the Larder

THE GUIDE TO SCOTLAND'S FOOD AND DRINK

EDITED BY DONALD REID

the
Larder
THE GUIDE TO SCOTLAND'S FOOD AND DRINK

SFQC | FOOD WITH THOUGHT

This edition published in Great Britain in 2010 by The List Ltd in association with SFQC

Copyright © 2010 The List Ltd, 14 High Street, Edinburgh EH1 1TE

The first edition of The Larder was published in 2009 by The List Ltd in association with SFQC and with the support of SOPA: Scottish Organic Producers Association.

A CIP catalogue record for this book is available from the British Library.

ISBN 978 0 9557513 3 2

Printed by Acorn Web Offset Ltd, Normanton, West Yorkshire

The Scottish Government

SCOTLAND OF FOOD & DRINK

The List and SFQC gratefully acknowledge the support of the Scottish Government, who have recognised the role of The Larder in promoting Scotland as A Land of Food and Drink.

Editor Donald Reid

Assistant Editor Jay Thundercliffe

Subeditor Rhona Taylor

Contributors & Researchers Will Bain, Sîan Bevan, Catherine Brown, Steve Brown, John Cooke, Gordon Davidson, Catharina Day, Cate Devine, Hannah Ewan, Rob Fletcher, Poppy Gilroy, Catriona Graham, Erica Goodey, Nicki Holmyard, Jackie Hunter, Jo Laidlaw, Carol Main, Malcolm McGonigle, Robin McKelvie, Kirsten McKenzie, Colette Magee, Nicola Meighan, Andrea Pearson, David Pollock, James Pryor, Carine Seitz, Barry Shelby, Claire Simpson, Sarah Thomson, Christopher Trotter, Natalya Wells

Design & Production Neil Gallagher, studiomuse.co.uk

Cover image and studio photography Jannica Honey, jannicahoney.com

Advertising Sales Suzanne Watt

Digital Simon Dessain, Andy Carmichael, Bruce Combe, Iain McCusker

Accounts Georgette Renwick, Tasmin Campbell

Publisher Robin Hodge

Project Director Peter Brown (SFQC)

With thanks to
Anna Davies at Scotland Food & Drink, Alistair Prior of the Scottish Government Food & Drink team, Lorna Bruce and Gaynyr Dickson at VisitScotland, Scottish Viewpoint, Margaret Stewart and Laurent Vernet at QMS, SeafoodScotland, Sarah Milne of the Scottish Farmers' Markets Partnership, Pierre Leger of Clarks Speciality Foods, Jim Cowie, Nichola Fletcher, Jonathan Honeyman and John Webber, Charles MacLean, Mitchell Beazley Publishers, Gavin Munro, and the staff at SFQC

introduction

Scotland is renowned for its good food and drink.

This isn't everyone's perception. Were you to ban jokes about the Scots' diet from the Edinburgh Fringe, stand-up comedy routines would be left bereft. Others acknowledge some good food and drink coming from Scotland – usually whisky, beef and salmon – but haven't appreciated that there's a good deal more.

In these 160-pages we hope you'll find that there is much more. The excellence of whisky, beef and salmon shouldn't mask all the other food that's grown, made or landed around Scotland including game, cheese, bread, baking, fish, shellfish, smoked food, fruit, veg, honey and beer. In telling the stories behind this produce we're able to shed some light on both the fascinating heritage of food production and the developing contemporary culture of food that can be uncovered in every part of Scotland.

Local food is not, however, a quaint niche in the everyday challenge of feeding ourselves well. Buying local food gives us a keener appreciation of the environmental, health, commercial and cultural aspects to food. Lower food miles, fresher produce, supporting local communities and taking pride in what's our own are now credible constituents of our purchasing decisions alongside the ever-present concerns of convenience and cost. There's no shortage of information on how convenient and cheap some food is, but rather less on the food that is closest to us and to some extent defines us.

This, therefore, is the second edition of a project begun in 2009 to answer some essentially simple questions: what is the food of Scotland, and where can you get hold of it? To provide a convincing answer, we felt it important that *The Larder* didn't become a glossy brochure full of marketing spin. Instead we aim to offer an insight into the food and drink scene in Scotland from an independent stance. The topics covered here are chosen by The List's editorial team who aim to find the most interesting and relevant stories, and to publish the most reliable and accurate information. As a result, *The Larder* is filled with the smaller, artisan and craft producers and shops that provide Scotland's food and drink with its richness, quality and human side. These are the very people you see at farmers' markets or in farm shops. who know about the food of Scotland because they make it, sell it and genuinely appreciate it.

We hope you find what's in *The Larder* informative, inspiring and appetising – but also practical. Despite the dominance of supermarkets and the convenience culture in our daily grocery shopping, there are still many thousands of small food shops in this country. We've tried to highlight the best and most useful. We haven't attempted to list every food producer in Scotland, but rather the places where the best food in Scotland can be bought. These range from up-market delis to family butchers going back generations, from farm shops with produce fresh from the field to artisan bakers with their irresistible smells. They, along with the restaurants run by chefs with an ever-greater enthusiasm for celebrating local produce, are the places where you can properly engage with something that's well worth believing in: the great tastes, smells, stories and culture of Scotland's food.

How to use the guide

The Larder is divided into chapters covering different types of food. The latter part of each chapter is a 'Where to Buy' section listing shops and outlets for that style of food. The only Where to Buy section not following the name of the preceeding chapter is Delis and General Food Shops, which comes after the opening chapter, The Food of Scotland.

Within each Where to Buy section, shops are grouped by geographical area, then listed alphabetically. Entries contain the following information:

Name of shop or business

Address, phone number and website, where applicable. If a business has several branches, these are either listed together in one entry or cross-referenced to a different geographical area of the country.

A general description of the shop or business. These have been compiled independently by List researchers.

▦ **Dougal's Deli**

Deli, Bread, Honey/Preserves

54 Bramble Parade, Stirling
01234 56789, www.dougalsdeli.co.uk
Tue–Sat 8am–7pm, Sun 9am–5pm.
Closed Mon.
Café, Web/mail order

A recent arrival, Dougal's Deli has quickly gained a reputation for all kinds of good local food, from ripe cheeses to honey made by the bees on owner Dougal Smith's organic orchard in the Ochil Hills. Some great tasting loaves, rolls and patisserie are baked freshly every morning in the neighbouring bakery, which makes Dougal's a top spot for morning coffee. Pick up weekly fruit and veg selections, or order directly online, with deliveries available to most of Central Scotland.

Speciality tag lines: these summarise the main specialities of the business, though not necessarily the complete range of food on offer

Opening hours. This indicates when the shop is open. If a business only offers mail order, the times given will refer to office hours.

Café: sit down food is available. Web/mail order: food can be purchased directly from a website, usually for delivery by mail.

The Directory

The Directory beginning on page 119 of *The Larder* contains useful information on restaurants, cook schools, visitor attractions and markets, as outlined on the Contents page opposite.

Restaurants in the Where to Eat section are grouped by geographical area, then listed alphabetically.

The hours shown for each restaurant are for **food served hours** (they may remain open longer). Note that in many parts of Scotland restaurants operate on reduced hours and days between October and April. In these months in particular we recommend you phone ahead to confirm that establishments are open when you expect.

The prices indicated are guideline figures showing either the **average price for two courses** for one from an à la carte menu or for the least expensive set price option.

Contents

What's in The Larder?

The shelves are well stocked in The Larder of Scotland.
Here are a few highlights.

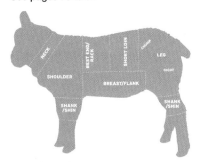

Fish spotter
Reel in all the information you need to know about our best fish and shellfish species.
See pages 78 to 84

Food from the Hills
Scotland's scenery is the source of some great food. **See page 35**

Lamb Cuts
A butcher and chef team up to help you get the best end from a piece of lamb.
See page 40

Where to Buy
The shops where you can buy Scottish produce. Lots of it – and lots of them, with 350 spread over the chapters of the guide. **See page 16**

Board of Cheese
Help pick out the best cheese for your table from Scotland's talented array of cheesemakers. **See page 66**

Wild in the Country
Head into the woods to forage for food with some of the country's top chefs. **See page 94**

Scot Choc
We nibble our way around Scotland's artisan chocolate makers and discover how they're mixing in a local flavour. **See page 58**

Market Rates
All Scotland's farmers' markets in one handy table. **See page 150**

Over a Barrel
Drink to the health of the brewers putting local beer on the map. **See page 108**

Where to Eat
Restaurants, bistros, cafés and even a few shacks all around Scotland where you'll find local food being sourced, cooked and served. **See page 120**

THE FOOD OF SCOTLAND

PHOTOS THIS PAGE AND OPPOSITE LOWER LEFT AND LOWER RIGHT: SCOTTISHVIEWPOINT.COM

We hae meat and we can eat...

The Scots' relationship with home-grown food is changing, and efforts to preserve our culinary traditions are gathering momentum. Catherine Brown offers a historical perspective.

Some hae meat and canna eat,
Some wad eat that want it;
But we hae meat, and we can eat
And sae the Lord be thankit.
Robert Burns, The Selkirk Grace

We hae meat, and we have seafood too. Massive rubbish dumps of oyster, mussel, scallop, whelk and limpet shells are the first evidence of enthusiastic Mesolithic seafood-eaters around our coast. Not content with just foraging the Scottish shore, they went on to make hooks for catching fish. It was the start of a long relationship between the Scots and food supplies from the sea that continues today.

Yet every generation faces the question of what's worth saving and what's not. We may still have a seafood industry, and can still eat seafood, but are we happy that so much of it is sold to enthusiastic seafood-eaters in other countries?

Were he around today, there's no doubt how Sir Walter Scott would have voted on this question. He was unhappy to see any of Scotland's heritage disappearing and, besides campaigning for other causes, he welcomed the publication in 1826 of the first Scottish cookery book to feature native culinary traditions: *The Cook and Housewife's Manual by Mistress Margaret (Meg) Dods*. These distinctive food traditions, he argued, should not be allowed to 'fall into oblivion in our day'.

There's no doubt either how Florence Marian McNeill would have voted on the seafood question. Born in

Orkney in 1885, and one of the first university-educated Scotswomen, she believed there was a cohesive force in folk culture and heritage that defined the identity of a country. In the period between two world wars she wrote *The Scots Kitchen* (1929), the first history of Scotland's food with recipes, which provided the evidence, among other things, of the seafood-eating Scots. She argued for saving the best traditions from the past.

But many people living in urban Scotland at this time were hard put to preserve their culinary heritage. Divorced from the sea, the land and its growing seasons, unemployed Dundee fathers – known as kettle-bilers – stayed at home while their wives worked in jute factories because they could be paid less than men. For these families, kettles of boiling water for tea replaced the porridge pots of previous times.

Less desperate was the scenario in my grandmother's cramped tenement kitchen, in similarly deprived urban Glasgow. Despite this, she still practised the art of clever economy cooking, coaxing wonderful flavours and aromas from cheap cuts of meat and vegetables in slow-cooked, meal-in-a-plate broths and stews. She baked on the girdle but never in the oven.

Rural Scots in the period between the wars were also more able to preserve their traditions. Vast geographical differences, from remote islands to fertile lowlands, had created such diverse foods as seaweed-fed mutton, from the isle of North Ronaldsay, and creamy cheeses from lush Ayrshire grasslands. Yet in the second half of the 20th century, nothing was safe from the rise of multiple food retailing,

'there are more cooks now who recognise that the intrinsic quality in Scotland's best beef, lamb, mutton, seafood and game is something to shout about'

the flood of ready-made meals and the multi-million pound export trade, which continued to remove not just seafood but so much more of the country's best food assets.

Protesting against these potential downsides have been the current generation of farmers, fishermen, producers, retailers and caterers – dedicated, determined and hard-working visionaries – who each make an important contribution towards the survival of traditional food ways and unique foods of the place. Now their combined effort is gathering momentum.

Compared with a decade ago, interested and culturally aware buyers can find more Scottish foods in the marketplace. There is more seafood at its peak of freshness just after catching; more naturally fed, properly matured native cattle and sheep; more available wild game; more fully sweetened soft fruits, picked at their peak of ripeness; more artisan producers of cheeses, smoked foods and specialist baking; more menus that tell the eater the full provenance of the food; more farmers' markets, farm shops and specialist retailers; and many more exciting new developments.

On the cooking front, I'm pleased to find my grandmother's thrifty traditions making a comeback. The

porridge pot is back in its rightful place along with economy broths and stews that fit the mood of the times. One Edinburgh butcher has recently reported such a demand for oxtails that he has had to import!

And there are more cooks now who recognise that the intrinsic quality in Scotland's best beef, lamb, mutton, seafood and game is something to shout about. Rather than smothering with too many added aromas, flavours and textures, they know that good cooking is when good things taste of what they are.

We hae meat and we can cook . . . so let's be thankful and vote yes to everything that's worth saving.

■ *Catherine Brown is an award-winning Scottish food writer and historian. Her book* Broths to Bannocks: Cooking in Scotland 1690 to the Present Day *has recently been updated and republished by Waverley Books.*

Scottish Terroir
or how regional food is finding its identity

PHOTOS ON P12 & 13: FOOD FROM ARGYLL

Local and regional food groups - cooperative associations of smaller-scale food growers, producers, distributors, shops and restaurants, are gaining a higher profile around Scotland, as Jackie Hunter found out.

Our interest in local food may have revived in recent years, but when large, complex systems of food production and distribution hold sway over so much of our food culture, it's not always a simple matter to serve it up. Driven not just by economic survival instincts, but by a genuine pride in the food of any given area and a loyalty to the concepts of artisanship, quality and commerce with a human face, small-scale food producers and businesses in Scotland are finding ways to cooperate.

Launched in 2002, Ayrshire Food Network has become one of the most successful examples of a burgeoning trend. The chief objectives of a food network are to increase the availability of regional food as well as accessibility to it, as AFN's founder Howard Wilkinson explains. 'Farmers markets are just one side of an equation; the creation of a food network has helped by making Ayrshire produce more widely available through its members, which include farm shops and delis.'

Food networks are doing Scotland a lot of good – it's not only independent producers, hotels, restaurants and shops that benefit, but local food groups also help to change public perception about the value and relevance of the food produced around them. Food groups may also achieve the critical mass required to influence policy on local issues regarding food, including regulation, procurement by publicly funded bodies and thorny problems such as the lack of local, small-scale abattoir provision.

More remote communities have, potentially, even more to gain. The problem of distributing local produce in Skye & Lochalsh was what inspired the creation of its Food Link network in 2000. As part of the pilot scheme, volunteer Ian 'the van' Morrison used his own vehicle to deliver local fish, fruit, vegetables, herbs, lamb, beer and so on from their producers to hotels, restaurants and shops in the region, who largely relied on deliveries from mainland suppliers hundreds of miles away. It was a rapid success and funding was awarded to upgrade the service. Food Link now moves more than £90,000 worth of goods per annum, compared to £6800 in its first year.

Before this one-van service existed, say its organisers, there was simply no marketplace there for local produce.

One of the newest networks and groups in Scotland is the Fife Food Network, founded by Viv Collie and Jimmy Wilson. Wilson explains: 'There was no one promoting the region's produce as an entity, so our starting point was Fife Farmers' Market, with which I was already involved. We now have a wide variety of produce to promote, from Crail seafood to arable vegetables, crops and meat. We're keen to build links between our producers, restaurants, hotels and shops, so that more local food is sold.'

By contrast, the main purpose of Food From Argyll – formerly a producers' co-operative – is to promote the region, and its local produce, throughout Britain. One way it does this is by targeting those not necessarily found browsing farm shops at the weekend. In 2007 Fergus Younger, now its co-ordinator, persuaded seven Argyll producers to run 'food to go' stalls at Connect music festival. It proved a popular alternative to the typical festival food, and now ten Argyll producers attend UK-wide festivals – including Rock Ness, Latitude and V Festival – under the Food From Argyll banner.

'It's not the producers' normal retail products, but high-quality, ready-to-eat food such as hot smoked-salmon rolls, steamed mussels, salmon pasta,' Younger says. 'We employ about 120 people from Argyll at the festivals too.'

In the Ayrshire Food Network, Howard Wilkinson says, another strong consideration of the 67 members across Ayrshire and Arran is to supply food to one another. 'You only have to go to the market before opening time to see the transactions from van to van – traders using one another's products. Corrie Mains supplies many of us with free-range eggs, for example.' Wilkinson also runs Petrie Foods in Kilmarnock, where all the dairy produce for their bakery comes from within 12 miles.

'We've reduced our carbon footprint by 20 per cent in three years,' he says. 'Most customers at the farmers market can relate to the fact that the food has travelled a short distance. But ultimately, he says, what the network offers visitors, whether from near or far, is 'the opportunity to have an authentic food experience'.

> FOOD NETWORKS IN SCOTLAND

In promoting local food and businesses, various food groups and networks around Scotland are helping to crystalise a greater appreciation of and pride in Scottish food, as well as meet the commercial challenges of distributing and selling good local produce.

The website for each group listed here should provide details on the producers, shops, markets and restaurants involved, as well as the principal activities of the network.

■ Aberdeenshire: Grampian Food Forum www.grampianfoodforum.co.uk; Community Food Initiatives North East www.cfine.org
■ Food from Argyll www.argyllandtheisles.com/food_from_argyll.html
■ Taste of Arran www.taste-of-arran.co.uk
■ Ayrshire Food Network (covering Ayrshire and Arran) www.ayrshirefoodnetwork.co.uk
■ Clyde Valley Farms Direct www.clydevalleyfarmsdirect.co.uk
■ Royal Deeside Larder www.discoverroyaldeeside.com

■ Savour the Flavours (Dumfries & Galloway) www.savourtheflavours.co.uk
■ East Lothian www.foodanddrinkeastlothian.com
■ Fife Food Network www.fifefarmersmarket.co.uk
■ Forth Valley Food Links www.fvfl.org.uk
■ Lewis and Harris Horticultural Producers www.stornowayfarmersmarket.co.uk
■ Lochaber Craft & Food Producers Association www.lcfpa.co.uk
■ North Highland Initiative/Mey Selections www.mey-selections.com
■ Orkney Quality Food and Drink www.oqfd.co.uk
■ Perthshire www.cittaslow.org.uk
■ Scottish Borders Food Network www.bordersfoodnetwork.co.uk
■ Shetland Islands www.foodshetland.com
■ Skye & Lochalsh www.tastelocal.co.uk

Future farming

Agriculture – the source of so much of our food – often has to fend off accusations of being stuck in the past, inflexible and unsustainable. But more promising visions of the path ahead can be found in Scotland, as Rob Fletcher uncovered.

While the EU was once the custodian of infamous wine lakes, butter mountains and ham hillsides, these surpluses – stockpiled largely due to the ever-increasing use of chemicals and machinery – are now seen as monuments to an unsustainable past. But, although highly intensive practices can damage the environment, in an age in which the world population is rising and food is expected to be a low-cost commodity, it is imperative that farmers continue to be productive. As a result, the current dilemma is how to increase, or at least maintain, agricultural yields by sustainable means.

As is often the case, some solutions are offered by more traditional methods of farming, and even crofting, with its small-scale plots and reliance on natural fertilisers, has come back into fashion in recent years, with organisations such as the National Trust for Scotland creating a crofting community at Balmacara, Wester Ross. Equally, native breeds are becoming increasingly popular, both for their better taste and their ability to thrive on minimal medicine and little more than a supply of fresh grass.

However, despite the low impact of these methods, 'with rising populations, we can't just turn the clock back,' reflects John Thomson, Director of Strategy and Communications at Scottish Natural Heritage (SNH). He observes the importance, where possible, of combining traditional techniques with state-of-the-art technology. 'We need to make the most of scientific advances such as GPS precision-farming, which allows famers to adjust the input

[fertilisers etc.] to suit the requirements of every part of every field.'

The combination of the traditional with the cutting edge has also been applied at Peelham in Berwickshire – a farm that has been praised for its forward-looking practices. Run by Chris and Denise Walton along with partner Amanda Cayley since 1993, its 680 acres produce pork, beef and lamb using organic techniques that include sowing clover to fix nitrogen in the soil, natural pest control, and growing rather than buying in essential foodstuffs for their livestock. Intriguingly, having gone organic, says Denise, 'the farm is more productive, the livestock more healthy and our crop yields have improved.' Winners of last year's Future Farmer Award, a competition run primarily by the Elizabeth Murray Trust, Denise reflects that the accolade has given them 'a renewed conviction that what we're doing is right. We've shown that the three pillars of sustainability – economic, environment and community – do actually work.'

The Future Farmer Award may be on the fringe of mainstream agriculture – its £4000 prize is dwarfed by the government subsidies that most farmers rely on. 'If subsidies went tomorrow, we would go under,' admits Denise. Yet the award is still valuable as it puts an emphasis not on theoretical models, but practical ideas that promote sustainable farming, and it is supported by mainstream organisations such as SNH and the National Farmers Union Scotland, who appreciate the role of this 'excellent award'.

As Denise Walton reflects: 'There is no such thing as a panacea that can be rolled out across all of Scotland. The essential element is to operate to the biological limits of your farm.' Whether you rely on organic and traditional methods, or rely on cutting-edge technology, Denise says: 'Knowing your patch, knowing your environment and knowing your market are the most important factors involved.'

■ www.futurefarmer.org.uk
www.peelham.co.uk

WHERE TO BUY

EDINBURGH & LOTHIANS

■ Bunney's
Deli, Cheese, Wine
96 High Street, North Berwick
01620 890245
www.fishermanskitchen.co.uk
Mon–Sat 9am–5.30pm. Closed Sun.
Web/mail order.
Rod and Lorna Bunney's delicatessen
has undergone a few changes in
the past year. Previously known as
Fisherman's Kitchen, and renowned for
its fresh fish, Bunney's has reined in the
fish to concentrate on the deli. Scottish
and continental cheeses and meats
are the order of the day here, backed
up by an impressively diverse range of
additional products, including wines and
spirits, biscuits and cakes, cook books
and pottery.

■ Damhead Organic Foods
Farm Shop, Box Scheme, Butcher,
Organic Foods
32a Damhead, Old Pentland Road,
Lothianburn
See Fruit & Veg Specialists.

■ Dobbies Farm Foodhall
Deli
Melville Nursery, Melville Nurseries,
Lasswade, Midlothian
0131 663 1941, www.dobbies.com
Mon & Wed–Fri 9am–8pm; Tue 9.30am–
8pm; Sat/Sun 9am–6pm.
Café.
Dobbies' passion for horticulture doesn't
stop at helping you grow fresh produce
– it extends to selling it in its farm food
halls. Choose from a good selection
of locally sourced fruit and vegetables,
fresh baked goods including a bread
and cakes, as well as honeys, jams
and preserves. The well stocked meat
and cheese counters groan with an
impressive array of goods from Scotland
and further afield, many of which are
organic. Treat yourself to a bottle of
champagne, a luxury pudding or some
Scottish hand-made chocolates.

■ Earthy Foods & Goods
Deli, Wholefoods, Fruit & Veg
33–41 Ratcliffe Terrace, Causewayside,
Edinburgh
0131 667 2967, www.earthy.co.uk
Mon–Fri 8am–7pm; Sat 9am–6pm; Sun
10am–6pm.
Café.
Earthy is a local produce store, market
garden and café, which sells fair-trade,
local, seasonal and organic foods.
Choose from a wide range of fresh fruit
and vegetables, meat, fish and dairy
items, all from passionate growers and
producers, as well as breads, pastries,
biscuits and cakes, pulses, pastas and
grains, teas, coffees, beers, wines and
a whole lot more. There are regular
tastings and producers' days – for a
chance to meet the faces behind the
food on offer.

■ Fenton Barns Farm Shop
Deli, Farm Shop, Fruit & Veg
Fenton Barns Farm, Near Drem, North
Berwick
01620 850294
www.fentonbarnsfarmshop.com
Mon–Sun 10am–5pm.
Café.
Fenton Barns Farm Shop brings the
cream of East Lothian produce into a
clean, airy space in which shopping
is a joy. Fresh seasonal fruit and veg,
sausages, cheeses and meats are all
available, as well as frozen meals and
sauces made on-site. To top it off, the
café and deli counter offers tarts, pâté
and game pies to take away, as well
as sweet treats and cakes. Truly a farm
shop with a difference.

■ Gosford Bothy Farm Shop
Deli, Farm Shop, Butcher, Northwood
Wild Boar
Gosford Estate, Aberlady
See Beef, Lamb & Other Meat.

■ Henderson's Deli
Deli, Wholefoods, Organic Foods
92 Hanover Street, Edinburgh
0131 225 6694
www.hendersonsofedinburgh.co.uk
Mon–Fri 8am–7pm; Sat 9am–6pm.
Closed Sun.
Café.
Founded by Janet Henderson in 1962,
Henderson's Deli is an Edinburgh
institution. Committed to selling
wholesome, natural food at reasonable
prices, there is also a salad bar
downstairs, bistro alongside and an art
gallery upstairs. Bread and cakes come
from Henderson's wholemeal bakehouse
on the same premises. An array of
vegetarian and vegan specialities are
available, along with locally grown fruit
and vegetables (organic where possible).
Salads, soups, sandwiches, ready-made
meals and fresh juices are available to
takeaway.

■ Herbie of Edinburgh
Deli, Cheese, Bread, Charcuterie
66 Raeburn Place, Edinburgh
0131 332 9888
www.herbieofedinburgh.co.uk
Mon–Fri 9am–7pm; Sat 9am–6pm.
Closed Sun.
When it comes to delis, the competition

CHEF'S CHOICE
FRED BERKMILLER ON SCOTTISH CHICKEN

Appellation d'origine contrôlée (AOC),
or 'authenticated source product',
is the French certification granted to
certain French wines, cheese, butter
and other food products including
Espelette pepper, Le Puy-En-Velay
lentils and Roquefort cheese. The
appellation exacts a very rigorous set
of clearly defined standards.

Poularde de Bresse was awarded
the AOC label in 1957 and since
then has become a highly regarded
product served at many famous tables
throughout France and around the
world. To qualify as a 'poularde' the
hen must not have produced any
eggs, must be a minimum of five
months old, have white feathers and
have spent at least three quarters
of its life free-range. It also should
weigh no less than 1.8kg and have
fed on maize.

When I was contemplating the idea
of serving Poularde de Bresse in my
restaurant I went to my good friend
Robin from Gartmorn Farm and asked
him if he could give me a 'poularde'
from his stocks.

The requested hens arrived and I
cooked them the way they should
be done, which is very slowly before
being finished with sautéed Scottish
girolles mushroom and creamed stock
reduction. What a treat! It might not
have been the real thing from home but
its a very tasty, moist and extremely
tender chicken.

We do not have a classification of
produce in Scotland but if we start
looking around us, what we have is
probably just as good as the more
famous equivalents – if not better in
certain cases.

■ *Fred Berkmiller and Betty Jourjon
run L'Escargot Bleu and L'Escargot
Blanc restaurants and own
L'Escargot Epicerie in Broughton Street,
Edinburgh, 0131 557 1600
www.lepicerie.co.uk
Gartmorn Farm by Alloa produces free-
range chicken, duck, turkey and guinea
fowl, 01259 750549
www.gartmornfarm.co.uk*

For the cheese bored,
we present our cheese board

Whether you want to round off a great dinner or fill a hearty sandwich, create a sophisticated soufflé or indulge in a toasted treat, there's nothing to compare with cheese for versatility and appeal. At Dobbies Farm Foodhall you'll find the best local cheeses available, often including hand-made farmhouse cheeses produced just a few miles from the store. We're proud to offer great local produce, but for brilliant brie and magnificent mozzarella we also search the world for the very best.

Choosing the right cheese makes all the difference – so we'll be delighted to make suggestions, or let you taste a little before you buy. And we even have the beer (many of them uniquely local), wine or port to complement your choice.

Garden Centre | Restaurant | In-store Butcher | Free Parking | Open 7 Days

Aberdeen: 01224 686 000 | Ayr: 01292 294 750
Dundee: 01382 530 333 | Dunfermline: 01383 842 757 | Edinburgh: 0131 663 1941
Milngavie: 01360 620 721 | Stirling: 01786 458 860

farm
FOODHALL
at Dobbies

in Stockbridge is stiff. Herbie, small as it is, can't offer the range of produce that Peckhams can a few doors down, nor can it stock a vast selection of cheeses. However, when you find yourself squeezed in there between the counter and the bread baskets, the walls lined with wine bottles and preserves, you'll find that you won't need to stop off anywhere else before heading off to Inverleith with an exceptionally greedy picnic.

Porto & Fi

■ Hilary's Deli
Deli, Fruit & Veg
7 Court Street, Haddington, East Lothian
01620 824220, www.hilarysdeli.com
Tue–Fri 10am–6pm; Sat 9am–5pm; Sun noon–4pm.
Café.
Established in 2010, this wee one-woman show in Haddington is already garnering a healthy reputation as a fine purveyor of high-quality deli goods, fresh fruit and veg (from Amisfield walled garden, less than a mile away), and artisan cheese. Grab a seat at one of the four tables and enjoy delicious soups, salads and freshly baked breads (even on Sunday) from nearby Waterloo Bistro, washed down with Hilary's own-blend coffee.

■ Victor Hugo
Deli
27–27 Melville Drive, Edinburgh
0131 667 1827, www.victorhugodeli.com
Mon–Sun 8am–10pm.
Café.
Now in its 70th year, the second-oldest deli in Scotland has deservedly become something of an Edinburgh institution. Within the cherry red exterior is a well-stocked shop with a good balance of everyday and more specialist items – from Gruth Dhu cheese to Rwandan coffee. Daily dishes offered – eat in or take-away – include a decent array of salads, bakes, daily specials and treats, while the menu for alfresco evening meals (BYOB) overlooking the meadows has been given a boost by a chef freshly dismounted from the Plumed Horse.

■ Kitchener's Delicatessen
Deli
127–129 Portobello High Street, Edinburgh
0131 669 9290
www.kitchenersdeli.co.uk
Mon–Sat 8am–5.30pm. Closed Sun.
Café.
Popular with locals, Kitchener's Deli offers an ideal stop for a warming bowl of home-made soup or to simply stock up the kitchen at home with organic honeys and jams or freshly baked cakes.

Their hearty supply of locally sourced bread often disappears by lunchtime, and its rustic rolls and wholesome tin loaves offer suitable accompaniments to their cheeses. Reflecting their commitment to Scottish produce, you'll find Scottish Dunsyre Blue and Mull of Kintyre Cheddar sitting among European varieties.

■ L'Escargot Bleu Epicerie
Deli, Wine, French produce
56 Broughton Street, Edinburgh
0131 556 1680, www.lepicerie.co.uk
Mon–Sat 10am–7.30pm. Closed Sun.
Café.
In the basement beneath award-winning restaurant L'Escargot Bleu lies L'Escargot Epicerie. This gastronomic treasure trove sells French cheeses, wines, terrines and saussisons, as well as cookware, freshly baked bread and ready meals cooked in the restaurant kitchens. If a stay in France has you dreaming of Banania hot chocolate or Rochambeau Sirop de Menthe, you'll find it here. There is also plenty on offer here that is carefully sourced from Scottish suppliers such as pork from Sunnyside Farm and poultry from Gartmorn Farm.

■ Harvey Nichols Foodmarket
Deli, Chocolate/Confectionary, Fruit & Veg, Wine
30–34 St Andrew Square, Edinburgh
0131 524 8322, www.harveynichols.com
Mon–Wed 10am–6pm; Thu 10am–8pm; Fri/Sat 10am–7pm; Sun 11am–6pm.
Café, Web/mail order.
The eternally stylish Foodmarket was slimmed down to around 1,500 square feet recently, making way for Yo Sushi! and the Chocolate Lounge. Nevertheless, it still stocks some of the finest artisan

foods and specialist international ingredients available. Those with a sweet tooth are spoilt with award-winning goodies from the 'Highland Chocolatier', and queues form for the weekly shipment of Poilâne bread. As well as the deli and foodmarket, the wine department is particularly impressive, with over 450 hand-picked wines and champagnes.

■ Pardovan Farm Shop
Farm Shop
Comely Park, Philpstoun, by Linlithgow
01506 834470
Thurs–Sun 10am–5pm.
It may be a modest shed on their farm just off the Queensferry–Linlithgow road, but Ian and Wilma Johnston have turned it into an Aladdin's Cave of good food. This large selection is sourced mainly locally, beginning with veg from their farm. From farther afield come produce such as steak pies from Falkirk, eggs from Fife, game from Duns and bread from Oliphants of Linlithgow. And the kids will love the friendly resident Highland cow and sow.

■ Peckham's
Deli
• 155–159 Bruntsfield Place, Edinburgh
0131 229 7054, www.peckhams.co.uk
Mon–Sat 8am–midnight; Sun 9am–midnight. Licensed until 10pm.
Café.
• 48 Raeburn Place, Edinburgh
0131 332 8844
Mon–Sat 8am–11pm; Sun 9am–10pm.
Café.
• 49 South Clerk Street, Edinburgh
0131 668 3737
Mon–Sat 8am–11pm; Sun 9am–11pm.
Café, Web/mail order.
See main entry in Greater Glasgow & Cydeside listings.

■ Porto & Fi

Deli, Fruit & Veg

47 Newhaven Main Street, Edinburgh
0131 551 1900
www.portofi.com
Mon–Sat 8am–8pm; Sun 10am–6pm.
Café.

This delicatessen and café has filled the gap in Newhaven for a friendly eaterie producing good food made from locally sourced, quality produce. Weekend brunch is particularly popular, but this shouldn't detract from the extremely competent dinner service. The deli counter houses a range of cheeses, while the wee shop downstairs sells fresh bread, dry goods, oils and preserves, as well as fruit and vegetables, and serves as a drop-off point for Phantassie Farm vegetable boxes.

■ Real Foods

Wholefoods, Organic Foods

• 8 Brougham Street, Edinburgh
0131 228 1201, www.realfoods.co.uk
Mon–Fri 9am–6.30pm; Sat 9am–6pm;
Sun 10am–5pm.
• 37 Broughton Street, Edinburgh
0131 557 1911
Mon–Wed & Fri 9am–7pm; Thu 9am–8pm; Sat 9am–6.30pm; Sun 10am–6pm.
Since opening in 1975, Real Foods has been at the forefront of natural, organic and vegetarian food in the capital. Now boasting over 10,000 health and wholefood lines and two stores, their staggering range of health and vitamin supplements is enough for a shop in itself. Both outlets have a vast array of pulses, fruit, nuts and cereals. Fresh organic fruit and vegetables are available as well as herbal and fruit teas, Asian and ethnic foods and other dry and fresh goods.

■ Relish

Deli

6 Commercial Street, Edinburgh
0131 476 1920
Mon–Sun 8am–8pm.
Café.

Relish is the local deli if you're based at Leith's Shore, where you can call in for a cup of coffee and a croissant on the way to work and pick up a nice bottle of wine on the way back home afterwards. A decent selection of Scottish and continental cheeses and charcuterie sits alongside fresh vegetables and dried products; and soup, sandwiches and Union Roasted coffee can be taken away or eaten in. Its sister café, Rocksalt, is just around the corner, located on Constitution Street.

■ Valvona & Crolla

Deli, Cheese, Bread, Wine, Italian produce

• 19 Elm Row, Edinburgh
0131 556 6066, www.valvonacrolla.com
Mon–Sat 8.30am–6pm; Sun 10.30am–4.30pm.
Café.
• Foodhall at Jenners, Princes Street, Edinburgh
0131 260 2242
Mon–Wed 9.30am–6pm; Thu 9.30am–8pm; Fri 9.30am–6.30pm; Sat 9am–6.30pm; Sun 11am–6pm.
Café.

Established in 1934, Valvona & Crolla is arguably the most famous delicatessen in Scotland. From the original premises on Elm Row they now run a Caffe Bar as well as the deli; the Vin Caffe on Multrees Walk; the foodhall and café in Jenners, Princes Street's most famous shop; and also in the Jenners outpost at Loch Lomond. While the two Jenners foodhalls have a stronger emphasis on Scottish products such as smoked fish, preserves and biscuits, the ceiling at the Elm Row shop suspends an array of continental salamis, hams and sausages, while the counter groans with cheeses and antipasti. All the cafés serve lunches, snacks and drinks using produce of the highest quality.

CHEF'S CHOICE

VAL BUCHANAN ON FOOD FROM LOCAL ALLOTMENTS

Being part of a real food community is why we work the crazy hours we do. Transforming food into a plateful of goodness for the soul and soil as well as the stomach underpins our menu and philosophy. At Woodend Barn we are surrounded by allotments and enthusiastic growers – more than 100 plots are in varying stages of development. Seasoned gardeners and complete novices all learn together – families and single people; biodynamic, organic and traditionally sceptical; methodical measurers of drills and rows and free-form planters. Among this, a virtuous circle of compost to café plate and back is gradually taking shape along with a local exchange network.

Some recent results have included the season's first rhubarb – cropped, delivered and served within a two-hour window; a bulging carrier bag of rain-kissed chard to make a colourful risotto, the leaves stripped and blanched and the stems softly sautéed; bright green, faintly luminous gooseberries paired with rich organic butter in a zesty crumble or served puréed with an oily mackerel salad; and green garlic resting in an oily confit for dressings and marinades.

The other regulars at the back door are our egg ladies, who bring trayfuls of local free-range eggs on a weekly basis. Rich and bright yellow, the eggs make the best pastry as well as an eye-catching egg mayonnaise.

With all these items, freshness is absolutely vital yet wholesalers are often not interested because of rapid deterioration or a lack of wide appeal. Using local food like this makes things more exciting for both ourselves and our customers, not less.

■ *Val and Calum Buchanan run Buchanans Bistro at Woodend Barn, Banchory, www.buchananfood.com. For Woodend Allotments contact mark@woodendbarn.co.uk, 01330 825431. Eggs, organic meat and charcuterie from Jenn & Dugie Foreman www.warkfarm.co.uk*

GREATER GLASGOW & CLYDESIDE

■ Ardardan Estate

Farm Shop

Ardardan Estate, Farm Shop, Cardross
01389 849188, www.ardardan.co.uk
Tue–Sun 10am–5pm. Closed Mon.
Café.
Run by the Montgomery family, Ardardan Estate is set in a walled garden surrounded by its own farm. The estate consists of plant nursery, tearoom and farm shop, which includes a deli counter with an impressive range of Scottish cheeses and home-made produce plus an olive bar. Priding itself on knowing the full traceability of its produce, it strives to stock as many Scottish and local products as possible. The farm's free-range eggs are a key ingredient in their delicious hand-made cakes, and the tearoom's scones are the best for miles around.

■ Berits & Brown

Deli, Wines

• 6 Wilson Street, Merchant City, Glasgow
0141 552 6980
www.beritsandbrown.com
Mon–Wed 8am–8pm; Thu 8am–10pm; Fri 8am–11pm; Sat 9am–11pm; Sun 9am–8pm.
Café.
• Centre West Shopping Centre, East Kilbride
01355 266878
Mon–Wed & Fri/Sat 9am–6pm; Thu 9am–8pm; Sun 10.30am–5pm.
Café.
• Unit 3, Maxim 3, 2 Parklands Avenue, Eurocentral
01698 733311
Mon–Fri 8am–5pm; Sat/Sun 10am–5pm.
Café.
Merchant City is rich in little boutiques, bars and cafés, with Berits & Brown a jewel among them. The deli stocks a good range of high-quality produce, alongside an impressive selection of wines. In their licensed café, breakfast is an ode to the free-range egg, while the evening menu tempts a return for dinner. The same owners operate a branch at Eurocentral. The original Berits & Brown in Kippen and a franchised outlet in East Kilbride are under separate management.

■ The Buffet Shop

Deli

30 Colquhoun Square, Helensburgh
01436 679990, www.thebuffetshop.co.uk
Mon–Sat 7am–5pm. Closed Sun.
Café.
For over 10 years Michael and Anne Chorley have been providing an array of quality Scottish and global foods to Helensburgh residents and the wider community, from cheeses and meats to locally made treats and 'the biggest olive selection in west Scotland'. The Chorleys dedication to quality means that much on offer is prepared in house so they can be certain it is without compromise. This commitment extends into the café where hot and cold meals and refreshments are available, made using the same top-notch ingredients sold in the shop.

■ Deli 1901

Deli, Preserves/Honey, Patisserie, Wine

11 Skirving Street, Shawlands, Glasgow
0141 632 1630, www.deli1901.co.uk
Mon–Sat 9am–7pm; Sun 10am–5pm.
Café.
Owned by award-winning chef team Colin and Eileen Campbell, Deli 1901 is a fine food emporium stocked with artisan products from around the globe. Closer to home, the deli counter has cheese from IJ Mellis and their own label jams, chutneys and coffee blends, plus take-away meals hand-made in the kitchens using fresh, high-quality local produce. They source the wine selection of over 120 bins using contacts from their restaurant days, so expect a cut above supermarket retail.

■ Delizique and Cafezique

Deli, Patisserie

76 and 70 Hyndland Street, Partick, Glasgow
0141 339 2000 / 0141 339 7180
Sun–Thurs 9am–7pm; Fri–Sat 9am–8pm.
Café.
Mhairi Taylor is the beaming face behind the success story that is Delizique and neighbouring Cafezique. With nearly ten years under its belt, Delizique is more astounding than ever, with a range of cold meats and cheeses, dried goods, herbs from Arran, local vegetables and freshly baked bread. The takeaway food can include salads made with the finest ingredients, fresh pies and soups. Cafezique serves up everything from coffee to three-course dinners, and has a laid-back yet fine-quality atmosphere.

■ Dobbies Farm Foodhall

Deli

• Crossford, By Carluke, Lanarkshire
01555 860205, www.dobbies.com
Mon & Wed–Fri 9am–8pm; Tue 9.30am–8pm; Sat/Sun 9am–6pm.
Café.
• Eastfield Road, Westerwood, Cumbernauld
01236 736 100
Mon & Wed & Fri–Sun 9am–6pm; Tue 9.30am–6pm; Thu 9am–8pm.
Café.

• Boclair Road, Milngavie, Glasgow
01360 620721
Summer: Mon & Wed–Fri 9am–8pm;
Tue 9.30am–8pm; Sat–Sun 9am–6pm.
Winter: Mon & Wed & Fri 9am–6pm; Tue
9.30am–6pm; Thu 9am–8pm; Sat–Sun
9am–6pm.
Café.
• Hawkhead Road, Paisley
0141 887 5422
Mon & Wed & Fri–Sun 9am–6pm; Tue
9.30am–6pm; Thu 9am–8pm.
Café.
See main entry in Edinburgh & Lothian
listings.

■ Eat Deli
Deli, Italian produce
16 Busby Rd, Clarkston, Glasgow
0141 638 7123, www. eat-deli.co.uk
Mon–Sat 8am–7pm; Sun 11am–5pm.
Café.
This Italian-influenced deli and café
is well known as a place to stop for
a Bei Nannini espresso and a pastry,
but it also has an astonishing range of
dried foods, organic juices, chocolates
and home-made dishes. Highlights
include The Fine Cheese Co fennel
crackers and Findlater's Fine Foods
excellent pâtés but it is probably the
various lasagnes, available in generous
portions, that make Eat Deli such a

well-loved feature of the Clarkston
high street.

■ Grassroots
*Deli, Wholefoods, Box Scheme,
Organic Foods*
20 Woodlands Road, Glasgow
0141 353 3278
www.grassrootsorganic.com
Mon–Wed 8.30am–6pm; Thu/Fri 8.30am–
7pm; Sat 9am–6pm; Sun 11am–5pm.
Grassroots is a friendly wholefood haven,
stocked with 2,000 or so lines of grains,
nuts, seeds, oils, herbs and spices. The
main fridge bursts with savoury treats
– smoked tofu, organic dairy and organic
meat from local farms – while the deli
counter displays freshly prepared meals
and snacks, almost all of which fits a raw
food diet, meaning uncooked, dairy-free,
gluten-free and completely unprocessed.
There's a good selection of organic fruit
and vegetables, and it boasts the city's
widest range of organic wine and beer
plus an adjoining holistic pharmacy.

■ Gusto and Relish
Deli
729–731 Pollokshaws Road, Glasgow
0141 424 1233, www.gustoandrelish.com
Mon–Fri 9.30am–6pm; Sat 10am–5pm;
Sun 10.30am–5pm.
Café.

Iain Manuell is a man who loves to make,
and share, good food. Each week he
conjures up his own pastrami, chorizo
and sausages as well as hummus
delicately flavoured with such things as
coriander or red pepper. On offer from
the deli counter are 22 different types of
cheese, a range of olives and antipasti
and a selection of organic fruit juices
and jams. Great fun for foodies on the
move or indeed anyone in search of a
comforting soup and sandwich.

■ Heart Buchanan
Deli
380 Byres Road, Glasgow
0141 334 7626
www.heartbuchanan.co.uk
Mon–Wed 8.30am–8pm; Thu–Sat
8.30am–9.30pm; Sun 10am–6pm.
Café.
This deli is a mecca for lovers of food,
with a counter stocked full of wonders,
shelves full of goodies and some well
chosen wines. One of the many fine
things about this deli is the selection of
reheatable dishes that are cooked up
for the next door café, chilled and ready
to take away. Having recently changed
hands there may be changes ahead,
but a dedication to sourcing the finest
quality foods – from local sources where
possible – is still top of the bill.

Delizique

subtly different focus, they all have an exciting comprehensive selection of high-quality items from local and global suppliers, snacks, meals and cakes from their own kitchens and bread fresh from the in-house bakery. Regular tasting trays and foodie events encourage window shoppers to take the next step.

■ Roots and Fruits

Wholefoods, Box Scheme, Fruit & Veg, Organic Foods
• 355 Byres Road, Glasgow
• 455–457 Great Western Road, Glasgow
See Fruit & Veg Specialists.

■ Valvona & Crolla Foodhall at Jenners

Deli, Whisky, Wine, Italian produce
Lomond Shores, Balloch, Dunbartonshire
01389 722200, www.valvonacrolla.co.uk
Mon–Sun 9.30am–6.30pm
See main entry in Edinburgh & Lothians listings.

■ Zuppa Deli

Deli
223a Fenwick Road, Giffnock, Glasgow
0141 620 1914, www.zuppadeli.com
Mon–Fri 8.30am–6pm; Sat 9am–5pm.
Closed Sun.
This Southside deli's emphasis on foods produced in Scotland and the UK plus a policy of stocking many Great Taste Award winners means there is a wealth of local treats on offer. The enticing range of carefully sourced regional food and drink comprises much that is made by small artisan producers within the same city and the wider region; from cheeses, preserves, pies and cakes to meat, fish and locally made ready meals. Home-made soups and sandwiches plus coffee and tea are also available for a midweek lunch.

SOUTHERN SCOTLAND

■ Borlands Deli

Deli
1 Main Street, Stewarton, Ayrshire
01560 482883, www.borlandsdeli.co.uk
Mon/Tues, Thur/Fri 8.30am–4pm; Wed 8.30am–2.30pm; Sat 8.30am–3pm.
Closed Sun.
Café.
Sandwiches and catering play an important part in this business, but for all aspects, including the retail deli, Ayrshire and other regional suppliers take centre stage. With over 20 county retailers stocked, as well as food and drink from Arran, you can expect to find Fencebay fish products, Graeme's local honey, Lime Tree Larder tablet, Galloway preserves and Little Doone's sweet balsamic dressing from Dalry. Dalduff Farm's ready

■ Kember & Jones

Deli
134 Byres Road, Glasgow
0141 337 3851
www.kemberandjones.co.uk
Mon–Sat 8am–10pm; Sun 9am–6pm.
Café, Web/mail order.
Established in 2004, Kember & Jones is something of a gourmet superstore. Everything about it speaks of quality: cabinets laden with fine continental delicacies, huge terracotta bowls of olives beside organic artisan bread (it stocks the delicious Poilâne) and a table of hip cookbooks that invite browsing as you wait. Choose from authentic pastas and sauces, chutneys and jams, Rococo and Prestat chocolates, luxury mueslis and cheeses, charcuterie, home-made pâtés and salads from the deli counter. It is always busy, so expect to queue.

■ Peckham's

Deli, Whisky, Wine, Beer
• 124–126 Byres Road, Glasgow
0141 357 1454, www.peckhams.co.uk
Mon–Sat 8.30am–midnight; Sun 9am–midnight.
Web/mail order.
• 43 Clarence Drive, Glasgow
0141 357 2909
Mon–Sat 8.30am–midnight; Sun 9am–midnight.
Café, Web/mail order.
• 61–65 Glassford Street, Glasgow
0141 553 0666
Mon–Sat 8am–10pm; Sun 10am–10pm.
Café, Web/mail order.
• 114 Kirkintilloch Road, Lenzie
0141 776 6050
Mon–Fri 7.30am–10pm; Sat 8am–10pm; Sun 9am–10pm.
Café, Web/mail order.
• 265 Mearns Road, Glasgow
0141 639 3782
Mon–Sun 8am–10pm.
Web/mail order.
A proper institution in the West End of Glasgow and beyond into Edinburgh and Aberdeen, Peckham's is both a reliable all-hours food stop and a place to pick up treats, gifts and hard-to-find ingredients. While each branch has a

Handmade, multi award winning cheeses, made with our milk from the family farm

Visit our Cheese Pantry: taste and buy direct from the creamery door

Try Connage Crowdie voted 'Best Cheese in Scotland' British Cheese Awards

Watch cheese being made

Available at specialist delis or from our website

Open Mon - Sat

Milton of Connage Farm, Ardersier, Inverness, Scotland, IV2 7QU   +44 (0)1667 462000

www.connage.co.uk

PORTOBELLO ORGANIC MARKET

BRIGHTON PARK – 1ST SATURDAY OF THE MONTH – 10AM -2PM

Saturday 4th September 2010 *first market!!*

Saturday 2nd October 2010

Saturday 6th November 2010

Saturday 4th December 2010

Saturday 8th January 2011

Lovely local and organic food & crafts.

Live music and face painting.

What better way to start your Saturday?

Printed on 100% recycled paper

To find out more contact Polly at PEDAL – Portobello Transition Town

polly@pedal-porty.org.uk | Tel: 0131-258-4483

www.pedal-porty.org.uk/food

It's our future

natural scotland

Pedal
Portobello Transition Town

PLUM CHUTNEY WITH ALE

BEETROOT & ORANGE CHUTNEY

SPICY TOMATO SALSA

SPICY CH

"The difference is in the taste"
www.mrsbridges.co.uk

meal range are also available, as well as wine, hampers and freshly baked bread.

■ Cairn Foods
Deli, Wholefoods
15 High Street, Biggar
01899 221770, www.cairnfoods.co.uk
Mon–Fri 9am–5.30pm; Sat 9.30am–5pm. Closed Sun.
Café, Web/mail order.
Evolved from a wholesale business brokering dried fruit and nuts, Cairn Foods stocks an extensive range of dried whole foods, chutneys, preserves, tea and coffee. As champions of home baking they provide an array of ingredients to indulge even the most accomplished baker. The chill cabinet contains a selection of locally produced cheese, smoked salmon, veggie sausage and haggis. They are sympathetic to dietary requirements and anything you can't find they will try to source for you.

■ Chisholms of Ayr
Deli
17 Carrick Street, Ayr
01292 269555
www.chisholmsofayrdeli.com
Mon–Sat 9am–5pm. Closed Sun.
Now a well-established good food stop in central Ayr, Chisholms has always set out its store by the quality of produce available on its doorstep. Thus a broad range of cheese is headed up by examples from Dunlop and Arran, smoked fish comes from Fencebay at Fairlie, pies from down the road at Dalduff and bacon and puddings from Ramsays over in Carluke.

■ Deli Beans
Deli, Cheese, Coffee
7 High Street, Peebles
01721 723461
Mon–Sat 9am–5.30pm. Closed Sun.
Café.
Unlike many Scottish county towns, Peebles has managed to hold on to its independent retailers. In the mix on the High Street are a handful of good food retailers, including Deli Beans. Supplying fresh deli goods, the emphasis is very much on locally sourced produce. The range of cheese and pâté keep regulars coming back, as does the Scottish roasted coffee. And if you fancy a picnic without the hassle, they will gladly put one together for you.

■ Dobbies Farm Foodhall
Deli
Old Toll, Holmston, Ayr
01292 294750, www.dobbies.com
Mon–Sat 9am–6pm; Sun 10am–6pm.
Café.
See main entry in Edinburgh & Lothians listings.

■ Fencebay Fisheries
Farm Shop, Fish
Fencefoot Farm, Fairlie, Ayrshire
See Fish & Shellfish.

■ The Olive Tree Deli
Deli, Wine
54 High Street, Biggar
01899 220125
www.theolivetreedeli.co.uk
Mon–Sat 9am–5.30pm; (limited hours on Sundays during December).
Café, Web/mail order.
This licensed delicatessen and coffee shop has become a popular stopping point in Biggar. Owner Ivan Stott is passionate about his produce and his knowledge will assist you through the selection of cheese and wine. Along with the usual deli fare, favourites are the award-winning Stornoway Black Pudding and home-made smoked mackerel pâté. Nothing is too much trouble for The Olive Tree; they will source anything outside their range, and supply buffet catering, party platters and sale or return on their wine.

■ Ravenstone Deli
Deli, Bread, Patisserie, Butcher
• 61–63 George Street, Whithorn, Dumfries & Galloway
01988 500329, www.ravenstonedeli.com
Tue–Sat 8.30pm–5pm. Closed Sun/Mon.
Café.
• 2 North Main Street, Wigtown, Dumfries & Galloway
Thu–Sat 8am–3pm. Closed Sun–Wed.
James Barton and Sara Guild have recently added a Wigtown branch to their original Whithorn deli, which stocks a range of local foods, from dairy items such as cheese and ice-cream to salmon smoked nearby and seasonal fruit and veg, some of which is home-grown. The in-store butcher prepares local meat and makes sausages and pies, and a range of speciality breads are freshly baked in the shop. Deli lunches and drinks are offered, or enjoy more substantial seasonal dishes on their 'pavement bistro' outside the Whithorn shop.

■ Whitmuir - The Organic Place
Farm Shop, Beef, Pork
Whitmuir Farm, Lamancha, West Linton, Peeblesshire
01968 661908
www.whitmuirtheorganicplace.co.uk
Mon–Sun 10am–6pm (summer open till 8pm Fri/Sat).
Café.
A fast-expanding operation, Whitmuir is based on a small, award-winning, organic farm north-west of Peebles. Beef, lamb, mutton and pork is reared, and butchered, on the farm, with organic vegetables, soft fruit and eggs also produced. A community-spirited farm supporters scheme provides the opportunity to receive regular deliveries of their produce, while a large, state-of-the-art green building opened in 2009 incorporates an impressive café/restaurant, art gallery and sizeable farm shop, which with over 2,000 lines carries one of the largest stocks of organic food in Scotland.

■ Woodland Farm Shop
Farm Shop
Woodland Farm, Girvan, Ayrshire
01465 710700, www.woodlandfarm.co.uk
Mon–Sun 9am–5pm.
Café.
Located on the coast just south of Girvan, Woodland Farm has become quite a landmark. The large stone complex encompasses a farm shop, 50-seater restaurant and coffee house, garden centre and trout pond, as well as the newly opened Woodland Bay Hotel. The shop is well stocked with a fine selection of seasonal home-grown fruit and vegetables, fresh home baking, local meat and poultry, as well as fish and deli items including cheeses, preserves and ice-cream.

CENTRAL SCOTLAND & FIFE

■ Berits & Brown
Deli, Wine
Main Street, Kippen
01786 870077, www.beritsandbrown.com
Mon–Sun 9am–5pm.
Café.
Kippen isn't, perhaps, the most obvious place from which to embark upon world domination, but it may yet happen. Berits & Brown was established here in 2004, quickly establishing itself as a classy but friendly good food shop, coffee stop and wine emporium. The concept was then expanded into a franchise business, with shops now open in England, Scotland and as far away as France.

■ Blairmains Farm Shop
Deli, Farm Shop
Manor Loan, Blairlogie
01259 762266
www.blairmainsfarmshop.co.uk
Mon–Sat 10am–5pm; Sun 11.30am–4pm.
Café.
Located at the foot of the Ochil Hills near Stirling, Blairmains is a busy but welcoming place. Its 'Coffee Bothy' is a well-established retreat for hearty home-baking, soups and filling lunches, while its new 'Coffee Bothy Express' offers a picturesque stop-off for a quick refuel.

The adjoining farm shop offers various local items such as eggs, fruit and bread alongside Scottish meat produce, flash-frozen exotic fruit, vegetables and pastries plus sweets, hampers and even furniture.

■ Dalchonzie Fruit Farm Shop
Preserves/Honey, Farm Shop, Fruit & Veg
Dalchonzie, Comrie, Perthshire
See Fruit & Veg Specialists.

■ Deli Ecosse
Deli, Patisserie, Wine
10 Ancaster Square, Callander
01877 331220, www.deliecosse.co.uk
April–Oct: Mon–Sun 8am–5.30pm;
Oct–April: Mon–Tues 8.30am–5pm.
Café.
A good place to stock up if you're in the Trossachs, Deli Ecosse is also a valuable pit-stop worth knowing about if you're travelling through. The cosy, homely converted church hall stocks good Scottish cheeses, meat, dried goods, home-made cakes and an unusual variety of Scottish wines, which make good conversation pieces if nothing else. There are a number of tables available for sit-in food, as well as take-away sandwiches and good coffee on offer.

■ Dobbies Farm Foodhall
Deli
• Western Approach Road, Dalgety Bay, Fife
01383 823841, www.dobbies.com
Mon & Wed–Fri 9am–7pm; Tue 9.30am–7pm; Sat 9am–6pm; Sun 10.30am–4.30pm.
Café.
• Whimbrell Place, Fife Leisure Park, Dunfermline
01383 842757
Mon & Wed & Fri/Sat 9am–6pm; Tue 9.30am–6pm; Thu 9am–8pm; Sun 10am–6pm.
• Huntingtower Park, Crieff Road, Perth
01738 638555
Mon & Wed–Fri 9am–8pm; Tue 9.30am–8pm; Sat/Sun 9am–6pm.
Café.
• Drip Road, Craigforth, Stirling
01786 458860
See main entry in Edinburgh & Lothians listings.

■ JL Gill
Deli, Coffee, Whisky, Beer
26 West High Street, Crieff
01764 653011
www.scottishproduce.co.uk
Mon–Sat 7.45am–5.30pm. Closed Sun.
A charming little food shop that looks like it belongs to times past. On the outside it looks like a traditional old greengrocer's; and on the inside it certainly lives up to its appearance. It stocks all the larder basics, such as oatcakes, preserves and cooking sauces. But you can also stock up the drinks cabinet at home with their extensive range of Scotch malt whiskies, Scottish wines and premium Scottish Ales and beers.

■ Gloagburn Farm Shop
Deli, Farm Shop, Beef, Lamb
Gloagburn, Tibbermore, Perth
01738 840864
www.gloagburnfarmshop.co.uk
Mon–Sun 9am–6pm.
Café.
Gloagburn is a friendly farm shop located at Tibbermore, near Perth. The shop stocks a wide variety of home-made produce, from meringues, cakes and savoury tarts to oatcakes, preserves and soup, which are also available to enjoy in their very popular and busy café. They also impress customers with their home-produced beef and lamb as well as Puddledub sausages, Hilton wild boar burgers and Hugh Grierson's organic lamb and beef. Both the shop and the café have been extended, reflecting the demand for their quality, local produce.

Where cooks buy ingredients
The best selection of locally-sourced seasonal, vegetarian, organic, ethical & wheat/gluten/dairy-free food in Edinburgh

realFOODS
37 Broughton Street, Edinburgh EH1 3JU
8 Brougham Street, Tollcross EH3 9JH
Shop online @ www.realfoods.co.uk

L'escargot Epicerie
The very best of France & Scotland

56a Broughton Street • EH1 3SA
Edinburgh • Tel: 0131 5561680
www.lepicerie.co.uk

CHEF'S CHOICE

TOM KITCHIN ON RED BERRIES

Scotland boasts some of the world's finest produce and we're lucky that our natural larder offers such an array of berries. We use lots of Scottish berries at The Kitchin, as they add a temptingly sweet flavour to any dish. I source most of my berries from Blairgowrie in Perthshire from the Bruce family. They have been farming in Perthshire for four generations, and have been producing berries for over 100 years.

The company is now managed by father and son team Bill and Geoff Bruce. Suppliers like the Bruce family give me lots of inspiration – they boast such a wealth of knowledge passed down from generation to generation and they truly know their product. They produce some of the best berries around, which they supply to Britain's best restaurants, including Heston Blumenthal's 3 Michelin star restaurant, The Fat Duck, as well as The Kitchin and our new restaurant, Castle Terrace.

They specialise in strawberries, raspberries, blueberries and blackberries, and all of the fruit is grown locally, hand-picked and packed right there on the farm. Berries rely on the right conditions to grow – similar to the way in which vineyards rely on the right weather conditions to produce the best grapes. The unique balance of the Scottish rain and the fertility of the soil around Perthshire offer an ideal climate for growing berries, helped along by the passion, knowledge and dedication of the Bruce family.

■ *Tom Kitchin is owner and chef of The Kitchin in Leith, 0131 553 0608, www.thekitchin.com, and director of Castle Terrace in Edinburgh's West End, 0131 229 1222 www.castleterracerestaurant.com Geoffrey Bruce Ltd is based near Meigle in the Vale of Strathmore, 01828 640228, www.geoffreybruce.co.uk*

■ House of Bruar

Deli, Cheese, Butcher, Fruit & Veg
By Blair Atholl, Perthshire
01796 483236
www.houseofbruar.com
Mon–Sun 8.30am–6pm (mid Nov–Easter 9am–5pm).
Café.
This independent department store has a large food hall whose policy of promoting Scottish produce shows in the wide range of regional items on offer. The reassuringly traditional in-house butchery specialises in locally reared beef and lamb, and produces a tempting selection of home-made sausages and pies. There is also a large selection of delicatessen items, from over 100 cheeses to confectionery, preserves and alcohol. There is also a 'market stall' selling seasonal fruit and vegetables from the local area. Recharge at the self-service restaurant offering a variety of snacks and hearty Scottish dishes.

■ House of Menzies

Wine
Castle Menzies Farm, Aberfeldy
See Whisky, Beer & Other Drinks.

■ Jamesfield Organic Centre

Farm Shop, Butcher, Organic Foods
Jamesfield Farm, Abernethy, Perthshire
01738 850498, www.seedsofhealth.co.uk/resources/meat/scotland/JamesfieldOrganicFarm.shtml
Mon–Sun 9am–5pm.
Café.
The large, purpose-built shop and restaurant constructed by Ian Miller on his mixed organic farm on the boundary between Perthshire and Fife at Abernethy includes a spacious and broadly stocked deli, a butchery and a café offering views over the Tay estuary. The centre acts as a showcase for produce that's mostly organic and definitely oriented to the local, not least the beef, lamb, chicken and vegetables from the surrounding 300-acre farm and its immediate neighbours.

■ The Little Italian Shop

Deli
33 Bell Street, St Andrews, Fife
01334 478396
www.thelittleitalianshop.co.uk
Mon–Sat 9am–6pm; Sun noon–5pm.
It may not stock much in the way of local Fife food (smoked salmon from the new East Pier Smokehouse being one exception) but this small and assured continental delicatessen is a highly respected part of the local food scene, with some top-notch imported cured meats, cheeses, oils, wine and coffee.

■ Loch Leven's Larder

Farm Shop
Channel Farm, Channel, Kinross, Perthshire
01592 841000
www.lochlevenslarder.com
Mon–Sun 9.30am–5.30pm.
Café.
Loch Leven's Larder combines vegetables from the surrounding fields with an impressively stocked farm deli and gift shop. Try before you buy at the popular café, which uses many of the seasonal ingredients that the shop sells. Beautifully located, the Larder and its attached, open-plan café overlook Loch Leven and serve as a base for walks along, and even around the loch's shoreline.

■ Lochend Farm Shop

Farm Shop
Lochend Farm, Scotlandwell, Kinross-shire
01592 840745
www.lochendfarmshop.co.uk
Cafe: Mon–Sun 9am–4.45pm
Farm shop: Mon–Sun 9am–6pm.
Café.
Lochend is located by the Kinross/Fife border at the eastern end of Loch Leven. This working farm specialises in growing root vegetables and raising beef, the shop has a decent deli section with local food incorporating produce from Fife and the wider region, as well as seasonal farm vegetables. There is also a coffee shop offering views out over the surrounding fields.

■ Mains of Taymouth Delicatessen

Deli, Chocolate/Confectionary, Ice Cream
Mains of Taymouth Courtyard, Kenmore, Perthshire
01887 830756
www.taymouthcourtyard.com
Mon–Sun 9am–5pm (later in summer).
Café.
The Mains of Taymouth Delicatessen manages to fulfill the roles of a grocer, a gelateria and a delicatessen without seeming crowded or unfocused. It's an airy, modern building with plenty of browsing space between aisles, and, because of the range, it has become important to tourist and local alike. Whether you need quality Perthshire beef for dinner, ice-cream to shush the kids, or some tartan-packaged biscuits to please Gran, Mains of Taymouth can deliver.

■ McNee's of Crieff

Deli, Chocolate/Confectionary
23 High Street, Crieff
01764 654582
www.mcneesofcrieff.co.uk

Mon–Sat 9am–5pm; Sun 11am–4pm.
A culinary labyrinth of locally sourced produce (home-made preserves, dry-cured bacon) and far-flung ingredients (Italian Vincotto, Spanish Brotes de Ajo), McNee's is a lively delicatessen and tempting chocolatier: the truffle range is a particular favourite. A lot of McNee's stock is created at home or on the premises – quiches, pies, cakes, jams etc – but nearby businesses are also well-represented: Dalchonzie Fruit Farm vinegars, for example, and Summer Harvest's cold-pressed rapeseed oil and dressings.

Menzies of Dunkeld

Deli, Cheese, Wine, Beer
1 Atholl Street, Dunkeld, Perthshire
01350 728028, www.scottish-deli.co.uk
Mon–Sat 9.30am–5.30pm. Closed Sun.
Café, Web/mail order.
See main entry for sister venue The Scottish Deli in Pitlochry.

Pestle & Mortar

Deli
41–43 Glasgow Road, Blanefield, Lanarkshire
01360 771110, www.pestlemortar.com
Mon–Fri 9.15am–7pm; Sat 9.15am–6pm; Sun 10am–5pm.
Café, Web/mail order.

Pestle and Mortar really is an act of indulgence. Based in the little village of Blanefield, this lovely shop is filled to the brim with fine foods and deli items. Its speciality is hampers packed with goodies and gift selections that come in wicker baskets wrapped with ribbons. Many of the items have won Great Taste awards – so, you're just going to have to find an excuse to treat yourself.

Pillars of Hercules Organic Farm Shop & Cafe

Farm Shop, Box Scheme, Organic Foods
Pillars of Hercules, Falkland, Fife
See Fruit & Veg Specialists.

Provender Brown

Deli, Cheese, Wine
23 George Street, Perth
01738 587300
www.provenderbrown.co.uk
Mon–Wed 9am–5pm; Thurs–Sat 9am–5.30pm.
Provender Brown is now well-established in Perth as the place to find deli bits and pieces. It stocks an impressive range of spices, oils and dressings, including Asian items and some Lebanese goodies. There is a good range of British farmhouse and continental cheeses and charcuterie. Stock up from a variety of olives and

other nibbles, or from the selection of French, Italian, Spanish and New World wines. Takeaway rolls are available for lunch.

The Scottish Deli

Deli, Cheese
96 Atholl road, Pitlochry
01796 473322, www.scottish-deli.co.uk
Mon–Sat 8.30am–5.30pm. Closed Sun.
The Scottish Deli has moved into the main street of Pitlochry and does a roaring trade at lunchtime with the extensive menu of gourmet sandwich fillings – in season, the salad leaves are grown on Alec Cruikshank's smallholding. The shop stocks a quality range of produce including Alec's personal selection of 70 cheeses. Down the road, Menzies of Dunkeld offers the same products as well as European and New World wines, Scottish beers and ciders.

Thompsons the Delicatessen

Deli, Bread, Patisserie
Drummond Street, Comrie
01764 670253
www.thompsonsdelicatessen.com
Mon–Sun 8am–5pm.
Café.
Daily shop-baked bread and a range of

home-baking – plus a wide selection of cheeses, oatcakes, olives and preserves – make this cosy Comrie deli and coffee-shop a popular yet relaxing haunt. They sell local fare, Scottish smoked salmon, 'the best seeded loaf in Perthshire' and plenty of goodies from further afield: co-owner Sophie is from Belgium and regularly visits to source chocolate treats.

NORTH EAST SCOTLAND

Baxters Highland Village
Deli, Preserves/Honey
Northern Preserve Works, Fochabers, Moray
01343 820666, www.baxters.co.uk
Mon–Sun 10am–5pm.
Café.
For decades Baxters has been synonymous with traditional tinned soups and jars of beetroot. These days they drape less tartan around the packaging and place more emphasis on convenience and the use of fresh, contemporary ingredients alongside the traditional staples. The Highland Village has four shops and two restaurants, and welcomes tourists. Other stores are located in Ocean Terminal in Edinburgh, Dunsdale Haugh in Selkirk, Blackford in Perthshire and Kelty in Fife.

Cairn Gourmet
Deli
52 High Street, Banchory
01330 825132
Mon–Sat 8.30am–5.30pm. Closed Sun.
Café.
The more prominently located of a couple of delis in the pretty Deeside town of Banchory, Cairn Gourmet has some well-stocked shelves of artisan-produced goods, with a good selection of cheeses, hams and cured meats. There are a few tables for sit-in coffee and snacks, and they also offer an outside catering service.

Dobbies Farm Foodhall
Deli
• **White Myers, Lang Stracht, Aberdeen**
01224 686 000, www.dobbies.com
Mon & Wed–Fri 9am–8pm; Tue 9.30am–8pm; Sat/Sun 9am–6pm.
Café.
• **Ethiebeaton Park, Monifieth, Dundee**
01382 530 333
Mon & Wed–Fri 9am–8pm; Tue 9.30am–8pm; Sat/Sun 9am–6pm.
Café.
See main entry in Edinburgh & Lothians listings.

Finzean Estate Farm Shop & Tea Room
Farm Shop, Preserves/Honey

Valvona & Crolla

Balnaboth, Finzean, Banchory, Aberdeenshire
01330 850710, www.finzean.com
Mon–Sat 9am–5pm; Sun 11am–5pm.
Café.
Finzean Farm Shop is located on the Finzean Estate, owned by the Farquharson family for sixteen decades. So far, so regal. The shop and café mingle together on the edge of Finzean village in a cottage-y looking stone building with a modern extension. Estate meat and game are on sale along with fresh fruit and vegetables, as well as dried goods and items such as jams made in the café kitchen. A pleasant place to eat or shop, careful sourcing is obvious throughout.

Food for Thought
Deli, Box Scheme
The Brae, New Deer, Turriff, Aberdeenshire
01771 644366
www.foodforthoughtdeli.co.uk
Tue–Thu 9am–5.30pm; Fri 9am–6pm; Sat 9am–5pm. Closed Sun/Mon.
A relatively unprepossessing local store set right in the heart of New Deer village,

Karen Woodhouse and Jane Hodgson's operation is a local dynamo for local food. Their veg box scheme serves north-east Aberdeenshire, while the deli stocks a range of hand-cut cheeses, local meat, Scottish beers, Ugie smoked salmon from Peterhead and Sandy Ingram's ham.

Gordon & MacPhail
Deli, Whisky, Wine, Beer
58–60 South Street, Elgin
See Whisky, Beer and Other Drinks.

The Green Grocer
Box Scheme, Organic Foods, Wholefoods
76 West High Street, Inverurie, Aberdeenshire
01467 620245
Mon–Sat 8.30am–6pm. Closed Sun.
Specialising in wholefoods, vegetarian and vegan ingredients, organic produce and local veg and fruit, the Green Grocer provides a wide range of products for cooking and eating well, rather than the more glamorised deli offering of fine foods or farm-shop array of meat and dairy produce. A veg box

scheme runs to Inverurie and Alford areas, to which other shop items can be added in.

■ Hammerton Store
Deli

336 Great Western Road, Aberdeen
01224 324449
www.hammertonstore.co.uk
Mon–Thu 8am–7pm; Fri 8am–7.30pm;
Sat 8am–6pm; Sun 9am–6pm.
This is Aberdeen's version of the kind of all-round general food store that is as much influenced by farm shops and old-fashioned provision merchants as it is by specialist continental delis. Owner Susan Watson has ensured that the bedrock of the shop is rooted in local and organic produce, including fruit and vegetables in season, with everyday items available alongside treats and luxuries. Then there are the extras which not only extend the range but also emphasise the values of the place: wine and real ale, cook books, ceramics and art on the walls.

■ Hattoncrook Farm Deli
Farm Shop, Beef

Hattoncrook, Whiterashes, Aberdeenshire
01651 882271
www.mcgregoraberdeenangus.com
Set deep in the Aberdeenshire farming hinterland east of Inverurie, the well-respected Hattoncrook Farm Deli is based on the McGregor family farm at Whiterashes. Aberdeen Angus, butchered on the farm, figures strongly in the products available, with ready meals and pies also made up on site, but there's also a decent range of other deli items as well including cheese, home-baking and wine.

■ Milton Haugh Farm Shop
Preserves/Honey, Farm Shop

Milton Haugh Farm Shop, Carmylie, By Arbroath, Angus
01241 860579, www.miltonhaugh.com
Mon–Sat 9am–5pm; Sun 10am–5pm.
Milton Haugh is a well-stocked farm shop near Arbroath, selling big sacks of farm-grown potatoes and other seasonal vegetables along with a range of jams and jellies made by the company under the brand name of Nicoll's of Strathmore. Also available is its own reared Shorthorn Cross beef as well as free-range chickens and eggs. Milton Haugh is also now the home base of Aberfeldy Oatmeal, selling bags of oatmeal, flour, oatcakes and biscuits.

■ Mitchells
Deli, Cheese, Ice Cream

Market Place, Inverurie, Aberdeenshire
See Cheese & Dairy.

■ Peckham's
Deli

• 45–51 Schoolhill, Aberdeen
01224 638 525, www.peckhams.co.uk
Mon–Fri 7am–10pm; Sat 8am–10pm; Sun 9am–10pm.
Café, Web/mail order.
• 234 Union Street, Aberdeen
01224 587 634
Mon–Fri 7am–10pm; Sat 8am–10pm; Sun 9am–10pm.
Web/mail order.
See main entry in Greater Glasgow and Clydeside listings.

■ Phoenix Community Stores
Deli

The Park, by Findhorn, Moray
01309 690110, www.phoenixshop.co.uk
Mon–Fri 10am–6pm; Sat 10am–5pm; Sun 11am–5pm.
Café, Web/mail order.
Located at the entrance to the famous Findhorn eco-village, the Phoenix Community Store started life as a specialist new age shop. It has now turned into a thriving community store, specialising in organic, Fairtrade and artisan foodstuffs. But it has retained some of its alternative tendencies and also houses an apothecary. What's more, the Phoenix is part of a community partnership and hundreds of local people own a share of the business.

■ Smithies
Deli

16 Keptie Street, Arbroath
01241 873344
Mon–Fri 9.30am–4.30pm; Sat 9.30am–4pm. Closed Sun.
Café.
Selling a good range of cheeses, salamis and olives among a pretty comprehensive stock of goodies to eat, the shop itself is rather fine having once been a butcher shop and a Lipton's grocer – the green shamrock tiling from that era remaining in place. Good coffee, cakes and sandwiches are served, making it a handy pit stop for the nearby station.

■ The Spey Larder
Deli

96–98 High Street, Aberlour on Spey, Moray
01340 871243, www.speylarder.co.uk
Mon–Sat 9am–5.30pm. Closed Sun.
It is the range of produce that impresses at the Spey Larder. As the name would suggest, it is the perfect place to stock up on all the deli larder basics, both continental and local – Connads cheese is a favourite, as is Ola rapeseed oil. A large selection of locally caught fish,

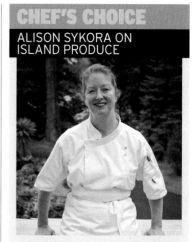

CHEF'S CHOICE

ALISON SYKORA ON ISLAND PRODUCE

It is such a privilege to be able to eat good food, and to celebrate the quality of each ingredient by doing as little as possible to it.

I have just eaten a delicious supper of mackerel, line-caught here on the Isle of Bute, and stuffed with oatmeal, a sauté of onions, parsley, black pepper, lemon juice and zest, with a huge portion of cavolo nero, (that beautiful black textured kale, until recently more often grown in British gardens as an ornamental plant, rather than an edible vegetable) steamed with garlic and white wine and, on the side, fresh roasted beetroot with a splash of cold-pressed Scottish rapeseed oil.

Each part of this meal (apart from the lemons and the wine) came from Scotland and the majority of the produce travelled no air miles, and even no road miles – in fact it all came in by shanks' pony. The mackerel was caught at Kerrycroy, only some 800 metres away, and the garden produce was freshly picked and carried by hand to the restaurant this morning, direct from the gardens right here at Mount Stuart.

My choice of all these ingredients is the glorious but often under-appreciated beetroot. It is brimming with colour and is also the current healthy choice. I have loved this root and its rainbow leaves (chard and beets are from the same family) since my childhood. Probably in part because of my Czech heritage and being brought up on borsch. From mid-summer onwards we ate bowlfuls of this sweet, earthy vegetable soup. Hot or cold, thin or thick, it is said that there are more recipes for borsch than there are days of the year, and I would happily eat beets on every single one of them.

■ Alison Sykora is Chef Manager at Mount Stuart on the Isle of Bute, 01700 503877
www.mountstuart.com

CHEF'S CHOICE

DAVID AND KATIE YOUNG ON SOURCING FROM THEIR LOCAL ESTATE

We are passionate about the quality, seasonality and provenance of the food we serve at The Cross and, whether sourcing for dinner or breakfast, we spend a great deal of time in seeking out the best local and Scottish suppliers.

At nearby Rothiemurchus Estate, Johnnie and Philippa Grant and their team share our commitment to excellence and enthusiasm for fantastic produce and good cooking.

Wild red and roe deer roam the estate, ensuring that the deer live a healthy life grazing the sweet grasses of the estate's forests and hills. Each animal is carefully selected, and hung for a few days before the Rothiemurchus butchers, Brian Dey and Fraser Sharp, expertly prepare it for our restaurant.

Highland beef is also farmed on the estate – the pedigree herd is traditionally reared and the cattle are naturally produced then they are 'hung' for four to five weeks on Rothiemurchus before it leaves on its short journey to The Cross.

Guests and restaurant critics alike admire the estate-reared produce that we use and the way in which we cook and present it, and many subsequently visit the Rothiemurchus Farm shop to buy fresh produce.

■ *David and Katie Young own The Cross at Kingussie, Inverness-shire, 01540 661166, www.thecross.co.uk Rothiemurchus Estate, by Aviemore, Inverness-shire, 01479 812345, www.rothiemurchus.net*

artisan cheeses and pâté is stocked, as well as fantastic bread. It has a good selection of local real ale and local wines, as well as wines from more far-flung destinations.

■ Taste Fresh

Deli
11 Union Street, Dundee
01382 224300, www.tastefresh.co.uk
Mon–Fri 8.30am–5pm; Sat 9.30am–4pm.
Closed Sun.
Located in the heart of Dundee, Taste Fresh's extensive range reflects a real passion for good, interesting food. The owner often sources and selects the products personally, deciding to stock them only when he is sure they are of the finest quality. Serving coeliacs with a long list of gluten-free products, they also allow the local to take centre stage, stocking crowd-pleasers such as Dundee cake, Orkney seafood, Puddledub pork and buffalo and the award-winning Stornoway black pudding.

HIGHLANDS, ISLANDS & ARGYLL

■ Brin Herb Nursery

Deli, Herbs/Plants
Flichity, Farr, Inverness
01808 521288
www.brinherbnursery.co.uk
25th Mar–27th Sep: Thu–Mon 11am–5.30pm.
Café.
Brin is a vibrant and prolific nursery, stocking over 300 herbs and wild flower plants, including 15 varieties of basil and 23 types of mint. The café/shop, the Schoolroom, is further extending its stock for 2010 with a good Scottish selection including cheeses, free-range poultry, cereals and preserves. Particularly good is the range of smoked meats and fish and their own fresh herbs, salads, fruit and vegetables. A weekend scheme features products from around the Highlands on their menu, and free tastings.

■ Cockles

Deli, Fish
11 Argyll Street, Lochgilphead
01546 606292
www.cocklesfinefoods.com
Mon–Fri 9.30am–5.30pm; Sat 9.30am–5pm. Closed for lunch 12.45pm–1.15pm.
Closed Sun.
A true all-rounder, Kay Hunter's small but enduring, well-stocked deli in Lochgilphead combines a role as handy food store for those looking for decent ingredients with a daily supply of fresh fish – much of it from nearby Tarbert

merchants, bread hand-baked nearby specially for the shop, and organic salad leaves from Ardfern. Also good for hand-cut cheeses, boxes of teas and bags of coffee beans, free-from foods and organic flour.

■ Corner on the Square

Deli, Wine
1 High Street, Beauly
0146 378 3000
www.corneronthesquare.co.uk
Mon–Sat 9am–5pm. Closed Sun.
Café.
Corner on the Square is a friendly delicatessen and eatery in the Highland village of Beauly, stocking an impressive range of local produce ranging from Highland herb hams, artisan cheeses and haggis to heather honey, preserves and Highland wheat beer. A particular emphasis on wine means whether you're looking for an Old or New World wine, knowledgeable staff are able to advise you on your purchase. They will also be more than happy to recommend a cheese to go with it and they offer a cheese board service all year round.

■ Delicate Essence

Deli
53 Marine Parade, Kirn, By Dunoon, Argyll
01369 707040
www.delicatessence.co.uk
Mon–Sat 10am–6pm. Closed Sun.
Situated in the small village of Kirn, close to Dunoon, this family-run delicatessen was a natural progression from the McColms' successful catering company Party Pieces. The shop stocks a range of local and regional deli items from baked goods and seafood from nearby Loch Fyne to cheeses, pâtés, preserves and fresh produce from local farms. The deli's commercial kitchen serves the catering arm of the business as well as supplying the shop with plenty of home-made soups, cooked meats, sandwiches and salad bowls.

■ Eden Deli

Deli
3 Main Street East, Inveraray
01499 302262
Mon–Thu 9.30am–5pm; Fri 9.30am–6pm; Sat 10am–6pm; Sun 11am–3pm.
A small but engaged shop, which despite its size takes an active role in promoting food from the Argyll region. The busy in-shop kitchen is used to prepare fresh food daily, including lunchtime rolls and soup, as well as picnic snacks, or you can pop in to take home some of their ready meals and tasty pies to enjoy for dinner.

House of Bruar

There is a choice of hand-cut artisan cheeses and other essential store-cupboard items, which are packed into the shop's remaining space, and you can also order seafood from local merchants Aray Fish and they will be dropped off at the shop for later collection.

◼ Kitchen Garden Delicatessen

Deli, Whisky

14 George Street, Oban
01631 566332
www.kitchengardenoban.co.uk
Mon–Sat 9am–5pm; Sun 11am–5pm.
Café.

This bustling enterprise is positively heaving with the best of Scottish produce. The small but overstuffed entrance reveals a bounty of rustic breads, artisan cheeses, fresh ground coffee and shelves groaning with hundreds of whisky brands. There's more browsing space in the back shop boasting a range of vinegars, preserves and chutneys plus more modern Scots delicacies such as Inverawe trout caviar and bloody mary salsa. There's a further mezzanine level that hosts a sprightly coffee shop, which makes the most of in-house items such as Isle of

Mull cheddar or smoked fish from local producers.

◼ Lochaber Farm Shop, Crafts & Café

Farm Shop, Lamb, Pork

Unit 5, Lochaber Rural Complex,
Torlundy, Fort William
01397 708686
www.lochaberfarmshop.com
Jun–Oct: Tue–Sat 10am–5pm; Sun 11am–4pm.
Nov–May: Wed–Sat 10am–5pm; Sun 11am–4pm.
Café.

Lochaber Farm Shop was established in 2004 to sell lamb, mutton, beef and free-range pork reared on the farm. In addition, it now stocks a range of locally sourced items, including free-range meat and poultry, and encompasses vegetables such as Ardnamushrooms, as well as Farmstead Fayre home-baking, Ard Darrich Preserves, smoked salmon, and special dietary goods featuring gluten- or dairy-free produce. With a wider community-minded aim to support small farmers in other parts of the world, it also stocks a range of Fairtrade teas, coffees, biscuits and chocolates.

◼ The Original Orkney Hamper Company

Deli

34a Scapa Crescent, Kirkwall, Orkney
01856 878 213
www.orkneyhampers.co.uk
Mon–Sat 10am–5pm; Sun 11am–4pm (summer months only).
Web/mail order.

The Original Orkney Hamper Company was established to make the island's excellent produce available further afield, producing hampers of fine food for delivery straight to your door. Mixed hampers offer a selection of produce such as smoked mussels, marinated herring, the world famous Orkney Island Gold beef, home-made traditional cheeses, preserves, sweet biscuits and oatcakes. There are also speciality cheese or seafood hampers as well as gift boxes, all available online.

◼ Rothiemurchus Farm Shop & Deli

Farm Shop, Beef, Game

Rothiemurchus Centre, Inverdruie, by Aviemore, Inverness-shire
01479 812345
www.rothiemurchus.net
Mon–Sun 9.30am–5.30pm.
Café, Web/mail order.

Established in 1985, Rothiemurchus Farm Shop started life selling fresh and smoked rainbow trout caught in the clear waters flowing down from high in the Cairngorms straight into its fishery. Before long a fully fledged farm shop was well stocked and selling a good choice of local produce, ranging from the estate's renowned venison and beef to Scottish artisan cheeses, wines and beers, locally hand-made truffles and a unique range of chutneys and preserves.

◼ Smiddie's Deli & Eaterie

Deli, Cheese, Preserves/Honey, Beer

21 Albert Street, Kirkwall, Orkney
01856 875576
Café.

Bang in the middle of Kirkwall's bustling Albert Street is Smiddie's Deli & Eaterie, with shop and café located downstairs and the restaurant above. Concentrating on selling mainly Orkney produce and home-made ready meals, Smiddie's has deftly positioned itself to cater for both the tourist market and the local customers. Food that will go the distance includes various Orkney preserves and cheeses. For enjoying closer to home are lunchpots and venison, seafood and steak pies, which are freshly made each day. There is a choice of over a dozen Orkney beers to provide plenty of liquid accompaniment to enjoy with your food.

BEEF, LAMB & OTHER MEAT

Haute cuisine

Scotland's hills, upland moors and Highland glens offer great scenery, but in addition to that they're the source of some excellent food. Gordon Davidson finds out more from the people championing the ultimate free-range food industry.

Scotland's hills and mountains are central to our national identity, great brooding heaps of stone and scree that anchor our nation, making us feel quietly indestructible in a way no featureless flatland ever could.

But what few appreciate is that these uplands, some 4.6 million hectares and 85 per cent of our land, offer something more – they are a source of natural and delicious foods that are only now being recognised for their health advantages and their distillation of a pollutant-free environment into something wonderful for the dinner table.

Almost as iconic as the hills themselves are the deer that live on them, and it is a mystery why venison is not our national dish. Grazing on a varied diet of hill grasses, young heather shoots and blaeberry bushes, deer develop meat that is peerless for flavour and almost entirely free of the saturated fats that bedevil other red meats.

It has taken an incomer, Christian Nissen, of Highland Game, to make real progress in introducing Scots to venison. His company's supermarket-friendly packaging and no-nonsense cooking instructions have changed the prevailing attitude from 'never tried it' to 'tried it once, that wasn'y too bad'.

'Venison is pure, natural and as "organic" as only wild produce can be,' says Nissen, a Dane who has lived here for 18 years. 'Wild venison is a beautifully tender, lean and succulent meat with little or no saturated fat, due to its natural origin. Its fat content is half that of beef and a quarter that of lamb. In fact, venison is so nutritious that even a serving smaller than the recommended portion will provide higher levels of nutrients and a state of satisfaction compared to other meats.'

Scotland's own deer-farming evangelist, John Fletcher, of Reediehill, Fife, still fears the Scots venison sector may be lacking the

John and Nichola Fletcher at Reediehill Farm in Fife

'I am convinced that deer farming has a huge amount to offer both to Scottish agriculture and the health of the Scottish public'

support it needs to survive, which he describes as a 'damn shame' given that many a Scottish artery could do with a dose of deer.

'Scotland's hill ground is perfect for really extensive grazing, where ruminant animals get a varied diet that is good for them, and which in turn gives them the perfect composition for human health,' says Dr Fletcher. 'Scottish deer do not get fed any cereals. From a biological point of view, animals fed chiefly on cereals produce meat with fats that are potentially toxic to humans. I am convinced that deer farming has a huge amount to offer both to Scottish agriculture and the health of the Scottish public.'

The land bestows the same blessing on Scotland's other great hill species, sheep, in particular the Blackface, which any shepherd will tell you is more wild than tame. Recent research found that hill-fed Blackface lambs were bursting with Omega 3.

Looking to increase returns for shepherds across the Highlands and Islands, farm adviser Fergus Younger is two years into the Argyll Hill Lamb project. 'What we have done is to create a specific hill-lamb brand, capturing the culture of hill flocks, the shepherd working alone with his dog, the purity of the hill, the scenery, the really good natural herbage these sheep eat – and the fit and active lifestyle they lead to find that food,' he says.

'These sheep live on hills up to Munro level – at 3000ft, it is just them and the deer. Up there you can taste the cleanness of the atmosphere, you are far away from the pollutants that settle over the cities.'

But Aileen McFadzean, the Blackface Sheep Breeders Association secretary, still fears that, pitched against the marketing might of other meats, hill-sheep producers may be bleating in the wind. 'Hill lamb is this unknown product. We try our best but it has not been advertised enough. So the public has forgotten about it, and all the attention tends to be on how wonderful Scotch beef is. Beef is good, but everyone in the know will tell you a good bit of hill lamb is better.'

Not all publicity is good publicity, however, the grouse being a case in point. Each year the public is bombarded with news stories about the start of the shooting season and the rush to get a brace or two from Scotland to London, convincing many people that this delicious bird is not for the likes of them.

This pains Scottish Countryside Alliance director Ross Montague, who emphasises that hill game does not carry the price-tag people expect. 'Grouse and venison are the ultimate wild, natural and free-range meats from Scotland's hills and moorlands. People really should give them a try.'
■ www.highlandgame.com
www.scottish-venison.info
www.scottish-blackface.co.uk

Perfect venison

Cooking tips from an expert

It is an iconic Scottish food; it is delicious; it is comparatively low in fat and cholesterol but high in iron; and is becoming easier to buy. Venison has much to offer the conscience as well as the body – important for people who want to feel reassured about what they eat as well as enjoy its taste. For deer are extensive grass-grazers and do not suffer the indignities of factory-farming.

Forget those negative messages that suggest venison is difficult. Follow two simple rules and cooking fabulous venison dishes is easy. The first is to buy good quality venison, and the right cut for your recipe. Do not be satisfied if it is poorly trimmed or butchered, or if it smells bad – that is not proper venison.

The second rule is to choose one of two basic ways of cooking venison because it is so lean. Cook steaks or joints pink or rare. To do this, brown the venison, part-cook it and then let it rest to finish the cooking. That way it always stays juicy and there is no need to lard it or wrap it in bacon. Alternatively, just braise or stew steaks or diced venison. Large joints do benefit from larding with fat. There is no need to marinate good venison, but you can if you prefer. And that's it. Perfect venison every time.
■ *Adapted from Nichola Fletcher's* Ultimate Venison Cookery.
www.seriouslygoodvenison.co.uk

ULTIMATE *Venison* COOKERY

Breeds of beef

With many farmers choosing larger and faster growing continental breeds such as Charolais and Limousin in the post-war era, Scotland's native breeds were on the decline. Here Rob Fletcher looks at four Scottish breeds whose grass-fuelled, flavoursome meat is back in fashion.

Aberdeen Angus

Luing

Belted Galloway

Highland

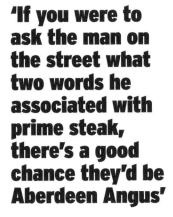

> **'If you were to ask the man on the street what two words he associated with prime steak, there's a good chance they'd be Aberdeen Angus'**

Aberdeen Angus
If you were to ask the man on the street what two words he associated with prime steak, there's a good chance they'd be 'Aberdeen Angus'. Developed from the cattle of the north east that were known as doddies and hummlies and refined in the early 19th century, the breed became official in 1862 with the establishment of a herd book. This long-standing pedigree combined with coats that would put the colour and texture of a pint of Guinness to shame, make the cattle very distinct and they are justly famed for the quality of their marbled meat.

Belted Galloway
Although Highlanders may adorn more postcards, these distinctive black and white cattle from the south west are almost as endearing. Registered as a breed in 1878, their distinctive white midriff, which distinguishes them from their near cousins, Black Galloways, was bred into them to make them easier to spot on the dark hillsides of their origin. And like their cousins, Belties share a hardy nature and can cope with their homeland's incessant rain. Their slow growth – they take three years to mature – gives the beef a depth of flavour that is second to none.

Luing
While these russet cattle now seem to be part of the furniture in much of the Highlands and Islands, their ease with their surroundings belies their relatively recent origins – created by the Cadzow brothers' attempts at crossing shorthorn and Highlanders, which began on the eponymous isle in 1947. As they were recognised as a distinct breed only in 1965, they are by no means the best known of our native cattle, but their incredibly laid-back temperament combined with their slow maturing mean that the beef is exceptionally tender and flavoursome.

Highland
Their hirsute nature combined with their starring role in the tourist industry mean many visitors can forget that they're grown to be eaten – to many, eating a Highland steak would be akin to ordering a Nessie-burger. However, despite their endearing appearance, these cattle, which were registered as a breed in 1885, taste considerably better than a plesiosaur sandwich – thanks largely to the fact that they are slaughtered only after 24 to 30 months, which gives their beef a rich, deep flavour.

Don't Mess with the Marag Dubh

Black pudding from Stornoway - or marag dubh as it is named in Gaelic - is a common sight on Scottish menus these days. David Pollock caught up with moves to secure its status and identity.

PHOTO: SCOTTISHVIEWPOINT.COM

Rather like a copyright scheme for local food, the European Protected Food Names system allows producers to ensure that only they can use a local designation for the foodstuffs which are synonymous with a region.

'We've applied for what's called Protected Geographical Indicator status,' says Claire MacLeod, a manager with Stornoway family butcher Charles MacLeod, one of a group of four butchers on the Isle of Lewis town seeking PFN status for Stornoway black pudding. 'It's really to protect the identity of our product, because we use a specific recipe and method of production which links back to the crofting industry.'

Compared to other black puddings, boudins and morcillas, the marag dubh has a number of unique characteristics. While most black puddings use blood from pigs, the Stornoway version uses sheep's, cow's or pig's blood – a throwback to the crofting heritage where all three animals were kept and recipes developed to ensure that every part of the animal was used. Rough Scottish oatmeal is used rather than barley or other cereals to soak up the blood, and beef suet is also a major constituent of the Hebridean recipe – with its low melting point it softens and lightens the texture of the pudding. The only other ingredients are onion, seasoning and water.

The Stornoway producers, all crofters themselves, use traditional family crofting recipes, and even today all dry ingredients are measured by 'handfuls', emphasising the experience, skills and judgment of the producers. 'In the last twenty years black pudding has gone from being the poor man's food to being an ingredient of choice for top chefs and a staple of specialist food retailers,' comments MacLeod. She is hopeful that the results of the application will be through before the end of 2010.

> EUROPEAN PROTECTED FOOD NAMES

Protected Designation of Origin (PDO)
Must be produced *and* processed *and* prepared in a specified geographical area. Everything must be done within the local area, in other words, and no ingredients may be sourced from elsewhere. 'The whole point of PFNs is to preserve the authenticity of a foodstuff which consumers recognise,' says David Lamb of the Scottish Agricultural College. Scottish foodstuffs which hold PDO status are Orkney beef, Orkney lamb and Shetland lamb.

Protected Geographical Indication (PGI)
Must be produced *or* processed *or* prepared in the geographical area. The difference from PDO is that some ingredients might be bought in from outside the immediate area. Scottish examples include Arbroath Smokies, Scottish farm salmon and Scotch Beef and Lamb. 'The main thing is that it has an association with being prepared in that area,' says Lamb. 'For example, had Arbroath smokies not sought and gained a PFN designation from the European Union, what would stop firms in England or Norway, for example, smoking a haddock and marketing it as an Arbroath smokie?'

Traditional Speciality Guaranteed (TSG)
'In this case the name must express the specific heritage of what's being produced, in terms of its tradition and custom,' says Lamb. This isn't used widely, though, and while traditionally farmed Gloucestershire Old Spot Pig has recently qualified, there aren't any Scottish products yet in the pipeline.

■ *For a comprehensive round up of food designations and labelling relevant to Scottish food, see pages 154–155*
■ *For full PFN listings see http://ec.europa.eu/agriculture/quality/*
(David Pollock)

They know my tipple, my love of Puccini and my plans for expansion.

If they know me, they know my business.

Meet other businesses to do business with.

A bank that's embedded in the local business community is far more likely to understand you, your business and the challenges it faces. That's why we provide event seminars and a members' network where you can connect with other members to create new business opportunities.

With over 70 Financial Solution Centres offering free conference facilities, you can gain access to a whole team of local banking specialists, credit facilities and solutions from Asset Finance to Independent Financial Advice. If that sounds like the kind of relationship you'd like to have with your bank, let's talk.

Call us on 08457 034567 today.

Always thinking beyond banking.

www.cbonline.co.uk | www.ybonline.co.uk

CB Clydesdale Bank | always thinking | Yorkshire Bank

C9206 EXP MAR 11

PHOTO: QMS

> LAMB OFFAL

The most popular is lamb's liver, which has a light, delicate flavour when taken from new season lamb. Kidneys have lost some favour in recent years, but there are some excellent traditional recipes involving both kidney and lamb hearts, which were traditionally stuffed and roasted. Sweetbreads from the lamb's neck glands have a limited season but are highly prized. Light and delicate, they make an excellent garnish or stuffing for a dish or can be served in their own right.

Haggis is another traditional product strongly linked to lamb. The main ingredients are lamb's offal with oatmeal, onions and spices being added to the mixture before it is enclosed in a natural casing. Traditional butchers still make haggis to recipes that are often handed down through the generations.

Cooking: Sauté the liver and finish with butter and sage – a drizzle of sherry wine vinegar also goes down well. A similar finish can be used for the sweetbreads, though white wine, cream and mushrooms also does the trick.

Always remember to trim the kidneys well and remove all the skin and fatty tissue in the centre. If you tend to find them too strong, soak in cold milk overnight then wash well before cooking. Always cook quickly and keep them pink to avoid toughness.

> POTTED HAGGIS

This simplified version of haggis can be made easily at home and doesn't require casings.

Ingredients:
225g (8oz) fresh diced Scotch Lamb liver
110g (4oz) beef suet
2 medium onions, chopped
225g (8oz, or 1 cup) pinhead oatmeal
2 tsp fresh dill, thinly cut
Optional 2 tsp of Drambuie, Islay whisky or your favourite liqueur (it can be heated and cooled to remove the alcohol).

Method:
Boil the liver and onions for 30 minutes in two cups of water. Drain, keeping aside a cup of the drained water (bree), and cool. Mince the cooled liver and onions together. Dry roast the oatmeal in the oven until golden coloured.
In a bowl, mix the minced liver/onion, suet, oatmeal, liqueur/whisky (optional), salt and pepper, and dill. Add the reserved cup of bree and mix to make a paste.
Pour the paste into a greased bowl covered with greased paper.
Steam for two hours or half an hour in a pressure cooker.
Serve warm.

WHERE TO BUY

EDINBURGH & LOTHIANS

■ Andersons Quality Butcher

Butcher
• 14–18 High Street, East Linton
01620 860232
Mon–Sat 8am–5pm; Sun 8am—1.30pm.
• 36 High Street, North Berwick
01620 892964
Mon–Sat 8am–5pm; Sun 8am–1.30pm.
A real family affair, John Anderson runs this award-winning North Berwick butcher shop, and an East Linton branch, with his wife Liz and three sons. They sell high quality meat, sourced locally – sometimes from only a couple of miles away – and often they place a note in the window to let customers know where exactly from. There is frequently a queue of people lining up to buy the various cuts of meat on offer, as well as their popular haggis, bridies and pies. Chatty and friendly staff are always around to give a helping hand and advice.

■ Ballencrieff Rare Pedigree Pigs

Farm Shop, Pork, Haggis/Sausages
Ballencrieff Gardens, by Longniddry, East Lothian
01875 870080 (home)
www.ballencrieffrppigs.co.uk
Tue–Sun 1–4pm.
Web/mail order.
Award-winning Ballencrieff are real pig farmers. Their Berkshire, Saddleback and Gloucester Old Spot sows run outside all year round, eating feed that is free of additives and growth promoters. They produce healthy pigs that grow slowly and naturally, and rarely need to see the vet. Home-cured bacon, pork and home-made sausages are the delicious results of this fastidious farming, and are available from Edinburgh and Haddington farmers' markets in addition to their focused little farm shop, where they only sell what they themselves produce, or choose from the cuts and products on offer from their online store.

■ Belhaven Smokehouse

Fish, Smokery
Beltonford, Dunbar, East Lothian
See Fish & Shellfish.

■ Boghall Butchers

Butcher, Beef, Game, Lamb
65 Margaret Avenue, Boghall, Bathgate
01506 630178
www.boghallbutchers.com
Mon/Tues & Thurs/Fri 7.30am–5pm;
Wed 7.30am—12.30pm; Sat 6am – 4pm.

Crombie's of Edinburgh

PHOTO: QMS

This modest neighbourhood butchers tucked away in Boghall punches way above its weight. Its legendary pies have locals queueing and judges at the UK Pie Awards smiling, winning two categories in 2010. Owner Paul Boyle's pie range is vast, the fillings imaginative. Everything is made on the premises, both savoury and sweet. Add their wholesome ready meals, from lamb casserole to lasagne, plus plenty of fresh veg and fruit, and it is, as they say, all good.

■ George Bower

Butcher, Beef, Game, Lamb
75 Raeburn Place, Stockbridge, Edinburgh
0131 332 3469
www.georgebowerbutchers.co.uk
Mon–Sat 8am–5pm. Closed Sun.
In the heart of Stockbridge, George Bowers has earned itself a reputation as one of the best quality butchers in Edinburgh. It sets itself apart by buying, plucking and dressing game, so don't be surprised if you find yourself leaving with a rabbit, hare or quail as well as sausages and bacon. Most produce is sourced locally but if the owner thinks the best chickens come from France or the tastiest wild boar from Italy then that's where he gets them.

■ Crombie's of Edinburgh

Butcher, Beef, Pork, Haggis/Sausages
97–101 Broughton Street, Edinburgh
0131 557 0111
www.crombiesofedinburgh.co.uk /
www.sausages.co.uk
Mon–Fri 8am–5.30pm; Sat 8am–5pm.
Closed Sun.
Crombie's of Edinburgh has something of a reputation for its range of award-winning sausages. Choose from an extraordinary selection of flavour combinations, for example lamb, rosemary and garlic; venison, pork and calvados; or boar, port & stilton, through to Sicilian, Cumberland, chorizo, South African Boerwors and merguez. In addition, their haggis is hand-made on the premises, and there's an impressive selection of well-sourced meats, game and poultry. Jonathan Crombie's grandfather – who founded the butchers in 1956 – would be proud.

■ Findlay's of Portobello

Deli, Butcher, Beef, Haggis/Sausages
116 Portobello High Street, Portobello,
Edinburgh
0131 669 2783
www.findlaysthebutchers.co.uk
Tue–Sat 8am–5pm. Closed Sun/Mon.
Web/mail order.

A family-run butcher providing free-range meat and poultry from farms around the Scottish borders, Findlays has been trading since 1974. They use only free-range cattle, selected and then hung for no less than two weeks to mature and enhance the flavour of the meat. Free-range pork is sourced from a farm in Hawick and the lamb from Peeblesshire. Renowned for their award-winning, hand-made products, they hold titles for their haggis, black pudding, beef sausage and bacon.

■ Gosford Bothy Farm Shop

Deli, Farm Shop, Butcher, Northwood
Wild Boar
Gosford Estate, Aberlady, East Lothian
01875 871234
www.gosfordfarmshop.co.uk
Mon–Sun 9.30am–5pm.
Café.

Bob at Gosford Farm has his own herd of wild boar, which (provided he can catch them) form the core of this excellent butchers and farm shop. All meat here is locally sourced, bought 'on the hoof' and butchered on-site, so the staff here know exactly what's going behind the counter. Seasonal vegetables, dry goods and Scottish artisan cheeses are all sourced with similar care, creating a one-stop shop for superb regional ingredients.

■ John Lawson Butchers

Butcher
• 8 Main Street, Broxburn, West Lothian
01506 852605
www.johnlawsonbutchers.co.uk
Mon–Sat 7am–6pm. Closed Sun.
• 16 East Main Street, Uphall, West Lothian
01506 855634
Mon–Sat 7am–6pm. Closed Sun.
• 8 Main Street, Winchburgh, West Lothian
01506 891018
Mon–Sat 7am–6pm. Closed Sun.

Lawson's is a family affair: founder John Lawson works with his two sons, as well as his brother Russell, from whose Midseat farm he sources the beef and lamb for sale in the three shops across West Lothian. In all their branches, you'll also find a comprehensive range of poultry, game, ready meals, pies, sausages and haggis, many of which have picked up awards in local competitions.

■ John Saunderson

Butcher
40 Leven Street, Edinburgh
0131 229 8348
www.johnsaunderson.co.uk
Mon–Fri 7.30am–5.30pm; Sat 7.30am–1pm. Closed Sun.

John Saunderson is the third generation of butcher to run this award-winning shop and, with over 80 years of experience between them, his staff are well placed to give advice to all passing carnivores. Stocking an impressive range of products from reputable and award-winning suppliers – free-range chickens and duck eggs from Linda Dick, game from George Bower, venison from Lochaber Game and pork from Ramsay of Carluke – you are guaranteed quality, traceable produce in this classic and timeless store.

■ Shaws

Butcher
• 6 Learmonth Avenue, Edinburgh
0131 315 2056, www.tendertaste.com
Mon–Sat 7.30am–5pm. Closed Sun.
• 56 High Street, Innerleithen, Peeblesshire

01896 830636,
www.tendertaste.com
Mon 6am–5pm; Tue 6am–1pm;
Wed–Fri 6am–5pm; Sat 7.30am–1pm.
Closed Sun.
Founded in 1828 in Lauder, this
family-run business has risen to
prominence over the past five years,
opening branches first in the Dobbies
Garden Centre in Melville (a finalist in
the search for Britain's best butcher),
then in Stockbridge and most recently
in Innerleithen. While George Bower
down the road may offer greater variety
and Waitrose across the road may be
cheaper, Shaws takes pride in doing
the simple things very, very well indeed.
The bacon, sausages and steaks in
particular are outstanding.

■ Whitmuir – The Organic Place

Farm Shop, Beef, Pork
Whitmuir Farm, Lamancha, West Linton,
Peeblesshire
See Delis & General Food.

GREATER GLASGOW & CLYDESIDE

■ James Allan

Butcher, Haggis/Sausages
85 Lauderdale Gardens, Glasgow
0141 334 8973
Mon–Fri 8am–5.30pm; Sat 8am–5pm.
Closed Sun.
With fine quality cuts of meat and
home-made produce, it's no wonder
that James Allan is one of the few
traditional butchers left in the West
End. All the meat comes from Scottish
producers, with items such as organic
Shetland lamb available in season. Their
legendary home-made sausages come
in at least 12 different varieties, such
as pork, basil and tomato or lamb and
cumin. Traditional pies and frozen ready
meals are made on site too.

■ Edenmill Farm Shop

Farm Shop, Beef, Haggis/Sausages,
Smokery
Blanefield, Glasgow
01360 771707, www.edenmillfarm.co.uk
Tue–Sun 9am–5pm. Closed Mon.
Web/mail order.
The shop specialises in fine cuts of its
own herd of Aberdeen Angus cattle and
even displays the ear-tag number of the
week's beef. They sell wild venison and
trout smoked in their own smokery and
a variety of local produce. Home-made
sausages include Edenmill pork with
fennel, garlic and Glengoyne whisky, and
the steak pies are sell-outs. The shop is
worth the trek to find it – but a van also
has their delicacies on offer elsewhere.

■ Ramsay of Carluke Ltd

Butcher, Pork, Haggis/Sausages,
Smokery
22 Mount Stewart Street, Carluke,
Lanarkshire
01555 772277
www.ramsayofcarluke.co.uk
Mon 8am–4pm; Tue–Fri 8am–4.30pm; Sat
8am–12.30pm. Closed Sun.
Web/mail order.
Ramsay of Carluke has been a local
family butcher for over 150 years. Using
only farm-assured outdoor free-range
pigs, they produce traditional Ayrshire
bacon, home-cured in large vats of old-
fashioned pickle. After curing, the sides
are left to mature before being divided
into traditional Ayrshire cuts, after
which much of the bacon is then slowly
smoked in their own smokehouse.
They produce a range of award-winning
sausages, puddings, haggis and cooked
hams using old family recipes. Mail order
available.

SOUTHERN SCOTLAND

■ Carmichael Estate Farm Meats

Farm Shop, Beef, Game, Lamb
Carmichael Visitor Centre, Warrenhill
Farm, A73 between Biggar and Lanark
01899 308336 or 01899 308169
www.carmichael.co.uk
Mon–Sun 10am–5pm (Nov–Feb hours
restricted: phone ahead to confirm).
Café, Web/mail order.
This estate farm in South Lanarkshire
prides itself on producing meat with total
traceability. Every animal is born, reared,
fattened, slaughtered, butchered,
packaged and processed on the farm.
Beef, lamb and venison (including lean
venison and mushroom sausages or
tasty cuts of smoked venison) are all
specialities. You can buy directly from
the estate shop, order by phone or
buy online.

■ Dalbeattie Fine Foods

Butcher, Haggis/Sausages, Pies
69 High Street, Dalbeattie, Dumfries
and Galloway
01556 610349
www.dalbeattiefinefoods.co.uk
Owner Alan Elliott headed over from
Northern Ireland in 2004 to open his
butchers in Dalbeattie at the tender age
of 19. He then took on the Scots at their
own game and produced an award-
winning haggis to go along with his
highly praised black pudding, sausages
and pies, and he was duly crowned the
UK Young Butcher of the Year in 2008.
A dedication to quality and a farming
background mean Alan has close ties to
local farmers ensuring the meat in the

CHEF'S CHOICE
DIDIER NEMESIEN ON HIS ON-FARM BUTCHER

Having an on-farm butchery means
I'm working directly with the butcher.
The farm stocks grass-fed Shorthorn
beef, hung in the butchery for at least
21 days, North Country Cheviot lamb
and pigs from Tamworth sows with a
Duroc boar. I can ask at any time for
any cut, unusual or classic. I get beef
skirt – bavette – and pope's eye, shin
of beef, pig's cheeks which I'll fry in a
mixed grill and trotters to make terrine.
I'll use off-cuts and bones for stock, I
can get pig's head, I can make haggis.
One hundred per cent of the animal is
used in different recipes – it's the maxim
of home-made.
  With everything here around us we're
very much tuned into the seasons,
whether it's a banquet with our farm
supporters with spring lamb as the
central dish or finding new ways to eat
salad in summer, using flowers and
leaves and all the seasonal veg.
I believe in the old-fashioned approach
and slow cooking, allowing time both in
farming and cooking. It's a great way to
show people the rich larder of Scotland.
■ *Didier Nemesien is head chef
at Whitmuir – The Organic Place,
Lamancha near Peebles
www.whitmuirtheorganicplace.co.uk*

shop and his produce are among the
best available.

■ Dalduff Farm Shop

Farm Shop
Crosshill, Maybole, Ayrshire
01655 740271, www.dalduff.co.uk
Mon–Sat 8am–4.30pm. Closed Sun.
Genetically modified produce is strictly
off the menu at this farm kitchen and
shop in South Ayrshire. Instead, a range
of locally reared beef, lamb and pork
is on offer, covering steaks and chops,
via mince rounds and pies, through
to quality home-made frozen meals,
including luxury lasagne or beef olives
in onion gravy. They will deliver to the

west coast of Scotland, or customers can pop in to the Maybole farm shop or buy from the Dalduff counter at various Dobbies and other outlets across the region.

■ Damn Delicious

Box Scheme, Butcher
• Thankerton Camp Farm, Thankerton, Biggar, South Lanarkshire
01899 308688
www.damndelicious.co.uk
Fri 2–7pm; Sat 9am–7pm.
• 108 High Street, Lanark, South Lanarkshire
01555 663193
Mon–Sat 8am–5pm. Closed Sun.
Web/mail order.

Michael Shannon has been farming in South Lanarkshire since 1996 and can state with pride that his livestock are reared on a green diet of grass and kale, 365 days a year. This traditional approach to farming is reflected in the taste and tenderness of his produce. Michael has established a successful online outlet for his quality beef and lamb and now has a shop on Lanark High Street. Damn Delicious has the advantage of 'on farm butchery' and welcomes requests for specific cuts. Alternatively you can select from an astounding array of online options.

■ WTS Forsyth & Sons

Bread, Patisserie, Butcher, Haggis/ Sausages
21–25 Eastgate, Peebles, Peeblesshire
01721 720833, www.forsyths.biz
Mon/Tue & Thu/Fri 7am–5.15pm; Wed 7am–1pm; Sat 7am–4.45pm. Closed Sun.
Web/mail order.

WTS Forsyth & Sons are a family-run butcher sourcing from quality herds while lambs come from farms in the Scottish Borders. Specialities include home-cured bacon, haggis, white and black puddings and pies. In addition, an in-house bakery produces shortbread, gingerbread, Selkirk bannocks and a selection of breads. Gluten-free pork sausages and burgers are available for celiac sufferer. You can expect to queue on Saturdays, an encouraging sign, but you can also order online using their comprehensive website.

■ Lindsay Grieve Traditional Butchers

Butcher, Haggis/Sausages
29 High Street, Hawick
01450 372109
www.lindsaygrievehaggis.co.uk
Mon–Fri 7am–5pm; Sat 7am–3.30pm.
Web/mail order.

St Andrew's Day, Hogmanay and Burns' Night are the busiest times of the year at Lindsay Grieve Traditional Butchers, whose award-winning haggis is prepared by hand to a traditional family recipe. This Borders butcher offers a mail-order service on his haggis, dispatching the mutton and oatmeal speciality from Hawick's High Street to the rest of the UK and beyond into Europe. A wide range of home-made sausages, pies, puddings and burgers are also available.

■ Hardiesmill

Beef, Haggis/Sausages, Smokery
Hardiesmill Place, Gordon, Berwickshire
01573 410797, www.hardiesmill.co.uk
Web/mail order.

Robin and Allison Tuke's 482-acre farm near Kelso is home to a herd of pure-bred Aberdeen Angus cattle. Firmly committed to a concept of 'farm to fork', everything at the farm is geared toward consistency in the pursuit of the best possible eating experience from their beef. Using seam cutting, their butchery produces the largest range of steaks in Britain (11 different muscles). Hardiesmill is also home to Tombuie Smokehouse and as a result, a range of smoked game, meats and cheeses are also available. They sell by web-order and farmers' markets, but try a trip to the farm for their 'ten steak experience',

an in-depth exploration of what affects beef, including a butchery demo and sampling (of all ten!).

■ Peelham Farm Produce

Beef, Lamb, Pork, Organic Foods
Peelham Farm, Foulden, Berwickshire
01890 781328, www.peelham.co.uk
Web/mail order.

If you fancy owning – and eating – your own pig, Peelham Farm's 'own a Tamworth' scheme aims to connect families with supply, as well as filling up their freezers with high-quality organic meat. Their ethical approach means veal is no longer off the menu – field-raised calves live free-range with their mothers for around nine months producing a rose veal that is both delicious and compassionate. Recent winners of a 'Future Farmer' award for their sustainable approach.

■ Shaws

Butcher
12 Market Place, Lauder, Berwickshire
01578 722306, www.tendertaste.com
Mon & Fri 7.30am–5.30pm; Tue–Thur 8am–5.30pm; Sat 8am–1pm. Closed Sun.
See main entry in Edinburgh & Lothian listings.

■ Tarelgin Farm Foods & Smokehouse

Farm Shop, Butcher, Smokery
West Tarelgin Farm, Coalhall, Ayrshire
0129 259 0590, www.tarelgin.com
Mon–Sat 9am–4.30pm; Sun 10.30am–2.30pm.
Web/mail order.

Set on West Tarelgin Farm, which lies approximately halfway between Ayr and Cumnnock on the A70, this farm shop is a prime outlet for meat raised on the farm and processed in the on-farm butchery. The addition of a smokehouse has added to the range, with salmon from Loch Duart, and they also do the occasional turn at fairs and farmers' markets smoking fish in half barrels covered with hessian sacking.

■ Tombuie Smokehouse

Cheese, Game, Smokery
Hardiesmill Place, Gordon, Berwickshire
01887 820127, www.tombuie.com
Web/mail order.
See entry for Hardiesmill.

CENTRAL SCOTLAND & FIFE

■ The Aberfoyle Butchers

Butcher, Haggis/Sausages
Mayfield, 206 Main Street, Aberfoyle
01877 382473

www.aberfoylebutcher.co.uk
Mon–Sat 8am–5pm. Closed Sun.
Web/mail order.

Running a traditional family business in the heart of the Trossachs, Jonathan Honeyman has established himself as one of Scotland's foremost butchers. At ease passing on his skills and knowledge to trainee butchers, chefs and the general public, Honeyman has always placed quality, heritage and respect for the seasons at the heart of his operation. His 'Legend' range seeks out 'premier cru' meat, game and poultry that reflect the true characteristics of a particular breed, cut, geographical provenance or particular diet.

■ Ballathie Good Food Company

Butcher, Beef, Game, Haggis/Sausages
Ballathie Estate, Kinclaven, Stanley, Perthshire
01250 876219
www.ballathiegoodfood.com
Tues–Sat 9.30am–5.30pm; Sun 10am–5.30pm.
Café, Web/mail order.

Pies, gourmet sausages, burgers and speciality cooked meats are the forte here at the Ballathie Good Food Company, where the Milligan family take the Aberdeen Angus beef and rare-breed pork from their own estate to make their produce. Wild venison and a range of wild game, which roam naturally on the 1,700-acre estate, are available in season. All goods are available from their farm shop in Perthshire; alternatively all packages are shipped for next day delivery.

■ Brig Farm Shop

Farm Shop
Gateside Home Farm, Bridge Of Earn, Perthshire
See Fruit & Veg Specialists.

■ Fletchers of Auchtermuchty

Farm Shop, Game, Farmed venison
Reediehill, Auchtermuchty, Cupar, Fife
01337 828369
www.seriouslygoodvenison.co.uk
Mon–Sun 8am–6pm.

The shop is essentially a porch on the outside of the Reediehill farmhouse, and an honesty box may be in operation, but both fresh and frozen venison from the farm is always available, along with useful cooking tips and some of the lauded books written by Nichola Fletcher. The best reason of all to come to the shop, arguably, is the chance to see the farm. Fletchers' venison can be found at most local farmers' markets.

CHEF'S CHOICE
PETE GOTTGENS ON GAME

For a chef, Scotland is the perfect natural larder, full of some of the world's finest fish, meat, vegetables, fruit and dairy . . . really, I'm spoilt. However, it's the game we have available to us that perhaps excites me more than anything. We took over Ardtalnaig Estate last year and from July until February we now have a superb choice of superb game on our doorstep. The estate is home to red deer, roe deer, grouse, duck, hare and pheasant, all of which feature on our menu.

Working closely with our game keeper, Ally McNaughton, I know just how the game is reared, where and on what it has fed and how it has been culled and hung, ready for the kitchen to take over. Hare in particular must be the most undervalued of all game in Scotland yet prepared carefully the fillets are fabulous – succulent and tender with a hint of gamey flavour.
■ *Pete Gottgens is chef/owner of Ardeonaig Hotel & Restaurant, South Road, Loch Tay, Ardeonaig, Perthshire, 01567 820400 www.ardeonaighotel.co.uk*

■ Gloagburn Farm Shop

Deli, Farm Shop, Beef, Haggis/Sausages
Gloagburn, Tibbermore, Perth
See Delis & General Food.

■ Hugh Grierson Organic

Beef, Lamb, Pork, Poultry/Eggs
Newmiln Farm, Tibbermore, Perth
01738 730201,
www.hughgrierson.co.uk
Buy from farm office.
Web/mail order.

Hugh and Sascha Grierson are committed organic farmers and active participants in the local food scene. They farm Aberdeen Angus, lamb, pork and, unusually in Scotland, a significant part of their business is in chicken. Most

CHEF'S CHOICE

TONY BORTHWICK ON WOODCOCK

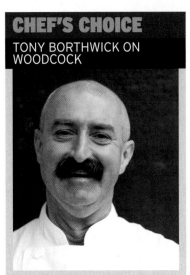

I love woodcock. Absolutely adorable little birds, beautiful, elusive, mysterious and hard to shoot, they have to be my favourite ingredient. It's a real pity they are so hard to get hold of, lunar cycles and all.

I love partridge (both red-legged and grey), which is a lot more readily available, but nothing beats a woodcock for flavour. I'm not keen on cooking them with their guts intact, but I do love to make the effort to cook the liver, heart and kidneys (albeit tiny organs) separately and to order, for me they complete the dish, with the head split.

I can't see past a few slices of autumn truffle and sliced ceps, celeriac purée, maybe a ravioli of mushrooms and a nice sauce flavoured with the chopped carcase of the bird. Cook it simply so you can taste how wonderful this little bird really is.
■ *Tony Borthwick is the chef-proprietor of The Plumed Horse in Leith. www.plumedhorse.co.uk*

recently vegetables have been added to their range. Their enthusiasm extends to a series of cooking tips and recipes on the website. Buy from them online, at Edinburgh Farmers' Market, or from the farm office.

■ House of Bruar
Deli, Butcher
By Blair Atholl, Perthshire
See Delis & General Food.

■ Simon Howie
Butcher, Game, Haggis/Sausages
• 112 High Street, Auchterarder, Perthshire
01764 664888
www.simonhowiefoods.co.uk
Mon–Sat 7am–5pm. Closed Sun.
• 270 High Street, Perth
01738 626376

Mon–Wed & Saturday 7am–5pm; Thu/Fri 7am–7pm.
Simon Howie's gleaming, hyper-styled shops in Perth and Auchterarder may be far removed from sawdust-strewn butchers of yore, but their produce and legacy are no less traditional. A family business, now into its fourth generation, the award-winning Perthshire institution supplies the Gleneagles and Old Course hotels among other restaurants and businesses, and its Auchterarder and Perth retail outlets have been named Scottish Butcher of the Year. While locally sourced game and hand-cured bacon are increasingly popular, their big breakfast deal (various sausages, black pudding, bacon and eggs) takes some beating.

■ Jamesfield Organic Centre
Farm Shop, Butcher, Organic Foods
Jamesfield Farm, Abernethy, Perthshire
See Delis & General Food.

■ Thomas Johnston Quality Butchers
Butcher, Haggis/sausages
• 2 Allan Crescent, Dunfermline, Flfe
01383 620658
Mon–Sat 8am–5pm. Closed Sun.
• 4 Main Street, Brightons, Polmont, Stirlingshire
01324 717126
Mon–Sat 8am–5pm. Closed Sun.
• 6/8 Cow Wynd, Falkirk, Stirlingshire
01324 623456
Mon–Sat 7am–5pm. Closed Sun.
• 25–27 High Street, Dunfermline, Fife
01383 724337
Mon–Sat 8am–5pm. Closed Sun.
• 7 Station Road, Oakley, Fife
01383 851660
Mon–Sat 8am–5pm. Closed Sun.
This multi-generation family concern with roots going back to 1861 is the best type of traditional butchery. From the quality meats raised in Scotland to their own potted and preserved meats, sausages, pies and ready meals, a visit to any one of their five shops in the Falkirk and Dunfermline areas will please traditionalists and foodies alike. From kitchens in Brightons come hand-made pies good enough to win, for instance, an award for Scotland's best sausage roll. On the non-meat front, there are Scottish tomatoes, eggs, honey and some fruit and veg.

■ D&A Kennedy
Butcher, Beef
36 High Street, Blairgowrie, Perthshire
01250 870358, www.kennedybeef.com
Mon–Sat 7am–5pm. Closed Sun.
Web/mail order.

Opened in 1982, D&A Kennedy have established themselves as one of Scotland's leading butchers. Alan Kennedy visits Forfar market every Wednesday to purchase livestock from tried and trusted local farms and suppliers, keen to assure traceability all the way from farm to plate, and beef is then hung for at least three weeks to ensure maximum tenderness and flavour. The Kennedys have been based at their Blairgowrie premises for the past ten years, and offer a nationwide mail order service.

■ McCallum the Butcher
Butcher, Beef, Haggis/Sausages
201 High Street, Auchterarder, Perthshire
01764 662128, www.bestbeef.co.uk
Mon–Sat 8am–5.15pm. Closed Sun.
Web/mail order.
A family butcher established in 1875, McCallum's prides itself on trusted, quality produce – not least naturally reared, local beef – and its long-standing relationships with Scotland's livestock farmers. While their spacious Auchterarder shop and affiliated Dunfermline Dobbies outlet are well stocked with meats, puddings, home-made pastries and specialities, they also offer a comprehensive online and mail-order service: award-winning haggis, Stornoway black pudding and venison sausages need never be out of your reach again.

■ Minick of St Andrews
Butcher
183 South Street, St Andrews, Fife
01334 472127
Mon–Fri 7.30am–5.30pm; Sat 7.30am–4pm. Closed Sun.
With high street shops under constant pressure from supermarkets, it's unusual to see a brand-new butcher, but this place opened in early 2010 to fill an obvious gap in St Andrews. Owner Stuart Minick has been the go-to man for butchery advice for shops around the country and in the States. The premises look modern, but their methods are traditional, and the meat comes mostly from Fife via the local St Andrew's Abattoir. Other products including pies are made in-house.

■ S Mitchell of Puddledub
Butcher, Water Buffalo
1 Cupar Road, Kennoway, Fife
01333 351245
www.puddledubbuffalo.co.uk
Mon–Sat 9am–5pm; Sat 9am–2pm.
Web/mail order.
Taking a step beyond the farmers' markets and direct supply, on which he'd founded his beef and water buffalo business, Steve Mitchell took over the

Simon Howie

butcher's shop in Kennoway, north of Leven, in 2009, as another outlet for his range of meat, which now includes 'Juicy' Jacob sheep. The expansion has continued with the opening of a butchery counter just across the Forth at West Craigie Farm Shop near South Queensferry.

■ Puddledub Pork & Fifeshire Bacon Co Ltd
Pork, Haggis/Sausages
Clentrie Farm, Auchtertool, Kirkcaldy, Fife
01592 780246, www.puddledub.co.uk
Mon–Fri 9am–5pm. (Phone in advance.)
Web/mail order.
Tom Mitchell is one of the founding fathers of the local food movement in Fife. His bacon, sausages, gammons and fresh pork cuts are well known at farmers' markets in Glasgow, Edinburgh, Perth and Fife; they can also be obtained from the farm – located between Kirkcaldy and Lochgelly – or online. Nephew Stephen runs his own business specialising in beef, water buffalo and lamb (see separate entry).

■ Rannoch Smokery
Smokery
Rannoch Smokery, Kinloch Rannoch, Perthshire
01796 472194
www.rannochsmokery.co.uk
Web/mail order.
Rannoch Smokery was founded in the late 1980s following a bad winter which prevented Ben Barclay's deer cull getting to market. Not to be defeated, he brined and smoked all of his meat, stopping it from going to waste and, in so doing,

created the first ever Rannoch Smokery smoked venison. The family business now produces smoked meats, game and poultry, as well as pates and chutneys, and distributes through a wide network of supermarkets and delis, as well as by mail order through their own website.

■ Stuart's of Buckhaven
Butcher, Pies
37 High Street, Leven, Fife
01333 429515
Mon–Sat 8am–5pm. Closed Sun.
Originally a bakery, this sixth-generation family butchers and bakers with shops across Fife began sourcing meat in the 1960s to guarantee the quality of their speciality pies. Current boss Alan Stuart founded the now highly prestigious World Scotch Pie Championship in 1999, an annual headline-grabber across the UK.

NORTH EAST SCOTLAND

■ Davidsons Specialist Butchers
Fruit & Veg, Butcher, Pies
Unit 1, Burn Lane, Inverurie, Aberdeenshire
01467 621212
www.davidsons-inverurie.co.uk
Mon–Sat 7.30am–5pm; Sun 10.30am–3pm.
With reputedly one of the largest selections of fresh meat in the UK, Davidsons also stock fish, fruit and veg, and a beautiful selection of their own pies. The latter are customarily savoury, but autumn brings apples, bought from neighbours and baked into pies

that don't hang around. Pork, lamb, raspberries and strawberries come from the family farm, with KellyBronze turkeys added to that list this year. Sourcing and responsibility are key – Davidsons are working towards carbon neutrality within two years.

■ The Deeside Smokehouse
Game, Haggis/Sausages, Smokery
Dinnet and Kinord Estate, Estate Office, Dinnet, Aboyne
01339 885341
www.thedeesidesmokehouse.com
Web/mail order.
Serena Humphrey's dynamic new operation not only incorporates an innovative smokehouse, but also a large vegetable garden and box scheme (trading as Royal Deeside Vegetables) and a local hamper business. Wild venison and pheasant from Dinnet and surrounding estates on Deeside are hot- and cold-smoked over whisky barrel chips, as well as made into salamis and chorizo. Along with smoked haggis, they're available online and from Dinnet Estate Office.

■ Finzean Estate Farm Shop & Tea Room
Farm Shop
Balnaboth, Finzean, Banchory, Aberdeenshire
See Delis & General Food.

■ Andrew Gordon Butchery and Fine Foods
Box Scheme, Butcher, Organic Foods
• 35–37 Chattan Place, Aberdeen
01224 587553
www.andrewgordonbutchery.com
Mon/Tue & Thu/Fri 7.30am–6.30pm; Wed 7.30am–1pm; Sat 7.30am–5.30pm.
• 32 Evan Street, Stonehaven
01569 767855
Mon/Tue & Thu/Fri 7.30am–6pm; Wed/Sat 7.30am–5.30pm. Closed Sun.
Shifting the emphasis of a modern butchers from beleaguered high-street remnant towards community food centre, Andrew Gordon's smart new shops in Aberdeen centre and Stonehaven not only stock quality local meats, but staff also show people how to treat them, running regular 'Foodie Nights' at the Aberdeen shop with preparation demos and tastings. The shops also stock a selection of organic, gluten-free and local produce, and they offer an organic vegetable box scheme.

■ Grant's Butchers
Butcher
187 Blackness Road, Dundee, Angus
01382 669556
Mon–Sat 7.30am–5.30pm. Closed Sun.
The numerous awards adorning the walls of this shop bear testimony to

CHEF'S CHOICE

CHRISTOPHER TROTTER ON FALKLAND BEEF

There has been a history of beef on the estate at Falkland in Fife for centuries, including the eponymous Falkland cow. While this has not been bred since the nineteenth century, there are cattle grazing its fields again. Last year's were Limousin cross breeds and I roasted them on the spit at the Big Tent festival. The meat was loose grained and full of flavour, and made excellent eating. This year Estate Manager Amelia Stevenson bought some Belted Galloways from their heartland in Dumfries and Galloway and these were ready for the festival – I roasting them again on the spit but also used the lesser bits to make burgers. The whole process of production from 'field to spit' took place within a 25-mile radius.
■ *Christopher Trotter is a Fife-based chef, writer and consultant. He organises the One Planet Food Village at the Big Tent Festival. His book* The Whole Hog *is published in September 2010.*

the quality and popularity of Grant's Butchers. An important part of the community since 1875, Grant's supplies many local businesses as well as a steady flow of regulars. With locally sourced beef, pork and lamb, it projects a sense of pride in the produce on offer – reflected in its various awards. Popular sellers are the range of enticingly flavoured burgers and the Balmoral chicken – fillets stuffed with haggis. Many other products can be enjoyed, from pots of soup to apple and rhubarb tarts made fresh daily.

■ D&A Kennedy
Butcher, Beef
12 Castle Street, Forfar, Angus
01307 462118
See main entry in Central Scotland & Fife listings.

■ Macbeth's
Butcher, Game, Haggis/Sausages
11 Tolbooth Street, Forres, Moray
01309 672254, www.macbeths.com

Mon–Fri 8am–5pm; Sat 8am–1pm.
Web/mail order.
A well respected and highly praised family-run butcher, Macbeth's rear their own grass-fed, native-breed beef. They also source local lamb, rare-breed pork from free-range pigs, wild venison from the Highlands and free-range chicken, ensuring that their meat is fully traceable. With the option to buy online as well as through the shop in Forres, Macbeth's quality products, which include home-made sausages and burgers as well as award-winning black pudding and haggis, are available across the UK.

■ Scott Brothers
Butcher
• 32 Nethergate, Dundee, Angus
01382 201342
Mon–Sat 8am–5.30pm. Closed Sun.
• 206 Strathmartine Road, Dundee, Angus
01382 819417
Mon–Sat 8am–5.30pm. Closed Sun.
Established in 1935, these popular butchers are now in the hands of the third generation of the family. The ethos remains traditional: stock is bought live from within a 30-mile radius, then butchered, hung, matured and prepared on-site. Specialising in pork, lamb and beef, each outlet also sells a range of freshly made ready meals, cooked meats and other deli items, as well as barbecue and party platters.

■ HM Sheridan
Butcher, Game, Haggis/Sausages
11 Bridge Street, Ballater
01339 755218
www.hmsheridan.co.uk
Mon–Sat 7am–5.15pm. Closed Sun.
Thriving under the guidance of John Sinclair and Barry Florence, former employees who were bequeathed the business by founder Mike Sheridan a few years ago, this Deeside butcher sources its beef, lamb and outdoor-reared pork from farms in the local area, along with venison and game birds from nearby estates. In addition, a large range of products are made within the shop, including traditional puddings, haggis and over 20 varieties of sausage.

■ The Store
Farm Shop, Butcher
Foveran, Newburgh, Ellon, Aberdeenshire
01358 788083
www.thestorecompany.co.uk
Mon–Sun 10am–5pm.
Café, Web/mail order.
A prominent and active local farm shop for the last decade, the Store is

located on the Booth family farm where grass-fed lamb and Aberdeen Angus beef are reared in small numbers. The well-stocked meat counter includes sausages and freshly made shepherd's pie, curry and lasagne, and various cuts and joints for the traditional Sunday roast – all prepared in the on-site butchery and kitchen. In addition, there's a range of locally sourced foods including vegetables and cheeses, while a new coffee shop offers a smart sit-in option to enjoy the sweet and savoury food on offer.

■ Wark Farm
Beef, Lamb, Pork, Charcuterie
Wark Farm, Cushnie, Alford
01975 581149
www.warkfarm.co.uk
10am–4.30pm on monthly Open Days.
Web/mail order.
This family-owned business is run by Dugie and Jenny Foreman in the low hills of Aberdeenshire. Wark specialises in meat and charcuterie that comes from traditional breed meats including Belted Galloway beef, Oxford, Sandy and Black pork, Hebridean lamb and Aylsebury duck. A familiar sight at local markets, they also hold monthly open days (Thursday, Friday and Saturday of a given weekend) and have a buyers' scheme. Their impressive range now includes pork pies, home-made confits, rilettes and even corned beef.

■ Watt the Butcher
Butcher, Beef
39–41 Murray Street, Montrose, Angus
01674 672777
Mon/Tue & Thu–Sat 8am–5.30pm; Wed 8am–1pm. Closed Sun.
Neil Watt was once in charge of meat at the Savoy hotel, and now owns this butchers, which acts as the exclusive outlet for the finely marbled flesh of pedigree Aberdeen Angus from the Glenbervie estate by Stonehaven. Watt has a formidable reputation for the quality and traceability of the meat on offer. Fresh liver and kidneys, as well as local lamb in season, are all available too.

HIGHLANDS, ISLANDS & ARGYLL

■ Briggs' Shetland Lamb
Lamb
Cuckron, Stromfirth, Weisdale, Shetland
www.briggs-shetlandlamb.co.uk
Web/mail order.
On his croft at Weisdale in the heart of the Shetland Mainland, Richard Briggs rears 100 per cent Shetland lambs, a breed recognised by the PDO

designation as a protected regional food name. Given their relatively small size they are a more manageable prospect sold as a whole lamb, and with all the processing taking place on Shetland a box can be ordered from the website with next-day delivery. Shetland lamb has a reputation for tender, sweet meat, and while Brigg's own animals are reared on classic island pasture, both hill-raised and seaweed-fed lamb from neighbouring crofts can be ordered.

■ Campbell Butchers

Butcher, Beef, Lamb, Haggis/Sausages
56 Frederick Crescent, Port Ellen, Isle of Islay
01496 300480
www.meatislay.co.uk
Mon–Sat 8.30am–5pm. Closed Sun.
Reopened in 2006 by Neil Campbell and Neil MacAffer, this butcher in Islay's east-coast ferry port has been an integrally involved in the revitalisation of local meat. Through links with Dunlossit Estate and the new, small-scale abbatoir, the Meat Islay brand offers beef and lamb entirely reared and processed on the island. A mobile van serves Jura and the west of the island with Campbell's produce, while Dunlossit's Market Hall sells local produce on Fridays from 11am to 4pm.

■ The Dounby Butchers

Farm Shop, Butcher, Lamb, Beef
Dounby, Orkney
01856 771777
Mon 9am–3pm; Tue–Fri 9am–5pm; Sat 9am–4pm. Closed Sun.
Web/mail order.
This family operation has built its reputation by stocking a growing range of local produce. Their specialities are lamb and Aberdeen Angus beef reared on the family farm. The Sinclairs manage the whole process from birth to butchers, maturing the beef for a minimum of three weeks. They also stock Westray pork, fish and shellfish from the surrounding Orkney waters, Orkney cheeses, bread, cakes and biscuits sourced from local bakers, oatmeal and beremeal from the local mill and local seasonal vegetables and tatties from nearby farms.

■ Globe Butchers

Butcher, Lamb
49–53 Commercial Road, Lerwick, Shetland Isles
01595 692819
www.globebutchers.co.uk
Web/mail order.
Established over 100 years ago, this

Dalbeattie Fine Foods

Lerwick-based butcher knows a thing or two about quality cuts. Shetland-reared lamb is a particular speciality (available from August to March), as well as beef and pork sourced from the north-east of Scotland. Summer barbecues are catered for with their selection of quality home-made sausages and burgers, as well as ready meals, including dishes such as meatballs in a tomato and herb sauce. Recipe ideas and helpful cooking instructions are also dished out regularly by the staff.

■ Lochaber Farm Shop, Crafts & Café

Farm Shop, Lamb, Pork
Unit 5, Lochaber Rural Complex, Torlundy, Fort William
See Delis & General Food.

■ Rothiemurchus Farm Shop & Deli

Farm Shop, Beef, Game
Rothiemurchus Centre, Inverdruie, by Aviemore, Inverness-shire
See Delis & General Food.

■ WJ MacDonald

Butcher, Stornoway Black Pudding
5 Francis Street, Stornoway, Isle of Lewis, Western Isles
01851 702077
www.wjmacdonald.com
Mon–Sat 7am–5.30pm. Closed Sun.
Web/mail order.
Despite a population of only 6,000, Stornoway manages to keep four

independent butchers in business (despite a couple of full-scale supermarkets). Now run by the Smith Brothers, this centrally located butcher claims to be the home of the original Stornoway black pudding, or Steornabhagh marag dubh. Macdonald's has keen prices and a personalised service with a chopping block at the end of the counter for bespoke cuts. In addition there's a small selection of goods from nearby Stag Bakery, packs of Wild West (Uig, Lewis) beef jerky and a freezer chest heaving with game birds and pre-packaged ostrich.

■ Charles MacLeod Ltd

Butcher, Lamb, Haggis/Sausages, Stornoway Black Pudding
Ropework Park, Matheson Road, Stornoway, Isle of Lewis, Western Isles
01851 702445
www.charlesmacleod.co.uk
Mon–Sat 8am–5.30pm. Closed Sun.
If you live in the Outer Hebrides, you'll know this butcher as Charlie Barley. In addition to the classic and increasingly famous black pudding, the Macleod family keep sheep on the Isle of Lewis and it is their lamb and mutton that you'll find here in season. Along with other Stornoway butchers, Charley Barley is part of a collective seeking to secure EU protection for Stornoway black pudding, so that no one elsewhere can claim to produce this marvellous product.

BREAD, CAKES & CHOCOLATE

Scottish artisan bakers

Patisserie Jacob

Everyone loves to have a small, charming bakery just around the corner, yet in Britain 95 per cent of the bread sold is made in factories. John Cooke spoke to some artisan bakers around Scotland who have started their businesses from scratch in the last few years.

MATTHEW ROBERTS
The Steamie Bakehouse,
Dunfermline.
www.steamiebakehouse.com

Inspiration for setting up?
Enjoyment of baking, and a desire to contribute to a healthier, more sustainable, and above all, delicious food culture.

How did you go about it?
We started supplying the local deli/café out of our kitchen and as we grew we moved the baking into a garden shed.

Who is involved?
My wife, Zillah Scott, bakes scones and soda bread, takes photos of our produce, writes most of the blog and does the paperwork, while I bake and deliver the bread and write the website.

Where do you sell?
We supply two deli/cafés: Reuben's in Dunfermline, and Food For Thought in Burntisland. We also run a bread club, whereby groups of neighbours order from us then we deliver the whole order to one of their houses.

Your range?
All of our breads are naturally leavened, with an emphasis on wholegrains for nutrition and taste. Each week we bake three regular breads and a special.

What are you most proud of?
Our Hearth Haggerty – a flatbread made with wheat and rye dough sandwiching cheese, onions and fresh sage – represents many of our aims: it uses local ingredients (such as Anster cheese), it links to traditional food culture (it's inspired by Northumbria's Pan Haggerty), and it is a substantial, sustaining, healthy and delicious bread.

Plans for the future?
Building our wood-fired oven, which will increase our capacity. In the long term, a larger bakery will allow us to become a hub for community baking and encourage more people to make great bread.

Scottish baking heroes?
Falko's bakes some of the best bread and pastries I have ever eaten. The Engine Shed provides fantastic social value as well as fantastic food.

ANDREW WILSON
Different Breid, Glasgow.
www.differentbreid.co.uk

Inspiration for setting up?
I was fed up with not being able to get decent bread in this country so I decided to make it myself. Very importantly, Fi Buchanan (founder of Heart Buchanan) lent me space in her deli kitchen to get started.

Who is involved?
Just myself, which is great because I love baking and have complete control. Heart Buchanan also provide invaluable support and resources.

Where do you sell?
Always available at Heart Buchanan, and I also supply IJ Mellis Cheesemongers and Woodwinters. At the weekends I bake for Stravaigin restaurant, and sell at Stirling farmers' market every month.

Your range?
All my breads are sourdoughs/naturally fermented using different blends of stoneground organic flour.

What are you most proud of?

I do lots of bread-making classes to encourage passion about real bread, so it is rewarding to be told by a past pupil that they've stopped buying bread and are enjoying making their own.

Plans for the future?

Building my own unit for the space and resources to improve what I am doing.

**JACOB PHILIP
Patisserie Jacob, Edinburgh.
www.patisseriejacob.co.uk**

Inspiration for setting up?

I love this profession and I would do it with God's grace, even if I just got a minimum wage.

How did you go about it?

My girlfriend Erika and I set up in late 2009. I trained at Maison Blanc in Oxford and I was working as a pastry chef for the Members' Restaurant at the Scottish Parliament.

Where do you sell?

From our bakery in Gorgie Road, and we are hoping to do farmers' markets.

Your range?

All our breads are slow fermented for 12–14 hours to allow full flavour development. We do sourdough breads, plus focaccia, rolls, pizzas, croissants and pastries. We also make tarts and cakes, and our savouries include our signature pork and black pudding pie.

Plans for the future?

The immediate plan is to have a larger bakery/café in another Edinburgh suburb, and create finer patisserie/boulangerie.

Scottish baking heroes?

I really like Falko at Bruntsfield and Mhor Bread in Perthshire.

**JUSTIN TUNSTALL
Tunstall's Organic Bakery,
Dunkeld.
www.tunstallsbakery.co.uk**

Inspiration for setting up?

My wife and I believe in organic and sustainable principles and don't agree that food needs to be produced using petro chemicals that are bad for the environment. Also, we couldn't find a good-quality local bakery so we decided to set one up.

How did you go about it?

I attended bakery courses and took inspiration from the likes of Andrew Whitley, Dan Lepard and Richard Bertinet. And then, with very little practical experience, opened the bakery four years ago.

Who is involved?

We're a very small, family-run bakery.

Where do you sell?

Local delis, restaurants and coffee shops and you'll find us at most of the local farmers' and community markets.

Your range?

Everything in our range – including classic whites, ciabatta, pagnotta, pain au levain, wholemeal – is made from scratch so we know exactly what goes into every product.

Plans for the future?

To set up our own retail outlet.

Scottish baking heroes?

Tapa Bakehouse in Glasgow. They produce a fantastic range.

**DAVID HOYLE
Findhorn Bakery,
Findhorn.
www.findhornbakery.co.uk**

Inspiration for setting up?

The Village Bakery in Penrith.

How did you go about it?

We were originally part of Phoenix wholefood shop in Findhorn ecovillage. Fresh bread was a natural extension.

Who is involved?

We have two trained bakers plus a support team. Jan Boultbee and I are the working co-owners.

Where do you sell?

Our adjacent Bakehouse Café is the main customer. We also sell to a number of specialist shops and attend farmers' markets.

Your range?

We bake seven days a week, using a range of fresh organic doughs – wheat, rye, spelt and gluten free. We make sourdough and yeasted breads.

What are you most proud of?

Surviving as a traditional small village bakery, maintaining a high standard of baking and being blessed by great local suppliers.

Plans for the future?

Our very rural location is a limiting factor, so the future is probably in cakes and healthy snacks.

Scottish baking heroes?

While not artisan, we have a lot of respect for Maclean's Bakery, a small. local bakery that has developed into a regional brand.

**CARLIEN DUJARDIN
Patisserie Dujardin,
Linlithgow.
www.patisseriedujardin.com**

Inspiration for setting up?

We wanted to produce some bread using organic ingredients, without any additives or shelf-life extenders – a clean product suitable for people with wheat sensitivities and intolerances.

How did you go about it?

After sourcing our ingredients and experimenting with recipes, we set up in a local industrial unit. Now, our products are 99% organic and 25% wheatfree.

Who is involved?

Myself and Michael Bennett, owner of Epulum restaurant in Linlithgow.

Where do you sell?

Linlithgow farmer's market and on Saturdays from Epulum restaurant. We also supply cafés, delis and restaurants, such as Grassroots and Biblocafe in Glasgow and Earthy in Edinburgh.

Your range?

Spelt and sesame loaves, light rye bread and special-recipe sourdough (using spelt and rye starters). Wheat-free cakes, puddings and desserts.

Plans for the future?

To supply Scotland with quality artisan, wheat-free breads and cakes.

Scottish baking heroes?

Falko in Morningside, Edinburgh.

Hawick Balls

Everyone knows the one about rugby players and oddly shaped balls. As Jo Laidlaw discovers, there's some Border confectionary equally deserving of its place in the rugby lexicon.

'The resulting sweet looks a bit like a pickled onion (or, according to some, a sheep's testicle). The flavour is buttery with a hard crunch setting them apart from other Borders sweeties'

Hawick's late, great Bill McLaren was famously never without a poke of the traditional sweeties named after his home town. He used them to start conversations, elicit information and garner gossip that would then be added to his 'big sheets' – the detailed information he used to support his rugby commentary. Despite McLaren's deserved reputation for impartiality, however, the members of the England team were apparently never invited to partake of his sweeties.

Now produced by Greenock-based Golden Casket, legend has it that Hawick Balls were first made in the town in the 1850s by one Jessie McVittie. She used to 'pull' her boiled sugar mix by hanging it over a nail and allowing gravity to stretch it out. Although the exact recipe remains secret, today the bools are made in open copper pans – which caramelise the sugar – with oil of peppermint providing a minty hint. The resulting sweet looks a bit like a pickled onion (or, according to some, a sheep's

testicle). The flavour is buttery and actually quite grown-up, with a hard crunch setting them apart from other traditional sweeties from Borders towns such as Jethart Snails and Berwick Cockles, which have a rock-like texture.

Scots are famous for their sweet tooth and, although Hawick Balls have moved away somewhat from their original place and method of production, they still feel like that rare beast – a local, traditional product that's both accessible and fun.

Easy as pie

Nicki Holmyard **looks at the different types of pastry used by the makers of Scotland's famous savoury pies.**

PHOTOS: SIMPLE SIMON PIES

L ook in the window of any good Scots baker and you will see a variety of tasty Scotch pies and Forfar bridies, alongside newer interlopers such as venison, curry, pork and haggis pies. They are all part of a rich tradition that has seen Scotland become famous for the quality of its savoury baking.

Even the Aberdeen Butterie, the flat, flaky, breakfast pastry that is the Scots' equivalent of the croissant, has a distinct savoury taste.

The Scotch Pie, the staple of the football terrace, is high quality fare these days and even has its own club and a world championship in its 12th year. This is organised annually by Alan Stuart, from Stuart's of Buckhaven. 'These were set up to encourage bakers to source top quality ingredients – and consumers to eat more pies – in the wake of several food scares in the 1990s,' he says.

The success of any pie depends partly on the type and quality of the pastry used. These are many and varied, and each baker swears by different flours, fats and mixing or rolling methods.

Cold-water crust, shortcrust, puff pastry and suet crust all rely on rubbing or folding fat into flour, adding water and then rolling out, whereas with hot-water crust, the fat is boiled with water, then poured into the flour to make a moulding pastry. Lard is traditionally used for savoury pastry, and vegetable shortening for vegetarian pies.

Forfar bridies are made with shortcrust pastry, while traditional

'The Scotch Pie, the staple of the football terrace, is high quality fare these days and even has its own club and a world championship in its 12th year'

bridies – such as those made famous by Stephens Bakery in Dunfermline – use puff pastry.

For his Scotch pies, Alan Stuart uses a thin boiled pastry made from three different flours, which is heat-formed into pie shapes, then left to dry before filling to give it a crisp texture.

Bernard Alessi, of Simple Simon Pies, makes up a demi puff pastry, which is half the thickness of traditional puff. He rolls it into a spiral, then cuts across the layers, which allows the pastry to shed fat during the

cooking process and crisp up. 'This, together with top quality ingredients, makes the perfect pie and I can't make them fast enough!' he says.

The hot-water crust for the Melton Mowbray-style pork pies made by Robert Corrigan, of Acanthus Hand-Made Pies, uses organic, unbleached flour with a touch of wholemeal, and fine Italian lard. 'This doesn't have a strong smell and its low melting temperature doesn't leave a greasy taste in the mouth, giving it excellent eating qualities,' he says.

A Scottish cheese board

Red Anster

The sister of the crumbly pressed cheese made by Jane Stewart of the St Andrews Cheese Company near Anstruther in Fife (www. standrewscheese.co.uk), it's made from unpasteurised cow's milk and is naturally flavoured with garlic and chives. The orange colour comes from annatto, a natural plant extract.

As the only naturally flavoured artisan or farmhouse cheese made in Scotland, Red Anster is out on its own. Simple crowdie can be flavoured with herbs or peppercorns, such as Loch Arthur's Crannog. If you like this style of cheese but not the flavouring, original Anster has a fresh, lemony tang while Connage's Cromal is an organic, light and crumbly cheese with clean flavours made from pasteurised cow's milk.

Ailsa Craig

Attractively shaped and named after the landmark island in the Firth of Clyde, this is an individual, fresh, fragile goat's cheese with a bloomy rind and a light and fluffy texture. Made by Ann Dorward in Dunlop, it's one of the very few goat's cheeses made in Scotland, and still only made in limited quantities.

Putting a plain goat's or ewe's milk cheese on a cheese board opens up another broad avenue of tastes and textures. Ann Dorward makes a number of these, including Glazert and Bonnet, both goat's milk cheeses. Based at Millaires, Sorbie by Newton Stewart, Galloway Farm Cheeses also makes the aromatic, nutty-flavoured Cairnsmore cheese using organic, unpasteurised ewe's milk, but only in the summer months.

Criffel

Made in Dumfriesshire by Barry Graham and the inspiring Loch Arthur Creamery (www.locharthur.org.uk), part of a Camphill community offering vocational opportunities to adults with learning disabilities, Criffel is an organic, unpasteurised cow's milk cheese with a sweet, creamy paste and a contrasting washed rind. Semi-soft in texture, it carries some strong, pungent flavours and is certainly a contender for the most impressive cheese currently being made in Scotland.

Criffel does stand out for its distinctive style but it is worth looking out for Lanark White, made seasonally from ewe's milk by Humphrey Errington in Lanarkshire, as well as his Maisie's Kebbuck, a slightly firmer, unpressed cow's milk cheese with a natural rind.

It's perfectly possible to fill your cheese board with artisan cheeses made in Scotland – in fact, you'll be spoilt for choice. The Larder has teamed up with Pierre Leger of much-respected cheese retailer and wholesaler Clarks Speciality Foods to assemble a local cheese board featuring some of the country's prime cuts.

■ *Clarks Speciality Foods*
www.clarksfoods.co.uk
Cheese board made using East Lothian wood available from Earthy Foods & Goods, Edinburgh (see p.16)

Dunsyre Blue

A soft blue, mould-ripened cheese made using unpasteurised milk from Ayrshire cows by Humphrey Errington on his farm by Carnwath in Lanarkshire (www.lanarkblue.com). When aged, the smooth, creamy-coloured cheese is streaked with blue-green mould, and while it has a spicy flavour, it's mellower and creamier than its seasonal sister cheese, Lanark Blue, made from ewe's milk.

A number of other blue cheeses are made in Scotland. Highland Fine Cheese's Strathdon Blue and Devenick Dairy's Badentoy Blue appeal to those looking for a milder, creamier blue, while Fatlips Castle Blue, made near Hawick by Jim and Annie Shanks, is produced in small rounds as a soft blue-veined cheese in the style of a blue camembert (cambozola).

Morangie Brie

As the name hints, this creamy, cow's milk brie is made near Tain by Ruaraidh Stone of Highland Fine Cheeses (www.hf-cheeses.com). It can be eaten as young as six weeks though it can mature for a number of months, with larger rounds tending to develop more flavour than smaller versions. The milk is pasteurised, so it won't ever reach the ripe tanginess of a cheese made from unpasteurised milk.

Alternatives include the organic brie, Clava, made by Connage Highland Dairy at Ardersier near Inverness (www. connage.co.uk), while the Devenick Dairy in Aberdeenshire (www.devenickdairy. co.uk) makes a brie-style called Monarch. In the Borders, Hawick's Standhill Cheesery (www.standhillcheesery.co.uk) has its Roxburgh Roondie.

Cambus o'May

A recent addition to the Scottish cheese scene, this pressed cheese from the eponymous Cambus o'May creamery on Royal Deeside (www. cambusomay.com) is made with unpasteurised milk. Using a technique called two-day curd, where the curds from two separate days' milking are mixed together to achieve a distinctive marbled effect, the cheese is pale in colour but has some lovely nutty and earthy flavours.

Alternatives to this include more familiar pressed cheeses such as a classic Dunlop (see p.71). Chris and Jeff Reade's Mull Cheddar is much loved, though undoubtedly fiercer when mature. Blarliath from Highland Fine Cheeses is an increasingly popular milder alternative cheddar-style farmhouse cheese.

The milky way

Milk – and what it can be turned into – are integral not only to the Scottish diet, but also to our culinary heritage, writes Carine Seitz.

Whether it's in our afternoon coffee or morning bowl of cereal, most of us drink milk every day without giving it any thought beyond whether it's fresh.

But what is milk and where does it come from? Well, most commonly, cows. The characteristics of milk can vary depending on two things: the breed of cow, and the grass and other feed it consumes.

Jersey and Guernsey cows produce milk with a particularly rich and creamy taste due to a higher level of butterfat. It has an almost yellow hue and is especially suitable for making cream and ice-cream. Brown Swiss cows' milk has higher protein levels and is good for cheese.

The majority of dairy cows in Scotland, however, are black and white Holstein Friesians or Ayrshires. The latter, defined as a breed in the 1870s in south-west Scotland, are strong, rugged cattle with an ability to forage for themselves in poorer terrain and less favorable climatic conditions. These qualities, along with strong milk yields and generally good health, make the brown-and-white Ayrshires outstanding commercial cattle for Scottish dairy farms. It's no coincidence that the largest producing Scottish farms are found in Dumfries & Galloway and Ayrshire, where rainfall levels are higher and the grass grows long and lush in the summers too damp for reliable grain production.

In Scotland, the milk found in shops has been pasteurised to kill off harmful micro-organisms. This process involves heating the milk to 72C for 15 to 30 seconds and then cooling it rapidly (UHT is Ultra Heat Treated, giving it a longer shelf life). It is also often homogenised, when the milk undergoes a process that forces the milk through small holes at high pressure, breaking up the fat globules. This spreads the fat evenly throughout the milk and prevents a creamy layer forming at the top, resulting in a more uniform consistency and a whiter colour because the greater numbers of fat globules

'Jersey and Guernsey cows produce milk with a particularly rich and creamy taste due to a higher level of butterfat'

scatter the light more effectively.

Some people drink milk in its raw form – untreated and essentially straight from the cow. It contains enzymes, higher concentrations of vitamins and probiotics and tastes richer and creamier than treated milk but it may contain bacteria such as salmonella. Since 1983 it has been illegal to sell unpasteurised milk in Scotland.

Organic milk is produced from cows that have grazed on grass grown with no additional artificial pesticides, herbicides or fertilisers. Whole milk has nothing added or removed and, contrary to popular belief, is low in fat at around only 3.5 per cent. Skimmed has nearly all the fat removed, but consequently has lower levels of soluble vitamins, though conversely, slightly more calcium. With 2 per cent fat, semi-skimmed is the most popular milk in the UK.

All dairy products start life as milk. There's cream (produced by separating the fat from milk through centrifugation; the addition of bacterial culture produces crème fraîche and soured cream); butter (produced by churning cream); yoghurt (produced by live bacterial fermentation of milk with thicker yoghurts the result of separating the whey from the main curd); ice-cream (frozen sweetened custard most commonly made from cream, milk and egg yolk); and cheese, of which the varieties run into thousands.

To produce any cheese, the basic principles are essentially the same: starter cultures are added to milk, which then grow and ripen to develop flavours and aromas. Rennet is added to coagulate the liquid and turn it into curds and whey, which is then pressed to force out the whey. The cheese is then left to mature. Cream cheeses, including crowdie and fromage frais, are left for a matter of days, while soft cheeses of a camembert style are matured for around 60 to 90 days. Hard cheeses are matured for a long period – mature cheddars are left for six to nine months. The US writer Clifton Fadiman described cheese as 'milk's leap towards immortality.'

As an industry, however, Scottish dairies are under pressure. The latest figures collected by the Scottish Dairy Cattle Association show that there are only 1072 dairy farms left in Scotland, around a tenth of the figure 50 years ago. The National Farmers' Union also estimates that farmers can often lose money on every litre of milk they sell to supermarkets – so why do they do it? Dairy farming is a hard-working, traditional way of life. It is a skill passed down through generations: many farmers' fathers did it, and their fathers before them. Dairy products – milk, cream and artisan cheeses – are as much an integral part of our Scottish culinary heritage as seafood, game and beef.

>SOME OF THE INDEPENDENT SPECIALIST DAIRY PRODUCERS IN SCOTLAND:

Milk/Cream:

Arran Dairies
Brodick, Isle of Arran

Bonaly Farm Dairy
www.bonalyfarmdairy.co.uk
Loanhead, Midlothian

Clyde Organics
www.clydeorganics.co.uk
Muirhouse Fram, Carnwath, Lanarkshire

Grahams
www.grahamsfamilydairy.com
Airthrey Kerse Farm, Henderson Street, Bridge of Allan

Kerr's Dairy
www.kerrsdairy.co.uk
Strathmartine Road, Dundee

Mitchells
www.mitchells-scotland.com
Inverurie, Aberdeenshire

North Street Dairy
www.northstreetdairy.co.uk
22 North Street, Forfar, Angus

The Orkney Creamery
www.orkneyicecream.com
Crantit Dairy, St Ola, Orkney

Quothquan Farm
www.quothquanfarms.co.uk
Biggar, Lanarkshire

Yester Farm Dairies
www.yesterfarmdairies.co.uk
Gifford, East Lothian

Butter:

The Devenick Dairy
www.devenickdairy.co.uk
Banchory, Aberdeenshire

Grahams (see above)

Stichill Jerseys
Garden Cottage Farm, Kelso

Yoghurt:

The Devenick Dairy (see above)

Katy Rogers Creamery
www.knockraich.com/creamery.html
Knockraich Farm, Fintry, Stirlingshire

Loch Arthur Creamery
www.locharthur.org.uk
Beeswing, Dumfriesshire

Rowan Glen
www.dalefarm.co.uk
Newton Stewart, Galloway

West Highland Dairy
www.westhighlanddairy.co.uk
Achmore, Stromeferry, Ross-shire

For more on cheese and ice-cream producers and specialists, see elsewhere in this chapter and the online listings at www.thelarder.net

Flavour of the month

The availability of quality produce from diversifying dairy farms has fuelled a taste for ice-cream from our independent makers, writes Cate Devine.

The Scots-Italian culture may be alive and licking in Scotland but when it comes to making ice-cream it seems that tradition is dying out. Our taste for the old-fashioned milk-ice, brought to us by postwar Italian immigrants and made with milk, sugar and cornflour, is being overtaken by a preference for the creamy stuff – thanks to an unprecedented availability of top quality high-fat milk and double cream from Scottish farms. 'Even the Italians who come to visit us are amazed by the tremendous quality of our milk and cream,' says David Equi, whose fourth-generation ice-cream company, Equi of Hamilton, won top awards in six categories at this year's Royal Highland Show. 'Italian gelato is lighter because the quality of milk in Italy isn't that good. Their good milk all goes to making mozzarella.'

Equi produces some 300,000 litres of 14 per cent fat dairy ice-cream each year to a recipe adapted from his Italian great-grandfather's, and supplies bespoke flavours to the G1 Group and Rogano in Glasgow, as well as 12 Asda stores and 130 wholesalers. He also part-owns the famous Nardini's café in Largs, which

'Ironically, the low prices that supermarkets pay for milk have helped to boost the independent ice-cream sector'

makes its own luxury ice-cream using butter.

Ironically, the low prices that supermarkets pay for milk have helped to boost the independent ice-cream sector. Arran Dairies Ice Cream, for example, began in a desperate attempt to develop a market for the milk from the island's three remaining dairy farms (at one time there were 30). Sales have increased ten-fold in ten years to around 2400 litres a week. 'We doubled our market on the island in the first year alone, proving demand was certainly there,' says Alastair Dobson, managing director of Arran Dairies and the founder of Taste of Arran, a group of 11 food and drink producers on the island. Clients for his 14 per cent fat dairy ice-cream include the Macdonald hotel group throughout the UK, National Trust for Scotland properties and Dobbies garden centres. The supermarket trade is not an avenue Dobson chooses to go down.

Instead, a new business in bespoke ice-creams is developing. Dobson has so far created 70 flavours – including Scottish rhubarb ripple and Arran lemon verbena for the recent Open Golf at St Andrews. However, vanilla is the most popular: it's made up of three parts milk to one part cream. Arran milk has an unusually high fat content of up to 4.6 per cent; the cream 48 per cent, and the end product contains 12 per cent fat.

Bespoke ice-cream is popular with modern chefs who want to help to keep local, traditional skills alive and

who get a kick out of being able to name-check not only their supplier but in some cases even the cows that provided the necessaries. Which makes smaller artisan producers increasingly sought-after.

Meanwhile, at the delightfully named Meikle Dripps Farm at Thorntonhall, on the southside of Glasgow, Micki Henderson churns out some 270 litres of her bespoke handmade 8 per cent fat ice-cream each week to supply retail outlets and some of Glasgow's top restaurants including Crabshakk, Gamba, the Dining Room, Urban Brasserie and Red Onion. Flavours include black pepper, gingerbread, balsamic vinegar and liquorice. The business began four years ago as a way of supplementing income from Micki's husband John's dairy farm at a time when milk prices paid by supermarkets were plummeting. She now uses the farm's milk, cream and eggs. As a result, the company is unlikely to go down the supermarket route. 'We wouldn't want to grow too big because it would change our USP and we'd become just like everybody else,' says Micki.

■ *Equi is at 9–11 Burnbank Road, Hamilton, 01698 282494*
A Taste of Arran, Brodick, Isle of Arran, 01770 302374,
www.taste-of-arran.co.uk
Thorntonhall Farmhouse Ice Cream, Meikle Dripps Farm, Thorntonhall, Glasgow, 0141 644 2226,
www.thorntonhallicecream.co.uk
Cate Devine is The Herald's food writer.

Dunlop Cheese

Scotland's equivalent of Cheddar is enjoying a revival thanks to a number of artisan makers. Jackie Hunter looks at the story of Ayrshire's Dunlop.

Scotland doesn't produce many hard cheese varieties, but Dunlop is one that dates back to the 17th century, when farmer's wife Barbara Gilmour pioneered a process using unskimmed – or 'sweet' – milk from the Ayrshire cows at Hill Farm. Her method produced a distinctly creamy texture and mellow, nutty taste and was so widely copied that Dunlop soon became Scotland's equivalent of cheddar. It all but vanished in the mid 20th century owing to dairy-industry consolidation, but a quiet revival began two decades ago and is now blossoming as farmhouse cheeses, rather than mass-produced varieties, become increasingly sought after.

'We moved here in 1985 and opened up the dairy,' says Ann Dorward, of West Clerkland Farm in Ayrshire. 'Because we're only a mile from Dunlop village, it seemed obvious that Dunlop cheese was what we should make.' Although she follows the Gilmour method there is no actual recipe in existence, Ann points out. 'The cheese's characteristics depend purely on the grasslands where the cattle graze, the local climate and the weather. The area is what makes it unique and that's why we applied for PDO [Protected Destination of Origin] status four years ago. If it's ever granted we'll have to give our cheese a new name, because Dunlop has become a generic term – it can be made anywhere.' The Dorwards are presently the only Dunlop producers in Ayrshire, so a PDO status now would be theirs alone.

Pam Rodway and her husband Nick have been making Dunlop farther north, on their Moray farm, since 1997 (but this year have retired from cheesemaking). They always used Ayrshire cows, however, 'because they're synonymous with Dunlop, produce high-quality milk with small fat globules, respond well to organic husbandry and are healthy, hardy creatures that can spend long periods outdoors,' Pam says. The result? 'Similar to cheddar, but less acidic, not as strong-tasting.'

A much newer Dunlop producer is Connage Highland Dairy near Inverness. The farm has belonged to the Clark family for 60 years and converted to organic production in 1996, when brothers Callum and Cameron Clark built a high-spec dairy and began making cheese. 'Dunlop was one of our original cheeses,' says Jill Clark. 'It's a higher-moisture cheese, matured for five to seven months – about half the time of a cheddar – and mellow, but with a little kick at the end. It's very popular, probably because cheese-lovers are looking for good alternatives to what's widely available. There are currently more than 800 British cheeses – Dunlop is just a bit different.'

'Because we're only a mile from Dunlop village, it seemed obvious that Dunlop cheese was what we should make'

WHERE TO BUY

EDINBURGH & LOTHIANS

■ Clarks Speciality Foods
202 Brunsfield Place, Edinburgh
0131 656 0500, www.clarksfoods.co.uk
Mon–Fri 10am–6pm; Sat 9am–5pm;
Sun noon–4pm.
Clarks Speciality Foods is mainly a
wholesalers, supplying some of the
best hotels and restaurants in Scotland.
However, for the past five years the
good folk of Bruntsfield have been able
to shop in this gourmet emporium.
Specialising in farmhouse and artisan
cheese, they have 30 Scottish varieties,
including those from Cambus O'May.
There are also pastas, oils, olives,
vinegars and charcuterie and every
week fruit and veg arrives directly from
the Marché d'Intérêt National de Rungis
in Paris.

■ S Luca of Musselburgh
Patisserie, Chocolate/Confectionary,
Ice Cream
• 32–38 High Street, Musselburgh
0131 665 2237
 www.lucasicecream.co.uk
Mon–Sat 9am–10pm; Sun
10.30am–10pm.
• 16 Morningside Road, Edinburgh
0131 446 0233
Mon–Sun 9am–10pm.
Café.
Now into a third generation of ice-
cream making, S Luca continues to
delight Morningside and Musselburgh
locals with its renowned speciality.
Manufactured at its two outlets, Luca's
ice-cream can be enjoyed in a variety
of flavours, from the traditional to
the quirky. Its friendly and accessible
parlours offer a cross-section of
customers a treasure-trove of
confectionery, as well as quality comfort
food that serves as the perfect appetiser
for a classic ice-cream sundae.

■ IJ Mellis Cheesemonger
Cheese, Deli
• 6 Bakers Place, Edinburgh
0131 225 6566, www.mellischeese.co.uk
Mon–Fri 9am–6.30pm; Sat 9am–6pm;
Sun noon–5pm.
• 330 Morningside Road, Edinburgh
0131 447 8889
Mon–Wed 9am–6pm; Thu 9am–6.30pm;
Fri 9am–7pm; Sat 9am–6pm; Sun
11am–5pm.
• 30a Victoria Street, Edinburgh
0131 226 6215
Mon–Sat 9.30am–6pm; Sun noon–5pm.
Since opening his first premises in 1993,
Iain Mellis has established a mini empire

of cheesemonger's shops between
Edinburgh, Glasgow, Aberdeen and
St Andrews, though each shop has an
individual feel, with the Victoria Street
branch being something of a little sister
yet still sharing the same reputation for
supplying the best British farmhouse
cheeses. Well-trained, friendly staff are
on hand to help you choose from the
stacks of regional and global cheeses,
and are happy to let customers try before
they buy. With an array of local meats,
crackers, bread and chutneys for sale
alongside the cows', goats' and sheep's
cheeses, new customers will surely want
to make it part of their weekly shop.

GREATER GLASGOW & CLYDESIDE

■ IJ Mellis Cheesemonger
Cheese, Deli
492 Great Western Road, Glasgow
0141 339 8998, www.mellischeese.co.uk
Mon–Fri 9.30am–7pm; Sat 9am–6.30pm;
Sun 10am–5pm.
See main entry in Edinburgh & Lothians
listings.

CHEF'S CHOICE
GEOFFREY SMEDDLE ON
ANSTER CHEESE

Fife is hugely fortunate to have its own
landmark cheese production farm,
the St Andrews Farmhouse Cheese
Company, home of Anster cheese.
Ever since first tasting this traditional,
unpasteurised cheese, we have
always had their Anster on our trolley
of Scottish cheeses, and sometimes
even on the menu itself. Made by Jane
Stewart with milk from her husband's
dairy herd just a few miles from here,
it is a crumbly textured and complex
flavoured cheese of which all locals can
be justly proud. There is even a viewing
gallery where visitors can admire the
cheese production process, before you
buy some to take home. Try it.
■ *In 2010 Geoffrey Smeddle of The
Peat Inn won 'Chef of the Year' at
the CIS Awards, as well as his first
Michelin Star.*

■ George Mewes Cheese
Cheese, Bread
106 Byres Road, Glasgow
0141 334 5900
www.georgemewescheese.co.uk
Tue–Sat 10am–7pm; Sun 11am–5pm.
Closed Mon.
Having opened in the summer of
2010, this cheesemonger quickly
became a popular stop for Byres Road
shoppers. From the various artisan
breads to the stacks of cheeses
ranging from Scottish favourites such
as Anster, Lanark Blue and Isle of
Mull Cheddar to cheeses from around
the world, George Mewes carefully
sources all his produce and will happily
and knowledgeably enthuse about
his wares. Also for sale are items
complementing the cheeses, from
chutneys, oatcakes and crackers
to cured meats and the appropriate
equipment such as knives and boards.

SOUTHERN SCOTLAND

■ Ayrshire Farmhouse Ice Cream
Ice Cream
Catrine House Coffee Shop & Ice Cream
Parlour, Catrine House, Mauchline,
Ayrshire
01290 552093
www.ayrshireicecream.co.uk
Mon–Sun 10am–5pm.
Café.
A Scandanavian-style wooden chalet
is the new focal point for Jo and Willy
Templeton's farm-based ice-cream,
made from raw milk and cream from
their herd of pedigree Ayrshire cows.
The shop stocks a small selection of
local produce and deli items along
with various flavours of ice-cream and
fruit sorbet – at different times many
dozen varieties are made, ranging from
amaretto to whisky and marmalade
– alcohol is common, but you'll also find
nuts, Scottish raspberries and vanilla
from Madagascar.

■ Cream o' Galloway Dairy
Ice Cream
Rainton, Gatehouse-of-Fleet, Dumfries
& Galloway
01557 814040
www.creamogalloway.co.uk
Mid March–October: Mon–Sun 10am–
5pm (July–Aug closes 6pm).
Café.
Established in the early 1990s, Cream o'
Galloway has been producing fair-trade
dairy ice-cream and frozen smoothies
for over a decade. Using only the finest
organically grown ingredients to produce
their ice-creams, they are serious
about their commitment to reduce their

impact on the environment and always trade with ethical considerations at the forefront of their mind. You can keep the kids entertained on a day out at the visitor centre where they can spot wildlife and let off steam in the various play areas, both indoors and outdoors. Afterwards, enjoy a treat in the tearoom or ice-cream parlour where there are nearly 30 different flavours to choose from before buying more to take home from the shop.

■ Loch Arthur Creamery

Cheese, Bread, Farm Shop
Camphill Village Trust Ltd, Beeswing, Dumfries, Dumfriesshire
0138 776 0296, www.locharthur.org.uk
Mon–Fri 9am–5.30pm; Sat 10am–3pm. Closed Sun.
Web/mail order.

Grown out of the productive efforts of a diverse and vibrant community, Loch Arthur Creamery is a social enterprise committed to creating meaningful work and making a positive contribution to the local community. From humble beginnings in 1985 using the milk from their two Jersey and two Ayrshire cows, their cheeses have since grown to become recognised and sought after, winning awards and accolades in some of the UK's top competitions every year

The Cheesery

Connage Highland Dairy

Swiss in particular – this is the place to go if you're looking to buy a whole wheel of Gruyere. If there's something in particular you're after, Robertson will have the cheese ripened and ready for collection. The shop also stocks general delicatessen items.

■ IJ Mellis Cheesemongers
Cheese, Deli
149 South Street, St Andrews, Fife
01334 471 410, www.mellischeese.co.uk
Mon–Fri 9am–5.30pm; Sat 9am–6pm;
Sun 10am–5pm.
See main entry in Edinburgh & Lothians listings.

■ St Andrews Farmhouse Cheese Company
Cheese
Falside Farm, Anstruther, Fife
01333 312580
www.standrewscheese.co.uk
Mon–Sat 9.30am–4.30pm; Sun
11am–4.30pm.
Café.
Jane Stewart's highly regarded artisan cheese can be bought directly from the farm, along with a small selection of deli items, at the counter of the Butterpat Coffee Shop. The cheese-making can be seen from a viewing gallery adjoining the shop on production days – commonly Mondays, Tuesdays and Wednesdays, but check before visiting.

■ Stewart Tower Dairy
Ice Cream, Farm Shop
Stewart Tower Farm, Stanley, Perth
01738 710044, www.stewart-tower.co.uk
Mon–Sun 10am–4.30pm.
Café.
Using fresh whole milk from their herd of pedigree Holstein Friesian cows, Stewart Tower produces hand-made ice-creams in a staggering range of flavours, as well as fruit ices and frozen yoghurts to sell from their parlour in converted farm steadings. Visit the Round House coffee shop for home-made soup and a slice of cake or, in finer weather, relax on decking overlooking the Strathmore Valley. The farm shop stocks Scottish produce including fruit and vegetables from local farmers and suppliers and a range of preserves, cheeses and meats.

NORTH EAST SCOTLAND

■ Cambus O'May Cheese Co.
Cheese
Craigmyle, Torphins, Aberdeenshire
01339 889327, www.cambusomay.com
This 2009 start-up makes various traditional farmhouse-style pressed cheeses using raw milk, including the

---

since 1991. Their extensive range of cheeses and yoghurts are sold in their farm shop, other shops throughout the UK, and are also available via mail order.

■ Standhill Cheesery
Cheese
Standhill Farm, Minto, by Hawick
01835 870225
www.standhillcheesery.co.uk
The definition of a quirky, artisanal producer with just six cheeses available through farmers' markets and delis. It's two years since Standhill started production and the first batch of Minto Mellow Cheddar has now matured. Winter snow led to transport issues and a glut of milk, which was promptly transformed into a fresh crowdie, now a bestseller. Also popular is the fabulously named Fatlips Castle Blue – called after a local landmark, not one of the coos.

CENTRAL SCOTLAND & FIFE

■ B Jannettas
Ice Cream
31 South Street, St Andrews, Fife
01334 473285, www.jannettas.co.uk
Mon–Sat 9am–5.30pm; Sun
7am–5.30pm.
Café.
Jannetta's was one of the earliest Italian ice-cream parlours to open in Fife in the late 19th century. Since then, the original recipe has been handed down four generations and now comes in

---

more than 50 different flavours. Among Italian favourites such as raspberry are some Scottish tastes, for example tablet flavour, with chunks of crumbly fudge within. Everything is made on site behind the shop, and their café sits next door.

■ Luvians
Deli, Ice Cream, Whisky
93 Bonnygate, Cupar, Fife
01334 654820, www.luvians.com
Mon–Thu 9am–6pm; Fri/Sat
9am–6.30pm.
Vincent Fusaro is passionate about ice-cream. The business was started in 1955 by his father, and now comprises this branch as well as separate wine merchant and ice-cream parlour in St Andrews. Ice-cream making happens behind the Cupar premises, but at the front the large bottle shop also sells deli items with a mixture of French and Italian produce, and a selection of Scottish cheeses too.

■ McDonalds Cheese Shop
Cheese
Westfields, Balmoral Road, Rattray, Blairgowrie
01250 872493
www.mcdonaldscheeseshop.co.uk
Tue–Sat 9am–5pm. Closed Sun/Mon
(Jun–Aug open Sun 10am–4pm).
With a history stretching back nearly 50 years, McDonald's is a mini emporium of cheese owned by Caroline Robertson. The stock runs to 80 varieties of British and continental artisan styles and

---

eponymous Cambus O'May, crumblier Lairig Ghru and sharper Lochnagar. Though currently based in Torphins, the cheeses are available online as well as at many Aberdeenshire delicatessens, farm shops and grocers, and they hope to make a move soon to a dedicated cheesemaking facility on the Reids' family farm at Cambus O'May, just east of Ballater, which will include a viewing platform where visitors can watch the cheese being made.

■ The Cheesery

Cheese

9 Exchange Street, Dundee
01382 202160, www.thecheesery.co.uk
Mon 10.30am–5.30pm; Tue–Fri 9.30am–5.30pm; Sat 9.30am–5pm. Closed Sun.
Based in Dundee, this award-winning independent cheese specialist sells a range of quality regional and continental artisan cheeses. With an aim to offer customers new cheeses on a weekly basis, their range stretches to around 50 varieties, around half of which hail from the British Isles. Choose from an impressive array of accompaniments from olives, chutneys and savoury preserves to oatcakes and biscuits, and for real cheese aficionados there's a selection of kitchenware and utensils including hand-carved cheese and breadboards, platters and domes to enjoy you get maximum enjoyment.

■ The Devenick Dairy

Cheese, Farm Shop

Bishopston Farm, Banchory Devenick, Aberdeenshire
01224 782476
www.devenickdairy.co.uk
Mon–Fri 10am–6pm, Sat/Sun 10am–5pm.
Web/mail order.
A local family-run dairy farm based on the south-western outskirts of Aberdeen, Devenick Dairy produces a growing range of hand-crafted cheeses as well as yoghurts, including drinking yoghurt. The farm shop is tucked away but it's well stocked with fresh cream, butter, free-range eggs, ready meals and vegetables, as well as produce sourced from other local businesses including wild venison, chutneys, puddings and oatcakes. Devenick also supply to other retail outlets and their products can now be found widely across the north-east and beyond.

■ IJ Mellis Cheesemonger

Cheese, Deli

201 Rosemount Place, Aberdeen
01224 566530, www.mellischeese.co.uk
Mon–Fri 10am–5.30pm; Sat 9am–5.30pm. Closed Sun.
See main entry in Edinburgh & Lothians listings.

■ Mitchells

Deli, Cheese, Ice Cream

Market Place, Inverurie, Aberdeenshire
01467 621389
www.mitchells-scotland.com
Mon–Sat 7.30am–5.30pm. Sun 11am–4pm.
Café, Web/mail order.
'Naturally we're local' runs the strapline, and this neatly sums up this community-minded family dairy business. Milk and cream are produced by the Mitchell herd just outside Inverurie and delivered throughout the north-east. Their produce, including ice-cream, finds its way to the Mitchells shop and restaurant in Inverurie. A commitment to local producers is evident in the shop with the majority of items, including fruit and veg, fish and meat, baked goods, cereal, sweets and alcohol, coming from the wider regional community. Various hampers of local fare are available from the shop or online.

HIGHLANDS, ISLANDS & ARGYLL

■ Connage Highland Dairy

Cheese, Farm Shop, Organic Foods

Milton of Connage, Ardesier, Inverness
01667 462000, www.connage.co.uk
Mon–Sat 10am–4pm.
Web/mail order.
To see how the hand-made cheeses offered in the Connage Pantry are made, just look through the big window in this Ardesier farm shop. The process is laid bare, from the organic milk from Callum and Jill Clark's 140 cows grazing nearby, through to the stainless-steel baths churning out seven different cheeses. There are five hard and two soft varieties, almost all shining at award shows in the short time since this Morayshire gem began in 2006.

■ The Island Cheese Company Ltd

Cheese

Home Farm, Brodick, Isle of Arran
01770 302788, www.islandcheese.co.uk
Mon–Sat 9am–5pm; Sun 10am–5pm.
Web/mail order.
A family-run business established 15 years ago on the home farm of Brodick Castle, they produce a range of wax-sealed flavoured and deluxe cheddars for sale in their shop, through farmers' markets and a number of other outlets including farm shops, delicatessens and restaurants throughout the UK. Such is demand for their cheese that a mail order service is available, where a further array of Arran preserves and oatcakes, Scottish drinks and hand-made chocolates are also available.

If asked to name their champion produce, any chef worth his salt shouldn't have to think about it. Top quality seafood, game, poultry, meat, fresh produce, dairy, breads, baking and preserves are all now widely available from artisan producers from all over Scotland. The beauty is that, in the main, the produce is seasonal and local.

It's a tough call to single out a sole supplier or producer, but Thorntonhall Farmhouse Ice Cream gets my vote. Started in 2003 on the Meikle Dripps Farm, Thorntonhall, by John and Micki Henderson, their plan was simple but brilliant. Convert an existing barn into an ice-cream production unit and turn the milk surplus into the best ice cream available. It's the best because they combine milk that's fresh from the morning's milking with award-winning Corrie Mains Farm's free-range eggs, sugar and natural flavourings. And that's it – all good and free of artificial colourings, emulsifiers and stabilisers.

They don't whip any air into the ice cream, so the finished product is rich, luxuriant and heavy with cream. We team a slice of hot chocolate-chip brownie with a ball of their honeycomb ice cream for spectacular results, and a scoop of cream ice cream in a strawberry sundae is the perfect summer pudding.

■ *John Quigley is Chef Patron at Red Onion, 257 West Campbell Street, Glasgow, 0141 221 6000, www.red-onion.co.uk Thorntonhall Farmhouse Ice Cream, Meikle Dripps Farm, Thorntonhall, Glasgow, 0141 644 2226, www.thorntonhallicecream.co.uk*

FISH & SHELLFISH

Tackling Scotland's fish

Fish and shellfish rank among our most lauded produce, but there are issues of sustainability and less confidence generally in how to handle fish in the kitchen. With Seafood Scotland and chef Kevin MacGillivray, we offer a handy guide to recognising, understanding and cooking some of Scotland's best species.

Herring

The North Atlantic herring fishery takes place in spring and the North Sea fishery in late summer, when fish gather in large shoals to spawn.

Once the core of the Scottish fishing industry, herring stocks came near to collapse in the 1970s and are now monitored carefully to ensure that they are sustainable. The two fisheries have achieved Marine Stewardship Council (MSC) certification (for more on this, see p.155).

Herring is an oil-rich fish that's full of omega-3 fatty acids. Fresh herring is best in late spring and autumn, though it's also popular all year round in its smoked form, as kippers.

'Herring fillets are delicious coated in oatmeal and shallow-fried in a little oil or butter, then served with mustard,' says Kevin MacGillivray.

Mackerel

Mackerel is the most valuable pelagic (open-sea) fish species in Scotland, worth around £65 million per annum. It is caught mainly by large trawlers, with a small amount of hand-lining. The stocks fished by Scottish vessels have all achieved MSC certification.

Fresh mackerel is available from January to March and October to November and is a popular smoked product all year round. It's another fish that's full of omega-3 fatty acids.

'You can't beat a fresh whole mackerel either grilled or barbecued. Make sure the fish is gutted, then simply score the skin and cook on both sides until it is crisp, then serve with horseradish sauce,' says MacGillivray.

Haddock

Haddock is the most important whitefish species in Scotland and is fished all around the coast. It is available all year round, but is in best condition after May. Catches are worth more than £32 million each year. Haddock caught in the North Sea should achieve MSC certification in autumn 2010.

'Haddock are really versatile fish – dipping them in batter for fish and chips is just one option. Try grilling fillets for a few minutes with a dab of butter and lemon juice, or top them with breadcrumbs mixed with cheese for a crunchy finish. Bake them in a tomato, cream or cheese sauce, dip them in seasoned flour and shallow fry.'

Megrim

Megrim, a lesser known flatfish, is a good alternative to lemon sole being similar in taste and texture. It's one of the most commonly landed flatfish in Scotland yet much of the catch still heads off to Spain, where it's very popular .

Stocks of megrim are plentiful in summer months. To ensure that they are sustainable, megrim is subject to a minimum landing size of 20cm and also to catch limits.

'Ask your fishmonger to source megrim, then get him to fillet it. This delicate fish is good with strong flavours. Try grilling it for a few minutes with a pesto topping. Fillets are also good wrapped around a piece of salmon, dotted with butter and baked for ten minutes.'

Hake

Hake is also popular with the Spanish, Portuguese and Italians. It is a member of the cod family and swims in deep water. It has a long, slender body and is good for cutting into steaks. The flesh is quite soft, but firms up on cooking.

Northern European stocks have been subject to recovery plans that include catch and fishing effort controls. Scottish stocks are now robust and being fished sustainably.

'Hake has a mild flavour and few bones so is very good in a fish soup, casserole or tagine. Layer it with olives, onions, cherry tomatoes and pickled lemons, add seasoning and a dash of wine and cook for half an hour in the oven.'

Mussels

Most native mussels are farmed in Scottish sea lochs, an operation involving mussel spores settling naturally on ropes suspended from buoys or floating frames. Once attached they grow for two to three years to reach harvest size. They receive no feed, relying on plankton in the water and, as a result, are a very healthy, natural product.

Relatively inexpensive and available all year round, live mussels can be stored wrapped in a damp cloth in the fridge for a day or two.

'Wash the mussels, pull off any thin threads (beard) and discard shells that do not close when tapped. Cook them in garlic butter, with onions and a splash of white wine, or with tomatoes, onions and herbs, for 3-4 minutes until they are all open.'

Scallops

Scallops live on sandy, gravel seabeds and are fished either with dredges (95 per cent) or hand-dived (5 per cent). There's no taste difference between the two. New dredge designs make scallop fishing more environmentally friendly (see p.83), with less seabed contact, while seabed mapping technology helps fishermen to avoid sensitive areas and protect vulnerable habitats. The minimum landing size is 100–110mm across the shell.

If you find whole scallops difficult to shuck, ask your fishmonger to do it for you or buy ready-prepared scallops.

'Don't overcook scallops! Pan-fry them in a little rapeseed oil until just translucent. Finish with a knob of butter and a squeeze of lemon, and serve.'

Crab

The brown crab is the most common crab species in Scotland. It's used most often for dressed-crab salads and sandwiches. Dressing a crab involves combining the rich brown meat from the body of the crab with the plainer white meat of the claws, together with seasoning and lemon juice. The white meat can also be eaten picked from the claw shells.

Licensed fishermen use creels (pots) to catch crab, which are subject to a minimum landing size of 140mm shell width in Scotland. The catch is taken alive back to shore, where it may be stored in seawater tanks until needed.

'Make a stunning crab tart using a mixture of brown and white crab meat, a small can of sweet-corn, 4-6 eggs, 2oz Gruyère cheese and a small pot of cream. Pour into a pastry case and cook for 30 minutes at 180C.'

■ *Further information on all species, as well as recipes and updates on fisheries management and sustainability can be found on the Seafood Scotland website, www. seafoodscotland.org*

For more on the MSC certification scheme for sustainable fisheries, see p.155

■ *Kevin MacGillivray is President of the Federation of Chefs Scotland and Executive Chef of Barceló Troon Marine Hotel. He works with Seafood Scotland to help to promote sustainable Scottish seafood at consumer events throughout Scotland.*

PHOTOS: SUMMER ISLES FOODS

The Reek of Peat

The unmistakeable whiff of peat smoke is something we associate with crofting townships or whisky distilleries. For a few Scottish fish smokers, it's the sweet smell of success, as David Pollock discovers.

Peat's profile in the Scottish food and drink industry comes from whisky distillers drying germinated malt using fires created with peat fuel. This gives all such whiskies a particularly smoky aroma, and those which use a large amount in the malt drying process – such as Laphroaig, Lagavulin, Ardbeg and the other whiskies of Islay – a particularly overpowering scent and taste that's generally considered quite off-putting by those who haven't yet developed a nose for it.

In which case the use of peat rather than the traditional wood when smoking salmon and seafood in some smokehouses around the north-west coast of Scotland might be greeted with caution by those who remain wary of their stronger Scotches or, indeed, the smell of burning peat. The minority who deal in it swear by it, though, as a deserving alternative to wood-smoked seafood.

'What peat-smoking does for the fish,' says Christopher West, general manager of the Hebridean Smokehouse on North Uist, 'is impart a warm, aromatic flavour. The flavour of the fish is still there, in fact it's accentuated if anything, with a kind of sweet, peat-smoked backbone.

That's one surprising thing, actually. With shellfish and particularly with scallops the peat accentuates the natural sweetness of the shellfish to an incredible degree. People often ask if we add sugar, which is a common additive to shellfish, but in fact we don't use any at all.'

Not all are absolutely convinced, though, even in the West Highlands where peats burn in plenty of hearths. 'I've tasted peat-smoked salmon before,' says Alastair Gordon of the Sleepy Hollow Smokehouse in Ormiscraig near Ullapool, who smoke their fish using wood. 'It tastes good, but it can be a little overpowering for me. I prefer it only lightly smoked. It's all a matter of taste, of course.' Would he consider selling it? 'It's something we'd like to try in the future, actually.'

Whether peat-smokers like the Hebridean Smokehouse, Summer Isles Foods in Achiltibuie near Ullapool and Andy Race Fish Merchants in Mallaig are ahead of the curve or just marrying two distinctive Scots flavours into one specialist range of products, there's little doubt that peat offers a sense of terroir, a flavour of the land. According to Keith Dunbar of Summer Isles Foods, 'In our experience the peat from different areas can produce

smoke with different flavours: some quite acrid, some quiet sweet. The peat bank we use at Achnahaird Bay near Achiltibuie produces a nice sweet smelling peat smoke which we mix 50:50 with oak shavings so we get a stronger smoke flavour but one that is not overwhelming.'

■ *Hebridean Smokehouse*
www.hebrideansmokehouse.com
Sleepy Hollow Smokehouse
www.sleepyhollowsmokehouse.com
For details of other smoked fish producers and suppliers, see Where to Buy listings from p.85

Over 100 different species of fish and shellfish are landed into Scottish ports each year, weighing more than 400,000 tonnes and valued at around £400 million. This bounty makes Scotland one of the largest seafood producers in Europe!

Scottish fishermen care passionately about their industry. For them, fishing is not just a job, it is a way of life that has shaped their communities and families. As a result, sustainability and responsible fishing practices are uppermost in their mind, as they work to ensure the sea provides a living for them and for future generations.

As a consumer, you will find at your local fish monger, fish van and supermarket, anything from gorgeous Scottish langoustine - Scotland's most valuable seafood product - to healthy oil-rich mackerel and Scottish haddock, all packed with vitamins, minerals, protein, and Omega 3. Seafood is so good for all aspects of your health that the British Heart Foundation and British Nutrition Foundation recommend you eat at least two portions every week.

With so much top quality Scottish seafood around, you're spoilt for choice. In just minutes, you can pan fry, oven bake, poach or grill a wide variety of readily available quality Scottish seafood, and serve up a healthy, tasty dish. For mouth watering recipes and a wealth of information about Scottish stocks and the sustainable and responsible practices of the fishing industry, please visit our website www.seafoodscotland.org

Seafood Scotland works closely with all sectors of the Scottish seafood supply chain, from catching and processing, through to retail, food service and consumption. It encourages and facilitates cooperation to ensure that top quality seafood is available to the consumer.

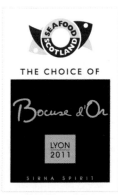

THE CHOICE OF

Bocuse d'Or

LYON
2011

SIRHA SPIRIT

Scottish monkfish, langoustine and crab have been chosen for the fish course at the Bocuse d'Or competition in Lyon in 2011, where the world's top chefs will compete for the golden statue.

18 Logie Mill, Logie Green Road, Edinburgh EH7 4HS
Tel/fax: +44 (0)131 557 9344
Email: enquiries@seafoodscotland.org
Web: www.seafoodscotland.org

PHOTO: SCOTTISHVIEWPOINT.COM

Getting Crabby

Lobster and langoustine may get the glamour roles in Scotland's stellar shellfish line-up, but crab is starting to nip at their heels, as Donald Reid found out in Orkney.

Unlike many parts of the British Isles, Orkney still has lots of small fishing boats. There are around 100 of them, at work around the coast, in the sounds and the large protected waters of Scapa Flow, giving a palpable sense of activity to harbours such as Stromness and Pierowall. The Orkney archipelago has 1000 miles of coastline, yet the relatively close grouping of the islands creates a lot of shallow, sheltered water, while the strong tidal streams around the Pentland Firth means that there's plenty of cleansing water movement and good feeding for all sorts of sealife.

The small boats, each employing two or three fishermen, are mostly at work laying and lifting creels, catching velvet crab, lobster and, in the main,

brown crab. Orkney has the largest brown crab fishery in the UK, landing 2000 tonnes a year, over 20 per cent of the total Scottish catch. In Stromness the Orkney Fishermens' Society operates one of Europe's largest and most sophisticated crab processing factories. A cooperative, with over 75 per cent of local crab fishermen belonging to it, the OFS employs 70 on-shore.

'There's £6 million coming into the local economy and being spread among what are peripheral communities,' says Stewart Crichton, general manager of OFS. 'Probably the biggest single cash income on islands such as Westray, Sanday, Stronsay, Hoy and Papa Westray is coming from someone fishing crab.'

Whole crabs have a much lower

market value than lobster or langoustine. Commercial processing, however, add significant value. Only five per cent of the crabs landed by local fishermen are sold whole. With the rest, the OFS factory produces the majority of the of bespoke crab products – such as dressed crab and claw meat – sold in UK by retailers such as Waitrose, M&S, Sainsbury and Morrisons. Around a third of their output is exported to France, Italy and the Far East.

Even still, Stewart Crichton produces the startling statistic that less than five per cent of UK population have ever eaten crab. Langoustine may be way out ahead in their economic worth to Scotland's fishing industry as a whole, and lobster clings hard to its luxury cachet, but for many crab has as much

'Orkney has the largest brown crab fishery in the UK, landing 2000 tonnes a year, over 20 per cent of the total Scottish catch'

to offer as its crustacean cousins. It does enjoy a more established place in Scottish food heritage – you'll find partan bree rather than lobster bisque in local cookbooks, and if you've got time, then cooking, dressing, picking and eating a crab is rewarding and tasty – albeit a little messy.

Until recently, crab were largely ignored as a commercial catch in Orkney. When the OFS was established in 1953 it was lobsters being packed onto chartered DC3 planes on their way to France. There was awareness of the potential for crab, but even 40 years later the on-shore operation still involved just four people processing the catch in a shed on Stromness pier. The new factory built by the OFS in the mid 1990s initially handled 200 tonnes of crab a year. It has been extended many times as capacity has increased ten-fold. One of the reasons for its success is that it has largely been funded by the fishermen themselves and share-holders in the wider community who supported them.

'If you look around the other food processors in Orkney,' says Crichton, 'the abattoir, the meat processing plant, the creamery, the salmon processing plant and the herring factory were all built by the local authority and leased to the operators. The OFS owns its own property

outright, and invests in it itself. If you're in your own building, you don't have to wait for the council before you do anything. It has enabled the business to keep investing to raise its standards.'

Part of the current investment is to ensure that the fishery remains viable. The OFS works closely with Orkney Sustainable Fisheries Limited, which now employs a shellfish sustainability officer. Their work includes tagging crabs to look at migration and movement around spawning, recording discard from pots to demonstrate the selectivity of the fishery, and analysing the size of the crabs caught (the average size of crab landed for processing in Orkney is currently ten per cent above the legal minimum) to understand the population structures.

There's also work underway looking into the fishery's relationship to other marine interests in Orkney. The same fast-moving waters that enrich the seas are also being explored in Scotland's foremost wave- and tidal-energy projects. Far from disrupting the fishing fleet, by keeping creels away from the renewable energy sites, no-take zones are created that contribute to the regeneration of stocks. It's an encouraging synergy, and offers further proof that at the moment there rarely seems to be a sideways step for the crab industry of Orkney.

PHOTO: SCOTTISHVIEWPOINT.COM

> CREELING VS. DREDGING

Jim Cowie of The Captain's Galley in Scrabster explains the different methods of catching crustaceans.
Creels are baited traps, set out and retrieved by fishermen and widely used on continental shelves around the world for the capture (mostly) of crustaceans. Creeling is a highly selective and thus sustainable method of fishing because fish are caught alive and immature or egg-carrying animals can be returned to the sea.

As a boy we constructed creels from willow or hazel, and fished them by hand, but they're now made from plastic-coated or galvanised wire with nylon netting, and virtually indestructible. Modern creels, or 'parlour pots', are also more complex and fitted with pot-locks, making escape impossible. These factors combined with mechanical hauling allow fishermen to work more creels and leave them longer on the seabed, thus increasing efficiency and fishing capacity.

Some crustaceans (langoustine), but mainly bivalve molluscs (such as scallops) are harvested by dredging. Dredges are metal-framed baskets with connected iron rings called a chain belly at the bottom. The lower edge of the frame has a raking bar, with or without teeth, depending on the targeted species. The catch is lifted from the sea bed by the raking bar and passed back into the basket.

Some dredging (and the closely related 'beam trawling') is quite damaging to the sea bed and indiscriminate in the fish and shellfish it captures. Thanks to ongoing experimental work, however, and through modern advances in gear technology, dredging is becoming more eco-friendly, with wider mesh sizes enabling immature shellfish to escape and lighter gear proving more fuel efficient and less damaging to the seabed.

PHOTO: HUMA HYDER

Spreading the net

Stuart Wilson's company supplies some of Britain's top restaurants with freshwater fish that are a little out of the ordinary. John Cooke finds out more.

There can't be too many Scottish fishermen who have top Michelin-starred chefs on speed-dial, but Stuart Wilson is no regular fish hunter.

His company, Trossach Country Foods, has built up an enviable reputation for supplying freshwater species that are far from the ubiquity of Scottish salmon. When Stuart hauls in his nets, it's pike, roach, perch, Arctic charr or eel that have him reaching for his Blackberry.

His customers include Andrew Fairlie at Gleneagles, Martin Wishart at Loch Lomond and the Roux brothers. Even the Queen sampled his Arctic charr via a Canadian Embassy dinner.

'It's the French chefs who are particularly excited about these fish, or switched-on locals who are looking for something out of the ordinary. They all love the fact that I call them on an evening from my boat and next morning they have a beautiful filleted fish that goes straight on the menu, with a strong story to tell about how the fish got there.'

Stuart's own story began on Loch Lomond with his work as a technician for the University of Glasgow Zoological Department. A by-product of their research was a supply of Arctic charr, a member of the salmon family that is a legacy of Scotland's ice age and remains the globe's most northerly fish. It's widespread locally, with at least 200 different populations identified in tens of thousands of Scottish inland lochs. And its firm flesh makes great eating too.

Stuart's first catches went to the Oak Tree Inn at Balmaha on the shores of Loch Lomond. Within a year, it was a regular big seller. This success fired Stuart's enthusiasm for the fish that he reckons has the potential to be the Scottish salmon of the next decades.

Today, a large proportion of the Arctic charr he supplies to renowned restaurants in Scotland and farther south comes from the west coast of Ireland, where it is raised, from Loch Tay stock, in on-land tanks. 'As a naturally shoaling fish that is quite happy swimming in tight groups, tank-raising is no problem, producing a healthy fish. With a closed system, there is also less environment impact on the wild surroundings too.'

Stuart is having his own positive impact on wild surroundings elsewhere. As yet another of the many strings to his bow, he has been netting in private fishing lochs for illegally introduced foreign species such as pike that are bad news for indigenous brown trout stocks. Stuart's catch keeps local anglers and superstar chefs equally happy.

Michel Roux describes the quality of the freshwater fish he supplies to La Gavroche in London as exceptional. 'When I first got delivery of an assorted box, my face lit up. It took me back to my childhood holidays fishing with my grandfather and cooking the fish the very same day. So fresh and pure a product on our doorstep – it would be a shame not to use it.'

WHERE TO BUY

EDINBURGH & LOTHIANS

■ George Armstrong Fishmonger

Fish, Smokery

80 Raeburn Place, Edinburgh
0131 315 2033
www.armstrongsofstockbridge.com
Tue–Fri 7am–5.30pm; Sat 7am–5pm.
Closed Sun/Mon.

This excellent fishmonger in Stockbridge sources fish from Scotland's coast as well as more exotic produce such as tuna from Sri Lanka and swordfish from Equador. The staff are particularly friendly and will prepare your fish to suit your needs. (They'll also give you tips for cooking it.) There's a smokery on site and a good selection of shellfish.

■ Belhaven Smokehouse

Fish, Smokery

Beltonford, Dunbar, East Lothian
01368 864025
www.belhavensmokehouse.com
Mon–Sun 10am–5pm.
Web/mail order.

Established in 1975, Belhaven is one of only a few independent fish farm processors in Scotland. Their Dunbar smoked salmon is made by smoking a fillet over oak chips from whisky barrels then preserving it using a traditional rum cure. Belhaven has a shop open all week – as well as their own fresh, marinated and smoked trout, they also stock smoked cheese and Ballencrieff smoked bacon and premium sausages.

■ Clark Brothers Fish Merchant

Fish, Smokery

220 New Street, Musselburgh
0131 665 6181
Sat & Mon 7am–5pm; Tue–Thu 7am–5.30pm. Closed Sun.

Inverawe Smokehouses

Live lobster tanks and wriggling razor clams are testament to the freshness of the seafood at the Clark Brothers' harbourside Musselburgh outlet. This reputable fishmonger has been in business for more than 100 years and the outstanding quality and variety of its range help to draw regular queues. Alongside cod, haddock and salmon are more exotic fish – jumbo tiger prawns, swordfish and tuna. Their speciality is smoked salmon from their smokery.

■ Eddie's Seafood Market

Fish

7 Roseneath Street, Edinburgh
0131 229 4207
Tue–Fri 7.30am–6pm; Sat 7.30am–5pm.

Eddie's Seafood Market, true to its name, has the feel of a mini market. Supplier to many of Edinburgh's restaurants, it overflows with sealife: Scotland's waters provide most of the fish and there's a

particularly wide range of home-grown shellfish. Lobsters and langoustines meander around a large tank while exotic sea creatures packed into ice-filled boxes on the floor might include snapper or even a whole shark. Everything is palpably fresh, from swordfish and tuna (sliced from the fillet in front of you) to haddock. Very busy at times, it's best to arrive early in order not to miss out.

■ Something Fishy

Fish, Smokery

16a Broughton St, Edinburgh
0131 556 7614
Tue–Fri 8am–5.30pm; Sat 8am–5pm.
Closed Sun–Mon.

This traditional, independent fishmonger offers a large and varied selection of fresh fish – from monkfish, bass and bream, to Pollack and salmon and a whole host of shellfish. They also produce their own delicious smoked

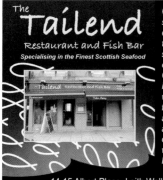

salmon and haddock, which they smoke on the premises using traditional methods. A family business, they are happy to guide you through your choice, will fillet your fish for you if required and can advise on cooking methods.

GREATER GLASGOW & CLYDESIDE

■ Alan Beveridge
Fish, Game
1121 Pollokshaws Rd, Shawlands, Glasgow
0141 649 5067
Tue–Fri 8.30am–5.30pm; Sat 8.30am–5pm; Closed Sun/Mon.
With more than 35 years' experience, this family fishmonger has an impressive selection of seafood. From outlets on Glasgow's Pollokshaws, Fenwick and Byres Roads, choose from an array of fresh fish including glistening sardines, squid, skate, herring, meaty monkfish and tuna and shellfish, with Scottish pheasant, rabbit and venison too when in season. Friendly and knowledgeable staff will guide you through the buying process and offer advice on preparation and recipes.

■ The Fish People
Fish, Game, Poultry/Eggs, Smoked meats
350 Scotland Street, Glasgow
0141 429 1609
Tue–Fri 7am–5.30pm; Sat 7am–1pm. Closed Sun/Mon.
Directly outside Shields Road subway station, this is the place to find a wide selection of the highest quality fresh fish and shellfish; alongside pickled or smoked fish and wild smoked venison, rabbit, duck and pigeon. You may have unknowingly sampled its wares at one of the quality restaurants and delis it supplies in Glasgow and farther afield. Competitive prices on sides of Loch Fyne smoked salmon are hard to resist and they'll source products, even offering free delivery.

■ The Fish Plaice
Fish, Game
1 St Andrews Street, Glasgow
0141 552 2337
Tue–Sat 8.30am–5.30pm. Closed Sun/Mon.
Follow the fishy aroma up a narrow alley and you'll come across this old-style fishmonger installed in a railway arch, freshly hosed and glisteningly clean. Outside are boxes of whelks, oysters and rope-grown mussels; move inside next to the well-used gutting table to encounter a broad selection from haddock and cod through to trendier

Mhor Fish

seabass, bream and scallops. From August to March it's also the place for Perthshire game, freshly plucked or skinned as nature dictates on the premises.

SOUTHERN SCOTLAND

■ Burns Country Smokehouse
Smokery
Grange Mains Farmhouse, School Road, Minishant, Ayrshire
01292 442773, www.burnsmoke.com
Mon–Sat 10am–5pm; Sun noon–5pm. Café, Web/mail order.
Seeking to use the most traditional methods, Burns Country Smokehouse takes a week to produce their smoked salmon, from harvesting through to packing. They burn oak staves from malt whisky barrels to fuel the kiln and give the products their unique flavour,

with all their processes are executed by hand. They also produce premium smoked bacon, utilising pork from a farm which has won a Freedom Food award from the RSPCA for the quality of their husbandry. Visit the award-winning farm shop to choose from an array of their own, and other locally sourced produce.

■ Dee Fish
Fish
146 King Street, Castle Douglas
01556 502788, www.deefish.net
Tue–Fri 9.30am–4.30pm; Sat 9.30am–1pm. Closed Sun/Mon.
A family-run business, Dee Fish has its own trawlers that keep its shops in Castle Douglas and Dalbeattie supplied with scallops, lobsters, prawns and a variety of white fish. Their nearby smokehouse produces oak-smoked salmon, trout and haddock, as well as smoked meat and game for local

butchers. They only smoke Grade A Scottish farmed salmon or wild salmon which has been caught by half-netters and stake nets on the rivers Nith, Cree and Dee. A variety of seafood is available to buy online.

■ Fencebay Fisheries

Farm Shop, Fish
Fencefoot Farm, Fairlie, Ayrshire
01475 568918, www.fencebay.co.uk
Mon–Sat 9am–5pm; Sun 10am–4pm.
Café, Web/mail order.
UKTV Local Food Hero, Fencebay Fisheries is a food chain in its own right. There is a farm shop selling a range of foods produced by local Ayrshire farmers, fishermen and country folk. Their smokehouse produces a number of smoked goods, and in addition to their own farmed rainbow trout, owners Jill and Bernard Thain smoke herring landed at Largs' pier. There's also a craftshop and Fins Restaurant, offering Scottish seafood platters fresh from the sea.

■ Tarelgin Farm Foods & Smokehouse

Butcher, Haggis/Sausages, Smokery
West Tarelgin Farm, Coalhall, Ayrshire
See Beef, Lamb & Other Meat.

CENTRAL SCOTLAND & FIFE

■ Dunkeld Smoked Salmon

Fish, Smokery
Springwells Smokehouse, Brae Street, Dunkeld
01350 727639
www.dunkeldsmokedsalmon.com
Tue–Sun 9.30am–4pm. Mar–Oct: Closed Sun.
Web/mail order.
Tucked along a side-street in Dunkeld and almost casting distance from the River Tay, the Springwells smokehouse began life smoking fish caught locally. That service is still on offer, but their well-regarded smoking techniques are also applied to Loch Duart salmon, organic sea trout from Shetland and wild salmon obtained in small quantities from west-coast fishermen. It's all sold from a shop on site and online.

■ East Pier Smokehouse

Fish, Smokery
East Pier, East Shore, St Monans, Fife
01333 405030, www.eastpier.co.uk
Mon–Sun 11am–4.30pm.
Web/mail order.
A new smokehouse for the Fife coast, East Pier sources its salmon from the RSPCA-monitored farms of Loch Duart. Their range includes a robustly flavoured '3-day smoke', a lightly smoked 'lox-

style' and a third option that's cured in beetroot juice before being smoked, creating a pink-hued, sweetly flavoured fish in a Scandinavian style. Call in at the smokehouse, arrange collection in Edinburgh or buy online.

■ Fish in Crieff

Fish, Game, Poultry/Eggs
30 East High Street, Crieff, Perthshire
01764 654509
Tue–Fri 6am–5pm; Sat 6am–4pm. Closed Sun/Mon.
Bedecked with creels, fishing nets, mini-lighthouses and other seafaring paraphernalia, Fish in Crieff prides itself on being able to source 'anything from the sea' given a couple of days' notice. Alongside a wide range of fresh fish and shellfish bought direct from Scrabster and transported overnight, 'Nick Nairn's favourite fish shop in Scotland' also supplies a range of game and poultry, delicatessen produce, home-made fish quiches and salmon terrines. It has a lovely wee cookery-book library too.

■ Mhor Fish

Fish
75/77 Main Street, Callander
01877 330213, www.mhor.net
Mon–Sun 10am–10pm.
Café.
The enlightened face of fish and chips, this trendy little fish café doubles up as a fishmonger, with a counter piled high with oysters, mussels, prawns and other fish delivered fresh from the north coast of Scotland. Expect sustainable pollock or coley rather than cod or haddock, with even the takeaway adopting a progressive attitude to taste and quality with chips cooked in beef dripping and fish available grilled rather than battered. Learn more about seafood on one of their day courses – the website has further details.

■ HS Murray

Fish
7 Hope Street, Inverkeithing
01383 412684
Tue–Fri 8am–5pm; Sat 8am–1pm. Closed Sun/Mon.
A family fishmonger since around 1922, HS Murray takes delivery of fish from Newhaven Fishmarket in Edinburgh. These are filleted in the store, while prawns are from Pittenween in the East Neuk of Fife and local boats supply scallops and langoustines. Other suppliers from the area provide free-range hen and duck eggs, tomatoes and samphire in summer. They are suppliers to nearby restaurants including Aberdour's Room With a View, Murray's also offer a free local delivery service.

CHEF'S CHOICE
ANDREW RADFORD ON THE FRESHEST LANGOUSTINES

It goes back to my days cooking on the Royal Scotsman train in my mid-twenties, and one memory in particular. We had pulled in to the station near Kyle of Lochalsh and the guests had left the train and gone off on an excursion. We had a break before they came back for their evening meal, and two or three of us were sitting in the dining car, watching the sun set over Skye, when we saw the silhouette of a man walking along the platform towards us. It turned out to be a fisherman with a bucket in each hand containing the most amazing langoustines, fresh out of his brother's nets. We bought them and just cooked them briefly and simply to add to the evening's menu as starter. I haven't tasted prawns like them since. It was that combination of the setting, the view and the spontaneity of it.

When I'm on the east coast, though, there's nothing like buying some fresh smoked haddock to make a traditional cullen skink. I don't want cream in it or any modern flourishes, just the basic recipe made with milk or even water. And good bread to go with it – that, for me, is the taste of Scotland.'

■ *Andrew Radford is proprietor of the Edinburgh restaurants Atrium (Cambridge Street, 0131 228 8882, www.atriumrestaurant.co.uk), Blue (Cambridge Street, 0131 221 1222, www.bluescotland.co.uk) and Café St Honoré (34 North West Thistle Street Lane, 0131 226 2211, www.cafesthonore.com*

CHEF'S CHOICE

JIM COWIE ON LINE-CAUGHT SEABASS

'Silver bars' (wild salmon) or 'silver darlings' (herring) may well be better known – who ever thinks of 'silver beauties' – wild seabass? They're elusive, certainly, but nonetheless native to our shores. We get ours from local anglers who cast from the beach on the other side of the bay from our restaurant.

The majority of seabass sold in restaurants and supermarkets in Scotland is not indigenous. There's no comparison between one that comes rod-caught from the fresh, clear waters around our beaches and those that are farmed in the Mediterranean and then flown to us.

I love when our customers feel passionate enough about their favourite seafood meal or most memorable dining experiences that they want to share the memory with me. There's no coincidence that it's always inextricably linked to what's in season, fresh and local. Even back in the 17th century, herbalist Nicholas Culpeper was warning people of the dangers in eating food out of season. 'Raw cucumber in winter,' he wrote, 'is cold in the third degree, one degree colder and it would be poison'. If we maintained this principle throughout, we as a nation would be much healthier, as would our fish stocks. Sustainability, conservation and seasonality are all inextricably linked.

As with all of mother nature's treasures, as the seabass season draws to an end in the early autumn, we move on, holding the memory and looking forward to enjoying them again next year.

■ *Jim Cowie is owner-chef at The Captain's Galley, Scrabster, by Thurso, 01847 894999, www.captainsgalley.co.uk*

NORTH EAST SCOTLAND

■ Iain R Spink Original Smokies from Arbroath
Fish, Smokery
Forehills Farmhouse, Carmyllie, Arbroath, Angus
01241 860303
www.arbroathsmokies.com
An Arbroath smokie, hot from the barrel and eaten with your fingers from its greaseproof paper wrapping, is right up there with any world class street food. If Iain Spink has any trout, try that hot smoked too. The traditional smoking takes place at various food events through the year and weekly farmers' markets in Fife – look out for, or sniff out, the plumes of beech and oak smoke.

■ M&M Spink
Fish, Smokery
10 Marketgate, Arbroath, Angus
01241 875287
www.arbroathsmokies.co.uk
Mon–Sat 8am–5pm; Sat 10am–4pm.
Web/mail order.
When Rick Stein waxes lyrical about an Arbroath Smokie you know it's likely to be good. Bill Spink, a fish merchant based in Arbroath, has been producing these hot smoked haddock delicacies since 1965; his smoked salmon is also renowned and wet fish for sale include crab, crayfish tails and lemon sole.

■ Stephens Fish Merchants
Fish
• 74 High Street, Montrose, Angus
01674 672276
Tue & Thu–Fri 8am–5pm; Wed 8am–1pm; Sat 8am–4.30pm. Closed Sun/Mon.
• 11 High Street, Brechin, Angus
01356 622037
Mon/Tue & Thu/Fri 8.30am–4.30pm; Wed 8.30am–4.30pm; Sat 8.30am–2pm. Closed Sun.
A fishmonger with branches in Montrose and Brechin. The choice is small but exquisitely fresh, rather than adopting the policy of stocking a great variety at the expense of quality. Besides very good haddock, plaice, lemon sole, kippers and smoked haddock, it sells local duck eggs, local honey and jams.

■ Ugie Salmon Fishings
Fish, Smokery
The Fish House, Crolf Road, Peterhead, Aberdeenshire
01779 476209, www.ugie-salmon.co.uk
Mon–Fri 9am–5pm.
Web/mail order.
Located in Peterhead, Ugie Salmon Fishings is based in a fish house built on the River Ugie in 1585, the only building in Peterhead to survive more than four centuries. Used by salmon fishermen for over 100 years, nowadays Ugie Salmon Fishings uses this unique building for curing, hanging and smoking locally caught wild Atlantic salmon (when in season) and top quality farmed Scottish salmon. A visit to the fish house gives a unique opportunity to sample a taste of history.

HIGHLANDS, ISLANDS & ARGYLL

■ Cockles
Deli, Fish
11 Argyll Street, Lochgilphead
See Delis & General Food

■ Gigha Halibut
Fish
Gigha Halibut Limited, Isle of Gigha, Argyll
01700 821226, www.gighahalibut.co.uk
Gigha Halibut specialises in the production of sustainable Scottish Atlantic halibut. Farming in a replenishable and controlled way, the halibut are grown over three years using a unique land-based farming system that harnesses the clean waters from the Sound of Gigha. The fish are reared to organic standards and handled with the utmost care to ensure they are healthy and happy. As well as supplying some of the world's leading restaurants, they produce smoked halibut, using oak chips from the Craigallachie distillery on Speyside.

■ The Hand-Made Fish Co
Fish, Smokery
Toll Clock Shopping Centre, Lerwick, Shetland
01950 422214, www.handmadefish.co.uk
Mon/Tues & Thurs–Sat 10.30am–5pm. Closed Wed & Sun.
At Havra's Hand-Made Fish Company, Dave and Tricia Parham produce smoked haddock and smoked organic salmon from the island of Skerries. Experimenting with the effects of various woods such as beech, olive and juniper, they also have a supply of old oak whisky barrels for general smoking purposes. One of Rick Stein's Food Heroes, the Parhams use ethically caught haddock, cod, salmon, hake and ray, all taken fresh from the boat every day.

■ Inverawe Smokehouses
Fish, Smokery
Inverawe Smokehouses, Taynuilt, Argyll
01866 822209
www.smokedsalmon.co.uk
Mon–Sun 8.30am–5.30pm. Closed Christmas Eve to mid Mar.
Café, Web/mail order.

Iain R Spink Original Smokies from Arbroath

Attention to detail, control over sourcing and an insistence on traditional methods has kept the Inverawe Smokehouse at the vanguard of the luxury fish market. The Campbell-Preston operation on the River Awe not only prepares smokes and packages the product; they also farm their own fish and shellfish. Their two-day smoking process involving real oak (no chips or shavings) creates an instantly recognisable deep flavour. It's no wonder customers include Rick Stein, Harvey Nicks and the royal family. The smokery welcomes visitors and there's a café, shop and smokehouse tour.

■ Jollys of Orkney
Smokery, Fish
Scott's Road, Hatston, Kirkwall, Orkney
01856 872417, www.jollyfish.co.uk
Mon–Fri 8.30am–5pm; Sat 9am–2pm.
Web/mail order.
Operating from a small shop in Kirkwall and with online ordering available, Jolly's of Orkney may have changed ownership in 2010 but it continues with a primary focus as a fishmongers and smokery business. Originally founded over 50 years ago, it sells fresh fish and local shellfish, as well as a variety of traditionally smoked and cured seafood. Orkney cheeses and confectionery are also on offer – with all items sold either individually or as part of a range of selection boxes and traditional hampers.

■ Loch Fyne Oysters
Fish, Butcher, Smokery, Wine
Clachan Farm, Cairndow, Argyll
01499 600264, www.lochfyne.com
Apr–Sep: Mon–Sun 9am–9pm; Oct–Mar Mon–Sun 9am–6pm.
Café.
Founded by John Noble and Andy Lane back in the early 1980s, this sumptuously stocked farm shop has built a fine, widespread reputation for environmental sustainability, which of course usually equals fresh flavours and quality. The shop, which is based in the same building as the renowned restaurant, sells an assortment of self-produced oysters, mussels, langoustines and scallops along with locally smoked salmon and a variety of other deli items ranging from meats to jams, wines, and chocolates, mostly coming from sustainable organic suppliers.

■ Lochleven Shellfish
Fish
Loch Leven, Onich, Fort William
01855 821444
www.lochlevenseafoodcafe.co.uk
Mon–Sun 9am–5.30pm.
Café.
On the shores of beautiful Loch Leven, this enterprising shop and restaurant has developed in the last few years from customer demand for shellfish to take home with them. Weather permitting, this successful shop now stocks live lobster, langoustines, crab, mussels, surf clams, razor clams, scallops and oysters. They also sell frozen and cooked fish, or will happily cook your lobster or crab for you while you wait. A range of pretty Spanish cookware is for sale, as well as paella kits to put them to good use.

■ Andy Race Fish Merchants
Fish, Smokery
The Harbour, Mallaig, Inverness-shire
01687 462626, www.andyrace.co.uk
Mon–Fri 9am–3.15pm. Closed Sat/Sun.
Andy Race Fish Merchants are renowned for their Scottish peat-smoked fish, including kippers, organic salmon and other high quality shellfish, all traditionally smoked without using any dyes. Having supplied to many of Scotland's most prestigious hotels for over 25 years, demand merited introducing a mail order service to benefit the wider public. Taster packs are available – with no charge for delivery – to provide smaller quantities of the most popular products such as smoked trout, kippers, organic salmon and mackerel to try.

■ Summer Isles Foods
Fish, Smokery
The Smokehouse, Achiltibuie, Ullapool, Ross-shire
01854 622 353
www.summerislesfoods.co.uk
Mon–Sun 9.30am–5pm (during summer months only).
Web/mail order.
Founded in the 1970s when Keith Dunbar and his wife Sheila fell in love with the area while on holiday, their subtly smoked salmon is still created from the original recipe using a blend of rum, molasses and smoke from peat and whisky barrel chippings. The online shop contains a wide selection of smoked fish and cheese available for home delivery, while those visiting Achiltibuie can pop in to their factory and witness the smoking process in action.

FRUIT & VEG

Tom Lewis foraging in the woods near Monachyle Mhor

PHOTO: MELANIE LEWIS, WWW.MHOR.NET

Highland gathering

Eating local, for some, means foraging for the wild foods that grow right on our own doorstep, writes Andrea Pearson.

Scottish consumers have just about caught up to the fact that our home-grown produce is among the best in the world, but now many food-lovers are taking 'local' produce a step further. In recent years foraged berries, herbs, mushrooms and edible plants have started to make an appearance in some of Scotland's most innovative restaurants. It is now not unusual to find seaweed on the menu, as well as sorrel, wild garlic, chanterelles and even squirrel.

This reclamation of indigenous produce is happening around the globe. Last year the food world was surprised when Noma in Copenhagen was named the world's best restaurant, leapfrogging elBulli and The Fat Duck in the league tables. Noma eschews Mediterranean staples such as olives and tomatoes and sources food only from the northern hemisphere, including asparagus, barley and langoustines.

In Glasgow, the environmental project Urban Roots teaches people woodland skills including foraging for native food. Project co-ordinator Abi Mordin believes that people today have a desire to reconnect with the land and learn more about indigenous plants and foods. 'There is more awareness of climate change now and people want to eat local food and have a low-impact lifestyle. Although the Scottish climate is quite harsh we do have wonderful fruits, with almost 300 varieties of apple. Native birch trees produce a sap that can be used to make wine, and then there are plants like sticky willy, which grows everywhere. People think of it as a weed but it is edible and it's packed full of vitamins and very good for you.'

Foraging may be healthy and responsible but top chefs are turning to it more because wild foods yield stronger and more varied flavours. With a tastier, fresher, raw ingredient,

there is less need to add salts, fats and flavouring in the kitchen. Scottish mushrooms in particular are the big draw as each variety has a distinct flavour and texture. Ceps and chanterelles are meaty in texture and full of flavour while puff balls can be liquidised into a smooth, creamy soup, unlike any other mushroom.

Forager and chef Paul Hollern, who cooks and serves his harvests at Tattie Mac's in Glasgow, said: 'Wild food is available fresh, it has cleaner taste than anything bought in a supermarket. This is not a crusade against supermarkets, that would be unrealistic, but not all food has to be convenient. And the customers like what we are doing.'

In Perthshire Tim Dover focuses entirely on Scottish produce at his restaurant, The Roost, and feels that gathering his own wild food gives him more control over quality. 'The suppliers we rely on don't necessarily cook themselves, they are just piling

'With a tastier, fresher, raw ingredient, there is less need to add salts, fats and flavouring in the kitchen'

things into a box. As a chef I know exactly what I am looking for, the size, the shape, the quality and I take only what I need, there is nothing wasted. And I can pick something in the morning and serve it that night. If you get wild mushrooms from a supplier they might be five days old by the time they are on the table.'

Chanterelles and ceps cost from £15 to £35 a kilo but a good mushroom hunter can gather 30 kilos in one day, so these cost benefits can be passed on to the customer. And customers, in turn, seem to be enjoying the new adventure in eating. Last year Dover experimented with alexanders – a wild vegetable that resembles hogweed, once cultivated by the Romans and found by ruins or ancient church buildings. He placed them on the menu as part of a fish dish and found that people ordered the dish specifically to sample the unusual vegetable.

Successful foragers gain their knowledge from other foragers, backed up by reference books and websites.

This vital networking and sharing continues to inspire new aficionados and generates a kinship. 'I was lucky that someone taught me what to look for,' explains Hollern, 'And now I want others to learn. I take my two commis chefs with me now. We go out for the day and it has the same effect on morale as a night out – minus the alcohol and the agony of the next day.'

There are many easy starting points in Scotland that do not require reference books and training courses. Blackberry-picking is straightforward, a young nettle leaf can be blanched and used in risotto, elderflowers can be steeped to make a delicate syrup, while nasturtiums and even dandelion leaves can be used to enliven salads.

But while the benefits are many, the battle to change some eating prejudices may have some way to go, as Dover explains. 'I have to admit I eat dandelion salad but I haven't yet had the courage to serve it to my customers. Somehow I don't think they would appreciate paying to eat up my weeds.'

> SOME RESTAURANTS USING WILD FOODS:

Ardeonaig Hotel and Restaurant
Loch Tay, Perthshire
www.ardeonaighotel.co.uk

Cail Bruich
Glasgow and Bridge of Weir
www.cailbruich.co.uk

The Cross
Kingussie
www.thecross.co.uk

Monachyle Mhor
Balquhidder
www.mhor.net

The Roost
Kintillo, Bridge of Earn
www.theroostrestaurant.co.uk

Stravaigin
Glasgow
www.stravaigin.com

Tattie Macs
Glasgow
www.tattiemacs.co.uk

Wedgwood the Restaurant
Edinburgh
www.wedgwoodtherestaurant.co.uk

Foraging skills and courses:
Urban Roots
Toryglen Community Base,
Glasgow
0141 613 2766
www.urbanroots.org.uk

Forage Rangers
Edinburgh
0790 0515774
www.foragerangers.com

Books:
Seaweed and eat it
By Xa Milne and Fiona Houston
Published by Virgin Books

Wild Food
By Roger Phillips
Published by Pan/Macmillan
www.rogersmushrooms.com

PHOTO: MELANIE LEWIS, WWW.MHOR.NET

Yellow fever

Cold-pressed rapeseed oil is one of the more fashionable new products to appear on the local food scene in recent years. Donald Reid found out more about Scotland's other national oil.

The days when olive oil was only available in chemists isn't so far in the past, yet as a nation we've become very accustomed to using various cooking oils in the kitchen. The most recent is the introduction, since 2005, of premium oil produced from the fields of vivid yellow oilseed rape that appear in our countryside each May. While even the best rapeseed oils can't compete with olive oil for depth of taste and range of flavours, the fact that the new oils can be sourced locally is another clear attraction. It's relatively simple to process – harvested rapeseed is simply pressed to extract the oil, then left to settle, before being filtered and bottled. Much is also made of the comparative health benefits of rapeseed oil. Rich in Vitamin E and omega-3 and 6 fatty acids (rapeseed oil has ten times the level of omega-3 found in olive oil), it also has low saturated fat (6.6g per 100g compared to 14.3g in olive oil) and comparably high levels of cholesterol-lowering monounsaturated fat (59.3g per 100g compared to olive oil's 73g).

Summer Harvest
www.summerharvest oils.co.uk
Made from a single seed variety grown on Mark Bush's family farm in Madderty, Perthshire, this oil picked up a double gold star at the Great Taste Awards 2010. A clear, yellow-tinged oil, it has a mild, well-balanced and smooth flavour, with no bitter aftertaste. Summer Harvest are members of the recently established British Association of Cold Pressed Oil Producers (www.bacpop. org.uk), which has begun to set certain production standards to retain the health properties, clean taste and quality of rapeseed oil.

Ola Oils
www.olaoils.co.uk
From their farm near Inverurie in Aberdeenshire, John and Connie Storrie set up Ola (the Gaelic word for oil), in 2008. They cold press and bottle on the farm, producing a thicker and slightly more robustly flavoured oil, with a nuttier taste. As with a number of rapeseed oil producers, Ola have sought to add value by expanding their range beyond the simple oil itself to include various infused oils using lemon, garlic, herbs or chilli, as well as a series of ready-made salad dressings and flavoured marinades.

Mackintosh of Glendaveny
www.mackintoshof glendaveny.co.uk
On graduating from the Scottish Agricultural College. Gregor Mackintosh set up his company on the family farm near Peterhead which now grows and bottles their oil, which has a clear golden colour and a lingering peppery aftertaste. Macintosh is one of the firms using the term 'extra virgin' on their labels as part of the marketing push to convey rape oil as a premium oil. While there's a strict EU-regulated definition of 'extra virgin' with relation to olive oil, no such rules apply to rapeseed oil.

Oleifera
www.oleifera.co.uk

The first local rapeseed oil to appear in Scotland, Oleifera takes its name from the Latin for oil-bearing seed. Initiated by Coldstream farmer Jill McGregor, the oil is produced from rapeseed grown by various farmers in the Scottish Borders and Northumberland. Each bottle is traceable back to the field it was grown. Olifera has a light, fresh, flowery flavour that makes an attractive ingredient for mayonnaise and carrot cake, as well as providing crisp roast potatoes.

'Relatively simple to process, much is also made of the comparative health benefits of rapeseed oil'

› RAPESEED OIL

The chef's perspective by Steve Brown of pickledgreen, Edinburgh

Rapeseed offers options an all-round oil, given its ability to withstand the rigors of extreme heat – it has a flash point of around 230C – while bringing its light touch to almost every dish that enters the dining room.

In the early days of pickledgreen, I was bullish in my approach to locality and seasonality, trying to outlaw ingredients that came from anywhere other than within our borders. Although I have mellowed in my attitude and allowed certain ingredients to come from slightly further afield, rapeseed oil still takes pride of place in our kitchen.

For many years, extra virgin olive oil has been used to dress salads and the like, but not for cooking, as it has a low flash point and burns easily. Vegetable oil has a high flash point, but it's considered too bland and cloying to use for very much else.

Although it is possible to cook using rapeseed oil (as many restaurants do), we find that its distinctive grassy flavour can dominate. However, we use rapeseed oil to bring an aerated, whispy, almost dusty edge to dressings and to drizzle over toasts and fish dishes. We find that this use of rapeseed really highlights both the flavour of the oil and that of the ingredient it is dressing. We also use rapeseed to make our mayonnaise and our raspberry vinaigrette, finding that its nutty edge brings something truly special to the finished product.

The farmer's perspective by Mark Bush of Summer Harvest

Oilseed rape is a great addition to an arable cereal crop rotation (wheat, barley, oats). Its long tap root makes it useful as a soil conditioner thus improving the yield of the following crop. More recently it has been grown due to its quality as a premium culinary oil.

It is grown, harvested, dried and stored using the same machinery as other cereals, although harvesting can be more difficult and losses can be high particularly in strong winds due to the size of the seed. Oilseed rape responds extremely well to the Scottish climate due to the rain and the long hours of daylight during the summer. This is a vital time when the oil is maturing in the seeds.

As a bee-pollinated crop, bees are a vital part of the crop's lifecycle. With their populations threatened, oilseed rape is a great crop to help maintain bee numbers.

Fresh herbs: the vital ingredient

For some, fresh herbs tend to be associated with summer - the fragrant scent of rosemary, lavender and mint - as synonymous with a balmy summer evening as barbeques, midges and a long cool drink. However, the cold winter nights provide a great culinary opportunity to experiment with a variety of herbs. A warm stew laden with thyme and rosemary or a rack of lamb with a sprig of mint can warm the coldest of days. Fresh herbs are available all year round and can be used to really enhance the flavour or add the finishing touch to any meal.

Scotherbs, based in the Carse of Gowrie, Perthshire, are growing on 250 acres of fields and poly-tunnels nursing coriander, chervil, chives, mint, tarragon, parsley, rosemary and many more.

What began 25 years ago as a small farmhouse garden experiment selling to local restaurants and hotels, is now one of the largest herb growers in the UK, selling to many national retailers, major Scottish wholesalers and a growing number of food manufacturers, all keen to tap into the trend for healthy eating with natural flavours.

Fresh herbs are very much a versatile delicacy crying out for experimentation from both experienced chefs and culinary novices. You need not be a whizz in the kitchen to use fresh herbs in everyday cooking; pack size and availability now mean that they can be used in the same way as salt and pepper!

Scotherbs Ltd.
Longforgan, Near Dundee, DD2 5HU

Telephone 01382 360642

Scotherbs
THE VITAL INGREDIENT

www.scotherbs.co.uk

Pittormie Fruit Farm, Fife

PHOTO: EUAN CAMERON

'the industry faced another challenge, when supermarkets started demanding that their fresh fruit be pesticide-free and available for an extended season'

Bearing Fruit

The soft fruit industry in Scotland has long benefited from the appliance of science. Nicki Holmyard looks at the technology keeping Scottish berries in juicy good health.

Summer time is soft fruit time, and we all take for granted that a plentiful supply of ripe, juicy berries will be available for picking. Few people probably give a thought to the challenges that the Scottish climate presents in producing it, yet more than 70 per cent of the UK's soft fruit is grown in Tayside.

Scotland's raspberry crop alone is worth £12 million a year, and the blackcurrant crop £0.79 million (though this value rises significantly once processed). To keep competitive, up-to-date and attuned to the demands of the modern market, Scottish fruit farmers rely heavily on the help of scientific expertise and developments in research. The Scottish Crop Research Institute (SCRI) in Invergowrie, Dundee, has been researching crops and providing advice to growers since 1950. Its

commercial subsidiary, Mylnefield Research Services (MRS), was founded in 1989; it is a world-leading research centre for produce including soft fruit, and runs breeding programmes to develop new varieties.

Their Glen Ample raspberry is the most popular in the UK, while the Glen Lyon variety is the mainstay of the Spanish industry. Nearly all – 98 per cent – of UK and half of all world blackberries come from Invergowrie. In 2011 the Macaulay Land Use Research Institute is due to merge with the SCRI, which the organisations say will bring greater benefits to the industry.

Nikki Jennings, a raspberry breeder at MRS, works closely with the industry to breed new cultivars of raspberries and blackberries. Each new variety takes a minimum of 15 years to perfect. 'The current focus of our work is the

fresh market, but when SCRI began, the Scottish raspberry industry mainly supplied fruit for processing, jam making and canning. We developed the first spine-free cultivars to facilitate machine-picking, and have kept that trait in our breeding programmes ever since, because it is also better for hand-picking,' Jennings explains.

In the 1980s the industry went into decline as a result of competition from Eastern Europe, compounded by problems with raspberry root rot. Extensive research has since been carried out into the problem.

In the late 1990s the industry faced another challenge, when supermarkets started demanding that their fresh fruit be pesticide-free and available for an extended season, as well as having large berries, good flavour and appearance and a long shelf-life. To achieve this, Scottish growers had to turn their production systems around, bringing back hand-harvesting and introducing polythene tunnels.

Meanwhile, researchers stepped up research into disease-resistant strains and improved quality, and Julie Graham, a geneticist with the SCRI, developed molecular markers for these traits. According to Dr Graham, 'This work is very exciting because it will help speed up our breeding programme, make it more targeted and focused, and help Scottish fruit growers cope better with the next challenge that nature throws at them.'

WHERE TO BUY

EDINBURGH & LOTHIANS

■ Belhaven Fruit Farm and Ices

Fruit Ices, Fruit & Veg, Cider
Thistly Cross, Dunbar
01368 860573
www.belhavenfruitfarm.co.uk
May–Sep: Mon–Sun 10am–6pm.
Café.

Belhaven Fruit Farm has made life easier for fruit pickers with their table-top system, whereby strawberries are raised off the ground in poly tunnels, taking some of the strain out of the May to September harvest. Other summer berries to pick yourself include raspberries, blackcurrants, redcurrants and gooseberries. Belhaven also produce a range of Fruit Ices – an ice-cream style dessert free from dairy, fat and gluten. The farm has a café, open throughout the season, and it is also the home of Thistly Cross Cider, which is brewed on the premises.

■ Craigie's Farm Shop

Preserves/Honey, Farm Shop, Butcher
West Craigie Farm, South Queensferry,
Edinburgh, West Lothian
0131 319 1048, www.craigies.co.uk
Summer: Mon–Sun 9am–6pm.
Winter: Mon–Sun 9am–5pm.
Café.

Perched on a hillside with wonderful views down the River Forth, across Edinburgh and beyond to the Pentlands, Craigie's Farm is an expanding family-run enterprise based on a soft fruit farm. The farm shop sells a good range of seasonal, local foods including their own Jam Kitchen jams, and includes a fresh butchery counter run by Steve Mitchell of Puddledub. The busy café serves breakfasts, coffees and light meals, and there are plenty of activities for kids as well as pick-your-own, farm trails and walks nearby.

■ Crunchy Carrot

Box Scheme, Fruit & Veg, Wholefoods
43 High Street, Dunbar
01368 860000, www.crunchycarrot.co.uk
Mon–Tue & Thu–Fri 8am–5pm; Wed & Sat 8am–4pm.

Crunchy Carrot started off as a small vegetable box scheme and has now expanded into a well-stocked wholefoods shop. With products ranging from locally sourced fruit to imported organic nuts and spices, it covers all the bases. There's a comprehensive gluten-and dairy-free section, and of course plenty of quality local veg. Vegetable boxes are still delivered weekly and fortnightly, or you can pop into the friendly shop and pick up the goodies yourself.

■ Damhead Organic Foods

Farm Shop, Box Scheme, Fruit & Veg, Butcher, Organic Foods
32a Damhead, Old Pentland Road, Lothianburn
0131 445 7425, www.damhead.co.uk
Mon–Sun 10am–7pm (provisional).

After 20 years the founders have passed the business on to their son-in-law, Steven Mitchell. He's keen to keep improving the business and so while the organic fruit and veg boxes remain varied, the farm shop is being given a new lease of life. Whether delivered or bought in the shop, the range of produce goes beyond that of many competitors, from fruit and vegetables to pork, lamb and beef, and a large variety of pickles, spreads and preserves.

■ Dobbies Farm Foodhall

Deli
Melville Nursery, Melville Nurseries, Lasswade, Midlothian
See Delis & General Food.

in recent years with a shop and spacious café occupying a large, purpose-built wooden building, and both a garden shop and an expansive kids' play area immediately alongside. In the summer months the highlights are the luscious strawberries, raspberries and other soft fruit grown on the farm, with pick your own available. The shop also sells seasonal vegetables from the farm, along with their own jams and chutneys.

■ Blairgowrie Farm Shop
Farm Shop, Box Scheme, Fruit & Veg
14–16 Reform Street, Blairgowrie, Perthshire
01250 876528
www.blairgowriefarmshop.co.uk
Mon–Sat 8.30am–5.30pm; Jun–Sep & Dec: Sun 11am–4pm.
Blairgowrie Farm Shop sources its fruit and vegetables from local farms, and claims to get the produce on the shelf much more quickly than most supermarkets. It also offers many jams, chutneys and sauces made locally around Tayside. And if you need soft fruit for jam-making, it keeps some aside each day – it's all rather sweet and thoughtful.

■ Brig Farm Shop
Farm Shop, Beef, Game, Lamb, Pork
Gateside Home Farm, Bridge Of Earn, Perthshire
01738 813571, www.brigfarmshop.co.uk
Mon–Fri 8am–5pm; Sat–Sun 8am–6pm.
Café.
The café menu features home-made soups, fresh homebaking and daily specials as well as a range of sandwiches, toasties and baked potatoes. The smallish shop looks to keep food miles to a minimum by sourcing produce from the neighbouring Perthshire farms, and rarely sourcing from outwith Scottish soil. The range includes Puddledub pork, Hilton wild boar, Jim Fairlie lamb and mutton as well as their own beef.

■ Cairnie Fruit Farm
Preserves/Honey, Farm Shop, Fruit & Veg
Cairnie, Cupar, Fife
01334 655610
www.cairniefruitfarm.co.uk
Sep–Jun: Tue–Sun 10am–5pm. Closed Sun. Jul/Aug: Mon–Sun 9.30am–6pm.
Café.
Primarily a strawberry farm, Cairnie Fruit Farm's shop also sells home-grown raspberries, blackcurrants, redcurrants, gooseberries and tayberries, all of which are available on pick-your-own deals. They also produce their own range of jams, and sell gifts, homeware

and other grocery items, such as local oatcakes, sauces and marmalades. In addition to a child-friendly tearoom, their big attraction is a Maize Maze – a maze cut from a field of maize, which is harvested every October and regrown to a different theme the year after.

■ Dalchonzie Fruit Farm Shop
Preserves/Honey, Farm Shop, Fruit & Veg
Dalchonzie, Comrie, Perthshire
01764 670416, www.dalchonzie.co.uk
Mon–Sun 9.30am–4.30pm. (Closed from Christmas Day to April 1).
The Burberrys began growing fruit on their farm in 1989. They initially supplied to nationwide chain-stores, but gradually decided to refocus on being independent, community-minded and locally concerned instead (Dalchonzie's latest collaboration is with Perthshire rape seed oil entrepreneurs Summer Harvest). Their colourful chalet-style farm shop sells loads of quality fruit and 'spray-free' veg as well as deli produce, local crafts and scores of versatile home-made jams and preserves.

■ Muddy Boots Farm Shop
Farm Shop
Balmalcom Farm, Cupar
01337 830258
Mon–Sat 9am–5pm; Sun 10am–5pm.
Winter hours: Mon–Sat 10am–5pm; Sun 10am–4.30pm.
Café.
What began in a roadside tent selling soft fruit, when the Samson family made the decision to step away from loss-making supermarket supply, is now an appealing, family-friendly venue complete with waddling ducks, grass-sledging and acres of plastic greenhouses. The farm shop located in the old tractor barn stocks the farm's own juicy Tulamine raspberries in season, along with other farm-grown fruit and veg and a good range of staples and deli items from small suppliers.

■ Pillars of Hercules Organic Farm Shop & Cafe
Farm Shop, Box Scheme, Organic Foods
Pillars of Hercules, Falkland, Fife
01337 857749, www.pillars.co.uk
Mon–Sun 9am–6pm.
Café.
Dismiss this place as a harmless hippie enclave at your peril: over 25 years Bruce Bennett has created an organic farm, shop and café with charm, attitude and inspiring ethical principles. It also has great food: baskets full of produce from adjoining fields and polytunnels, as well as well-stocked shelves of organic wholefoods. A box scheme operates,

and you can admire the horticulture at close quarters on self-guided farm walks.

■ Pittormie Fruit Farm and Nursery
Preserves/Honey, Farm Shop, Fruit & Veg, Plants
Pittormie Fruit Farm, Dairsie, Fife
01334 870233
www.pittormiefruitfarm.co.uk
May–Oct: Mon–Sun 8am–7pm; Nov–Apr: Mon–Sun 9am–6pm.
A small, family-run farm shop, Pittormie sells their own seasonal range of strawberries, gooseberries, raspberries, currants, loganberries and tayberries through the summer months, as well as home-made jams, marmalade, chutney and lemon curd, as well as fresh vegetables. A wide range of shrubs and plants is also available, while fruit can be bought ready-picked or picked by hand. During the winter, business is transferred to a smaller 'egg shed'.

NORTH EAST SCOTLAND

■ Bridgefoot Organics
Box Scheme, Organic Foods
Bridgefoot, Newmachar, Aberdeenshire
01651 862041
www.bridgefootorganics.co.uk
Web/mail order.
Organic since 1991, Bridgefoot offers fresh vegetable boxes from the heart of Aberdeenshire, delivered weekly. As well as a wide variety of veggies, it also provides seasonal fruit, free-range eggs and some meat: customers put their own selections together. As part of its extended-family ethos, they work with Friends of the Earth to give volunteers the opportunity to help out on the farm in exchange for accommodation, home-made soup, bread and cheese.

■ Castleton Farm Shop
Farm Shop, Fruit & Veg
Fordoun, Laurencekirk, Aberdeenshire
01561 321155
www.castletonfarmshop.co.uk
May–Oct: Mon–Sat 9.30am–6pm, Sun 10.30am–6pm. Oct–Apr: Mon–Sat 9.30am–5pm, Sun 10.30–5pm.
Café.
Located just off the A90 between Stonehaven and Laurencekirk, this is one of a breed of large, smart farm shops and cafés built in recent years to complement progressive farms – many of them, as this, soft fruit growers. Various varieties of strawberries, raspberries and blueberries are available, alongside veg, meat, eggs, ice-cream and honey from Angus and Aberdeenshire suppliers.

Pillars of Hercules

■ Charleton Fruit Farm

Farm Shop, Fruit & Veg
Hillside, Montrose, Tayside
01674 830226
www.charleton-fruit-farm.co.uk
Apr–Jun & Nov/Dec: Mon–Sun 10.30am–
4.30pm; Jul/Aug: Mon–Sun 9am–5pm.
Café.
A family fruit farm just north of Montrose,
with pick-your-own and a variety of soft
fruit, as well as home-grown asparagus,
available in season. Good coffee and
light lunches are available from the
converted former stable, with kid-friendly
menus and outdoor play areas.

■ Food for Thought

Deli, Box Scheme
The Brae, New Deer, Turriff,
Aberdeenshire
See Delis & General Food.

■ The Green Grocer

Box Scheme, Organic Foods
76 West High Street, Inverurie,
Aberdeenshire
See Delis & General Food.

■ Huntly Herbs

Preserves/Honey, Veg
Whitestones of Tillathrowie, Braes of
Gartly, Huntly, Aberdeenshire
01466 720247
www.huntlyherbs.co.uk
Web/mail order.
Huntly Herbs specialises in making
preserves from its own range of fruit,
vegetables and herbs. Some are based
on traditional recipes, but others, such
as the Strathbogie Sizzler chutney, have
been uniquely developed. Everything
is hand-cooked in small batches so
the flavour is rich and intense – their
dill chutney was recently voted one of
The Independent newspaper's 50 best
food luxuries. They also grow almost
30 varieties of potato, including some
speciality and heritage varieties such
as Pink Fir Apple – available at Huntly
farmers' market.

■ Lenshaw Organics

Box Scheme, Organic Foods
Upper Lenshaw Farm, by Rothienorman,
Inverurie, Aberdeenshire
01464 871243
Doorstep sales by arrangement only.
Since buying the farm almost two
decades ago, Beryl and John Clarke
have worked hard to grow and rear
quality produce. They devote acres of
land to veg patches and free-ranging
animals. Upper Lenshaw is based
in Inverurie, but they deliver organic
vegetables and free-range pork and beef
anywhere within a 40-mile radius.

■ Mackays

Preserves/Honey
James Chalmers Road, Arbroath, Angus
01241 432500, www.mackays.com
Mon–Thu 9am–4.30pm; Fri 9am–3.30pm.
A manufacturer of jams, relishes and
chutneys, and the last commercial
marmalade producer in the Dundee
area, Mackays uses a traditional slow
boiling method in huge copper pans.
The jams, together with various branded
whisky marmalades, are sold under their
own and Mrs Bridges brands. There is a
shop on the premises open in the week.

■ Royal Deeside Vegetables

Box Scheme
Dinnet and Kinord Estate, Aboyne,
Aberdeenshire
01339 885341, www.deesideveg.co.uk
Using only the pesticide-free vegetables
grown in the two-acre walled garden
on Dinnet Estate, this vegetable box
scheme offers drop-off points on
Deeside and into Aberdeen. Linked to
the Deeside Smokehouse (see page 49).

■ Vital Veg

Box Scheme
North Tillydaff, Midmar, Inverurie
01330 833823, www.vitalveg.co.uk
Web/mail order.
Vital Veg offers an organic vegetable
box scheme, delivered weekly to your
door. It is deeply passionate about
homegrown produce, so much so that it
also offers vegetable starter plants to get
you up-and-running with your very own
vegetable patch. All its produce is either
grown on site or sourced locally, plus its
boxes are wide-ranging – allowing you
to specifically select 'detox' or 'smoothie
and juicing' combinations.

HIGHLANDS, ISLANDS & ARGYLL

■ Brin Herb Nursery

Deli
Flichity, Farr, Inverness
See Delis & General Food.

■ Macleod Organics

Box Scheme
Kylerona Farm, Ardersier, Inverness
01667 462555
www.macleodorganics.com
Web/mail order.
Based in Ardersier, Macleod Organics
deliver across a wide area of the
Highlands, and weekly from Inverness
to Nairn. Working towards sourcing all
their fruit and veg from organic Scottish
soil, Macleod's target is currently 90 per
cent fulfilled. You can request a whole
host of other items to be popped in your
vegetable box, from organic farm haggis
to totally degradable refuse sacks.

■ Natural Vegetable Company

Box Scheme
Clachandreggy, West Torbeck, Inverness
01463 250440, www.natvegco.com
Web/mail order.
A six-acre organic farm supplying local
hotels and restaurants, the Natural
Vegetable Company also offers a local
organic box scheme. It aims to supply
only Highland produce, specialising in a
natural range of seasonal varieties grown
on the farm – from herbs and salad leaves
in summer to root vegetables in winter, as
well as fruit. Both small and large boxes
are delivered weekly or fortnightly to
customers in the Inverness area.

■ Scotgro

Box Scheme
Broombank Farm, Auldearn, Nairn
07719 343097, www.scotgro.com
Web/mail order.
A box scheme set up by farmer Jock
Scott and manager Stuart MacCulloch
from Broombank Farm near Nairn.
Delivering to addresses in the Inverness,
Black Isle, Dingwall, Nairn and Forres
postcodes, boxes start from £10 and
include vegetables (mostly, though
not exclusively, organic) grown at
Broombank and surrounding farms.

WHISKY, BEER & OTHER DRINKS

Home Brew

High-quality water, historic recipes and a growing number of microbreweries means that Scotland is producing beers to rival those produced on the Continent, writes David Pollock.

PHOTO: SCOTTISHVIEWPOINT.COM

Traditionally, Scottish beers were more malty and less hoppy,' explains Lindsay Grant, CAMRA's Scotland & Northern Ireland Director. 'Although that distinction doesn't really exist any more. There are now a lot of Scots beers made with hops.'

Although Scotland's brewing tradition was strong throughout the 20th century, particularly in the renowned 'charmed circle' of Edinburgh, the beers produced north of the border enjoyed precious little goodwill outside the country at the time. 'I don't think there was a bias against them as such,' says Grant of the shilling-categorised beers that used to dominate. 'It was more to do with problems in transporting and marketing them anywhere else.'

The sea change for the nation came in 1991, when Edinburgh's Caledonian

'Cask ale is the area where variety is encouraged, and that's allowed more and more microbreweries to carve out a niche in the market'

brewery first started producing the hoppier Deuchars IPA. A hit at home and abroad, it's been the regular recipient of brewing awards ever since, including the title of CAMRA supreme champion beer of Britain in 2002. 'The cask beers being produced at the time were heavier and more wintery,' says Cameron Mather, of Caledonian Brewing Co, 'and Deuchars is simply a lighter and more refreshing drink. It was pretty unique among the Scottish beers of the time.'

This breakthrough came around the time that many Scottish breweries

were closing down in favour of larger national 'superbreweries' such as Scottish & Newcastle, whose production became more centralised. At the turn of the 20th century there were more than 40 breweries in Edinburgh, but now only Caledonian remains.

'Gone are the days when there were 50 different varieties of lager available. Now there are only seven or eight big brands sold on tap in bars. Cask ale is the area where variety is encouraged, and that's allowed more and more microbreweries to carve out

'This area is the "charmed circle", which all the breweries of the city once sat upon. It's very similar to the natural water supply at Burton upon Trent, which is the brewing centre of the UK'

you know you shouldn't

a niche in the market,' says Mather.

One positive factor that is mentioned frequently by those within the Scottish brewing industry is the particular quality of the country's water. In fact, that was a large part of the reason for Edinburgh's popularity with breweries. 'The city is set on volcanic rock,' says Mather, 'which incorporates a series of underground wells and water passages. This area is the "charmed circle", which all the breweries of the city once sat upon.

'It's very similar to the natural water supply at Burton upon Trent, which is the brewing centre of the UK.' Sadly, however, agricultural run-off has eroded the quality of this supply, and it's no longer suitable for brewing with.

'A lot of breweries now Burtonise their water artificially,' says Tuggy Delap, chairman of the Society of Independent Brewers (SIBA) Scotland

and co-director of Fyne Ales in Argyll. 'However, we don't and neither do a lot of the breweries in Scotland. We're all using the water from our Scottish hills and mountains, and it's good fortune for all the country's breweries – whether they're on the Black Isle, Skye, the Orkneys, in the Cairngorms – that we have access to this incredible water. And most of it falls out of the sky on our heads, so at least that's one delivery each week we don't have to pay for.'

At the same time, the rise of microbreweries (Grant says there are around 40 operating in Scotland now, of various sizes, which is roughly double the number of a decade ago) has led to a far greater variety of beers coming out of Scotland than ever before.

Among the more illustrious brands are Innis & Gunn, who age their beer in oak barrels, and Williams Bros Brewery, Alloa, which produces a

variety of beers made to historic Scots recipes, beginning with their most renowned range, the heather-infused Fraoch. Subsequent Williams ale revivals include Kelpie (infused with seaweed), Alba (Scots pine), Ebulum (elderberry) and Grozet (gooseberries).

Then there is the Fraserburgh-based Brewdog, who produce an iconoclastic and diverse range with names such as Trashy Blonde and Hardcore IPA, demonstrating that Scottish beers have at least overcome those marketing difficulties mentioned earlier.

'I find the beers produced in Scotland stand up really well to those produced on the Continent,' says Simon Briggs, head of sales at Great Grog wine merchants in Edinburgh, 'even those brewed to Czech or German purity laws. Our lager is almost as good, if not quite as light, but a lot of our ales are arguably better than anything you get on the Continent. That's certainly so in the case of really floral, characterful lines like Deuchars IPA or [Cairngorm Brewery's] Trade Winds.'

'Regardless of the quality of our water or the ingredients used,' concludes Grant, 'it all comes down to the ability of the brewer. As with any cottage industry, in the case of microbrewing, not everyone is going to be good at it. But some people will be very good indeed.'

PHOTO: SCOTTISH-VIEWPOINT.COM

Traquair House Brewery

Scottish Craft and Microbreweries

Edinburgh & Lothians

Caledonian Brewery
Edinburgh, 0131 337 1286
www.caledonian-brewery.co.uk Online Shop

Fowler's Real Ales
Prestoungrange Gothenburg, Prestonpans,
01875 819922, www.prestoungrange.org
Visit

Innis & Gunn
Edinburgh, www.innisandgunn.com

Stewart Brewing
Loanhead, Edinburgh, 0131 440 2442,
www.stewartbrewing.co.uk Shop

Thistly Cross Cider
Dunbar, 07956655123,
www.thistlycrosscider.co.uk Online Shop

Greater Glasgow & Clydeside

Houston Brewing Company
Houston, 01505 612620,
www.houston-brewing.co.uk
Visit

Kelburn Brewery
Barrhead, 0141 881 2138,
www.kelburnbrewery.com

West Beer
Glasgow, 0141 550 0135,
www.westbeer.com Shop / Visit

Southern Scotland

Broughton Ales
Broughton, 01899 830345,
www.broughtonales.co.uk Online Shop

Sulwath Brewery
Castle Douglas, 01556 604525,
www.sulwathbrewers.co.uk Shop / Visit

Traquair House Brewery
by Innerleithen, 01896 830323,
www.traquair.co.uk Online Shop / Shop

Central Scotland & Fife

Bridge of Allan Brewery
Bridge of Allan, 01786 834555,
www.bridgeofallan.co.uk
Online Shop / Shop / Visit

Fraoch Heather Ale/Williams Brothers Brewing
Alloa, 01259 725511, www.fraoch.com,
www.williamsbrosbrew.com Online Shop

Harviestoun Brewery
Alva, Clackmannanshire, 01259 769100,
www.harviestoun.com Online Shop / Shop

Inveralmond Brewery
Perth, 01738 449448,
www.inveralmond-brewery.co.uk Online Shop

Lade Inn House Ales
Kilmahog, www.theladeinn.com/microbrewery
Online Shop / Shop

Loch Leven Brewery
Loch Leven, 07745 223194,
www.lochlevenbrewery.com

Traditional Scottish Ales
Throsk, Stirling, 01786 817000,
www.traditionalscottishales.co.uk
Online Shop

Tryst Brewery
Falkirk, 01324 554000,
www.trystbrewery.co.uk Online Shop

North East Scotland

Brewdog
Fraserburgh, 01346 519 009,
www.brewdog.com Online Shop

Deeside Brewery
Aberdeenshire, 01339 883777,
www.deesidebrewery.co.uk

Highlands, Islands & Argyll

An Teallach Ale
Dundonnell, Garve, 01854 633306

Atlas Brewery
Kinlochleven, 01667 404555,
www.atlasbrewery.com Online Shop

Black Isle Brewery
Ross-shire, 01463 811875,
www.blackislebrewery.com Online Shop / Visit

Cairngorm Brewery
Aviemore, 01479 812222,
www.cairngormbrewery.com
Online Shop / Shop / Visit

Colonsay Brewery
Colonsay, 01951 200190,
www.colonsaybrewery.co.uk Online Shop

Fyne Ales
Cairndow, Loch Fyne, 01499 600120,
www.fyneales.com Online Shop

Highland Brewing Company
Swanney Brewery, by Evie, Mainland,
Orkney Islands, 01856 721700,
www.highlandbrewingcompany.co.uk
Online Shop

Hebridean Brewers
Stornoway, Isle of Lewis, 01851 700123,
www.hebridean-brewery.co.uk

Islay Ales
Bridgend, Isle of Islay, 01496 810014,
www.islayales.com Online Shop / Shop

The Isle of Arran Brewery
Claddich, Brodick, 01770 302353,
www.arranbrewery.com
Online Shop / Shop / Visit

Isle of Skye Brewery,
Uig, 01470 542477,
www.skyebrewery.co.uk Shop

Orkney Brewery
Quoyloo, Mainland, Orkney Islands, 01667
404555, www.sinclairbreweries.co.uk
Shop / Visit

Valhalla Brewery
Unst, Shetland, 01957 711658
www.valhallabrewery.co.uk Shop / Visit

Key:
Online Shop = direct purchase from
website available
Shop = retail shop at brewery
Visit = brewery tours routinely available

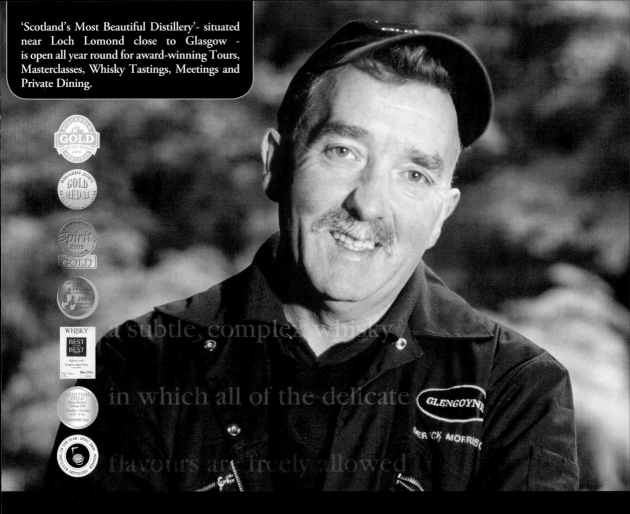

Whisky Words

How do you describe the flavours in whisky? If 'smoky', 'floral' or 'fruity' seem inadequate, whisky expert Charles MacLean's 'Whisky Wheel' helps reveal an imaginative array of possible definitions of a dram.

Whisky 'tasting' is something of a misnomer, since most of the work of evaluation is done by the nose not the palate. But it is difficult to put words to smells, and the language used is hotly debated. Just how effusive and allusive should one be? Until the late 1970s the whisky industry relied upon the flavour terminology and aromatic classifications used to describe wine and beer. These were found to be inadequate as they did not include the principal aromatic groups or the key terms needed to describe whisky. What is more, the words used were ambiguous or inaccurate when applied to whisky. The task of systematising and expanding upon the language of whisky was eloquently undertaken by Pentlands Scotch Whisky Research in 1979. They adopted a tasting wheel that could be used by the industry (rather than the consumer), for assessing new-make and mature spirit. In 1996/97, I collaborated with Dr Jim Swan and Dr Jennifer Newton of RR Tatlock & Thomson (Analytical and Consulting Chemists) to redraw the Whisky Wheel, with a view to making it less confusing for the non-specialist consumer.

> HOW TO READ THE WHEEL

The inner hub comprises the cardinal aromatic groups to be found in Scotch whisky. The middle tier breaks these down into secondary aromatic groups. And the outer rim supplies loose, hedonic, descriptors. So if a particular scent is discovered in a sample, it can be identified on the outer rim and then attributed to its aromatic group on the first tier. Not all the aromas (even aromatic groups) will be found in every malt whisky. Taste (ie. Mouth-feel and Primary Tastes) is measured on the smaller wheel. 'Complexity', 'Intensity' and 'Pungency' might also be scored.

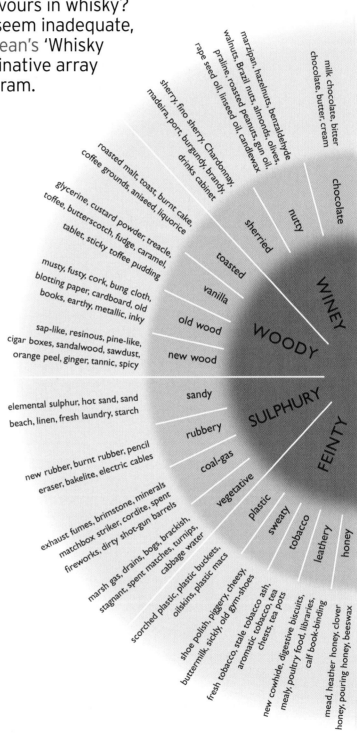

The Whisky Wheel is republished here with the kind permission of the author and Mitchell Beazley, publishers of *Malt Whisky* by Charles MacLean. A new edition of this book will appear in May 2011. Charles MacLean is one of Scotland's foremost whisky experts and writers. He is chairman of the Tasting Panel of the Scotch Malt Whisky Society.

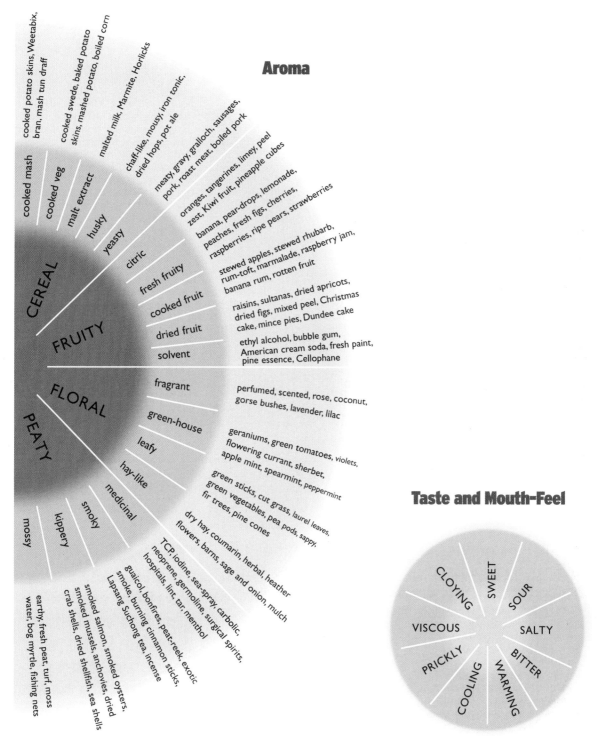

Aroma

cooked potato skins, Weetabix, bran, mash tun draff

cooked swede, baked potato skins, mashed potato, boiled corn

malted milk, Marmite, Horlicks

chaff-like, mousy, iron tonic, dried hops, pot ale

meaty, gravy, gralloch, sausages, pork, roast meat, boiled pork

oranges, tangerines, limey, peel zest, Kiwi fruit, pineapple cubes

banana, pear-drops, lemonade, peaches, fresh figs, cherries, raspberries, ripe pears, strawberries

stewed apples, stewed rhubarb, rum-toft, marmalade, raspberry jam, banana rum, rotten fruit

raisins, sultanas, dried apricots, dried figs, mixed peel, Christmas cake, mince pies, Dundee cake

ethyl alcohol, bubble gum, American cream soda, fresh paint, pine essence, Cellophane

perfumed, scented, rose, coconut, gorse bushes, lavender, lilac

geraniums, green tomatoes, violets, flowering currant, sherbet, apple mint, spearmint, peppermint

green sticks, cut grass, laurel leaves, green vegetables, pea pods, sappy, fir trees, pine cones

dry hay, coumarin, herbal, heather flowers, barns, sage and onion, mulch

TCP, iodine, sea-spray, carbolic, neoprene germoline, surgical spirits, hospitals, lint, tar, menthol

guaicol, bonfires, peat-reek, exotic smoke, burning cinnamon sticks, Lapsang Suchong tea, incense

smoked salmon, smoked oysters, smoked mussels, anchovies, dried crab shells, dried shellfish, sea shells

earthy, fresh peat, turf, moss water, bog myrtle, fishing nets

Wheel segment labels
cooked mash, cooked veg, malt extract, husky, yeasty, citric, fresh fruity, cooked fruit, dried fruit, solvent, fragrant, green-house, leafy, hay-like, medicinal, smoky, kippery, mossy

CEREAL, FRUITY, FLORAL, PEATY

Taste and Mouth-Feel

CLOYING, SWEET, SOUR, VISCOUS, SALTY, PRICKLY, BITTER, COOLING, WARMING

Gin Fling

Distilling Hendrick's Gin

It's seen as quintessentially English, but gin is now being produced by a number of Scottish distillers, as Jay Thundercliffe reports.

I
t has taken close to three centuries but gin has finally lived down its reputation as the scourge of society and a ruin of mothers. Today, the spirit is enjoying a renaissance. As Arthur Motley of Royal Mile Whiskies in Edinburgh points out: 'The market for small batch, carefully crafted gins has exploded over the last few years, and many top bars now have a huge range of specialist gins.'

For many, gin will be forever associated with England and London in particular – although 'London Dry' denotes a style of gin, not necessarily its origin, rather than the earlier and maltier genever gin of Holland. However, gin has been produced in Scotland for centuries, often in the form of distilled neutral spirit being sent down to England for redistillation, or rectification, with botanicals.

Given the Scots' heritage as master distillers it wasn't going to be long before they made a significant step onto the burgeoning marketplace. 'Our gin is based on recipes from 250 years ago when spirit was distilled in Edinburgh and then rectified with exotic flavourings and botanicals,' explains Jane Nicol of the Spencerfield Spirit Company, whose new Edinburgh Gin harks back to this earlier period as well as the Golden Age of cocktails in its 1920s-style labelling.

Gin lends itself to regional variations thanks to the various botanicals that can add distinction to the neutral spirit. Alongside the traditional juniper berries, citrus peel, coriander and cardomom seeds, angelica and orris root, many of today's producers are using Scottish ingredients. Edinburgh Gin includes Scottish juniper, heather and milk thistle, while the recently launched Caorunn gin features rowan berry and bog myrtle among others. Blackwoods gather all their botanicals from Shetland, and Boë Superior Gin from Stirling-based VC2 includes wild cassia bark from Skye.

Today's growing market in Scotland owes much to William Grants & Son, the family-owned distillers who pioneered the single malt industry when they bottled and marketed Glenfiddich in the 1950s. Their Hendrick's Gin, first produced nearly ten years ago, uses an infusion of rose petal and cucumber, and has proved very popular with its quirky branding and niche marketing. Hendrick's set the stage for the current market: 'I can't believe they have done it again,' says Arthur Motley. 'Other Scottish gin makers have a lot to thank Grants for.' With rumours and plans afoot regarding other local producers joining the trend, it might be time to raise the martini glass to a new wave of Scottish spirit.

'The market for small batch, carefully crafted gins has exploded over the last few years, and many top bars now have a huge range of specialist gins'

WHERE TO BUY

EDINBURGH & LOTHIANS

■ Artisan Roast

Coffee
57 Broughton St, Edinburgh
07590 590667, www.artisanroast.co.uk
Mon–Fri 8am–7.30pm; Sat/Sun & bank
holidays 10am–6.30pm.
Café.

With roastings around three times
weekly, at Artisan Roast beans are
rarely older than four days. Buying from
quality growers and paying more than
the Fairtrade base rate, their beans
come from estates, co-operatives
or collectives from Africa, Asia and
America. Originally a supplier of beans
who gave out tasting samples, such
was the coffee's popularity they started
selling it by the cup. They continue to
do so two years later and a Glasgow
branch has opened on Gibson Street
with snacks to go along with your brew.

■ Cadenhead's Whisky Shop

Whisky, Rum, Gin
172 Canongate, Edinburgh
0131 556 5864, www.wmcadenhead.com
Mon–Sat 10.30am–5.30pm. Closed Sun.

Web/mail order.
Scotland's oldest independent whisky
bottler has been operating since 1842,
bottling single cask whiskies and
selling direct to the customer. It offers
a huge range, from big brands such as
Glenlivet, Glenmorangie and Laphroaig
to the smaller Scottish distilleries. Each
of Cadenhead's cask whiskies spends
at least three years in the barrel, and
all are non-chill-filtered and free of
artificial colourings. There is a whisky
here for all budgets – from £3 to the
most expensive bottle in the world at
£50,000.

■ Cornelius

Wine, Beer
18–20 Easter Road, Edinburgh
0131 652 2405, www.corneliusbeers.com
Mon–Sat noon–9pm; Sun 1–7pm.

An independent beer and wine
specialist, Cornelius has one of the
widest selections of beer in the UK.
Far from carrying a staid selection of
beer, Cornelius leans towards the more
unusual, stocking a broad range of
interesting continental, American and
Scottish beers, including those from
micro-breweries. A similarly diverse
wine list is quirky and individual, while
a selection of malt whisky, spirits and
liqueurs is also available.

■ Demijohn

Organic Foods, Whisky, Liqueurs, Oils
and Vinegars
32 Victoria Street, Edinburgh
0131 225 3265, www.demijohn.co.uk
Mon–Sat 10am–6pm; Sun 11.30am–5pm.

Billed as the world's first liquid deli,
family-run Demijohn was inspired
by southern Italian wineries. Buy an
empty bottle and choose from an
array of predominantly British products
– including liqueurs, spirits, oils and
vinegars – to fill it. The bottle can then
be refilled at a reduced price. This policy
of reducing impact on the environment
is central to the company's ethos.
Producers are sourced locally and
vetted to ensure they use production
methods in line with Slow Food UK
principles.

■ Edinburgh Wine Merchants

Whisky, Wine, Beer
30B Raeburn Place, Edinburgh
0131 343 2347, www.edinburghwine.com
Mon–Fri 11am–8pm; Sat 10am–8pm; Sun
noon–7pm.

The Edinburgh branch of a chain of
award-winning wine merchants based
in Cambridge, this shop stocks a wide
variety of wines (particularly French),
Scottish beers, malt whiskies and a
good few other, more esoteric bottles.

CHEF'S CHOICE
MARTIN WISHART ON CURED HAM AND BEEF

The family run butchers Donaldsons of Orkney was established by Ewan and Erik Donaldson's grandfather in Kirkwall in 1965. I first met them five or six years ago at my restaurant – they'd been pointed here by Sandy Crombie, the butcher on Broughton Street in Edinburgh. I was especially interested in their cured ham. It's an unusual, bespoke product, with the meat dry cured for one or two days, moistened by a wee bit of whisky, then hung for a couple of weeks. It's smoked over whisky barrel chips then left to hang further. It's got a dark rind and a great aroma from the whisky, and you can't slice it like water-filled ham: the texture is such that it needs a slightly thicker cut. At Cameron House we serve it at lunch, laid on top of asparagus with a light gratin and classic hollandaise.

Ewan and Erik also do an unusual cure of a piece of beef topside, using a wet cure with blaeberry red wine from Orkney and fresh herbs. It's then hung for one to three months and lightly smoked over oak chips. It's a time-consuming job and they don't produce a lot, but it is sold to a few restaurants. It's very nice served with vegetables with an earthy flavour like beetroot, a celeriac remoulade with grain mustard or croquettes of horseradish.

■ *Martin Wishart is the chef-proprietor of Restaurant Martin Wishart in Leith, Martin Wishart at Loch Lomond and his eponymous Cookschool, also in Leith. A short film based on the original restaurant can be seen at www.martin-wishart.co.uk*
Donaldsons of Orkney is at 38 Albert Street, Kirkwall, www.donaldsonsoforkney.co.uk

The staff are friendly and though they may know a great deal about their subject, they aren't upset if you don't. Since their suppliers are often very small, there's a great deal for the layman to discover and also to set connoisseurial eyebrows twitching.

■ Fine Wine Company, The
Whisky, Wine, Beer
• 119 High Street, Portobello, Edinburgh
0131 669 7716
www.thefinewinecompany.co.uk
Tue noon–8pm; Wed/Thu 10am–8pm; Fri/Sat 10am–8.30pm. Closed Sun/Mon.
• 145 North High Street, Musselburgh
0131 665 0088
Mon/Tue noon–8pm; Wed/Thu 10am–8pm; Fri/Sat 10am–8.30pm. Closed Sun. Web/mail order.
Opened in 2003, this independent wine merchant offers all the benefits of a specialist retailer with none of the elitism, providing a helpful service whatever your level of wine knowledge. In addition to selling wine from around 14 regions, the Fine Wine Company also stocks around 34 varieties of Scottish ale, as well as a strong malt whisky selection. Its sister branch in Musselburgh also sells IJ Mellis cheeses to complement the tipple of your choice.

■ Great Grog
Wine, Beer
• 161 Bonnington Road, Edinburgh
0131 555 0222, www.greatgrog.co.uk
Mon–Sat 9am–6pm. Closed Sun.
• 1 Dalkeith Road, Edinburgh
0131 667 2855
Mon–Wed 11am–9pm; Thurs–Sat 11am–10pm; Sun 1–6pm.
A multi-faceted independent wine merchant, Great Grog's services extend to retail from their Dalkeith shop, wholesale from the warehouse in Bonnington and online; as well as tastings, courses and events. Established in 1999, they specialise in exclusive artisan wines. Delivery is free nationwide when you buy a minimum of 12 bottles – take a ready-made case from £58, create your own from the warehouse at Bonnington Road, or shop for individual bottles at their Dalkeith Road branch. Sign up to their email database for alerts about occasional rarities.

■ Glenfinlas Coffee
Coffee
Glenfinlas Ltd, 1 St Colme Street, Edinburgh
0131 220 8251
www.glenfinlascoffee.com
Web/mail order.
Glenfinlas is a coffee importer and distributer, looking after brands such as ethical trading company Green Mountain from Vermont, Calfornian Alpen Sierra and the George Howell Terroir Coffee Company. Online only, a vast section of coffees are available by mail order and are easily catagorised under single origin (coffees from an individual region, farm or estate); blended; flavoured or decaf. Glenfinlas Coffee also offers a wholesale service and supplies to a number of cafés and restaurants.

■ Henderson Wines
Whisky, Wine, Beer
109 Comiston Road, Edinburgh
0131 447 8580
www.hendersonwines.co.uk
Mon–Sat 10am–8pm; Sun 2–5pm.
Established in 2001, Henderson combines a specialist wine merchant with a corner off-licence par excellence. With over 1200 wines, as well as over 100 beers and 50 malts, even Bacchus himself would be spoilt for choice. What's more, if it's not in stock the friendly and informative staff will help you to track down that elusive bottle. Expect excellent quality and, thanks to regular promotions, there's something for everyone's wallet. Additional services include catering for weddings, glass hire, ice and free delivery throughout Edinburgh.

■ Howdah Tea and Coffee Company
Coffee, Tea
42 High Street, North Berwick, East Lothian
01620 894 245, www.howdah.co.uk
Mon–Sat 9.30am–5pm. Closed Sun.
Howdah Tea and Coffee is a remarkable wee shop and wholesalers tucked away on North Berwick High Street. A multitude of exotic teas and coffees are lined up on the counter, permeating the cosy shop with their fragrance. Real specialities are available here, including Kopi Luwak, the famous Civet coffee (yes, that civet coffee). Owners Pat and Mary Beale will roast beans to order, and happily offer their considerable know-how on the subject.

■ Inverarity One to One
Whisky, Wine, Cigars
1 Montrose Terrace Abbeyhill, Edinburgh
0131 661 8816, www.inverarity121.com
Mon–Wed 10am–6pm; Thu/Fri 11am–7pm; Sat 10am–4pm. Closed Sun. Web/mail order.
The public front of a company that's been trading to some of Scotland's biggest restaurants since the early 90s, Bath Street is the older, bigger sibling of Montrose Terrace in Edinburgh. One of Glasgow's only independent wine merchants, it stocks around 700 wines,

Cornelius

with a preference for smaller, family-run vineyards. Cigars range from a decent stock in Montrose Terrace to a walk-in humidor in Bath Street, and they stock four whiskies continuously.

■ Lockett Bros

Whisky, Wine
133 High Street, North Berwick,
East Lothian
01620 890799, www.lockettbros.co.uk
Web/mail order.
Inspired by a two-year journey harvesting grapes in Central Otago, New Zealand, Chris Lockett made the decision to become a wine merchant and opened his North Berwick shop in 2004. Together with his shop manager, Graham Kinniburgh, Lockett is a much-loved local independent retailer dedicated to sourcing exciting wines, selling a few New and Old World varieties exclusively through the shop. In addition, it stocks Scottish spirits and various malt whiskies.

■ Raeburn Fine Wines

Wine
21/23 Comely Bank Road, Edinburgh
0131 343 1159
www.raeburnfinewines.com
Mon–Sat 10am–6pm. Closed Sun.
Raeburn Fine Wines is a shipper, wholesaler and retailer of fine wine located in an unassuming shop in Stockbridge. The owner travels the world in search of quality wines, liaising personally with producers and, as a result, gives a very personal, high quality service. An excellent website lists their impressive stock and regular tasting evenings take place in The Vaults tasting room. As an aside, they also sell flowers that last well beyond those from many specialist florists.

■ Robert Graham

Whisky, Cigars
• 254 Canongate, Edinburgh
0131 556 2791, www.whisky-cigars.co.uk
Mon/Tue 10.30am–6pm; Wed–Fri
10.30am–7pm; Sun 11am–6pm.
• 194a Rose Street, Edinburgh
0131 226 1874
Mon–Wed 10.30am–6pm; Thu/Fri
10.30am–7pm; Sat 10.30am–5.30pm.
Closed Sun.
Web/mail order.
The impressive humidors are the raison d'être of these stores, and in the two Edinburgh branches you can even walk into them and browse the vast range of Cuban cigars. These and the smaller Glasgow shop offer everything for the tobacco enthusiast – pipes, loose tobacco, lighters of all shapes and sizes and a good range of quality whiskies including some rarer examples. Other treats include Scottish shortbread and preserves, French confectionery and a select number of international wines.

■ Royal Mile Whiskies

Whisky, Cigars
379 High Street, The Royal Mile,
Edinburgh
0131 225 3383
www.royalmilewhiskies.com
Mon–Sat 10am–6pm; Sun 12.30–6pm.
During the Edinburgh Fringe: Mon–Sat
10am–8pm; Sun 11am–6pm.
Web/mail order.
Established in 1991, Royal Mile Whiskies has become something of an institution. Browse through 1,000 malt whiskies and bourbons from Scotland and around the globe, including a selection of rare and collectors' items. There is also an unusually large range of absinthe, made less intimidating by spirit-loving staff who will help you to

choose. They'll also direct you to their second venture nearby, the Cigar Box, which offers a comprehensive range of Cuban cigars and an extensive selection of rums.

■ Valvona & Crolla

Deli, Cheese, Bread, Wine
19 Elm Row, Edinburgh
See Delis & General Food.

■ Villeneuve Wines

Whisky, Wine
• 49a Broughton Street, Edinburgh
0131 558 8441
www.villeneuvewines.com
Mon–Wed noon–10pm; Thu–Sat
10am–10pm; Sun 1–8pm.
• 82 High Street, Haddington
01620 822224
Mon–Thu 10am–7pm; Fri 10am–8pm; Sat
10am–8pm. Closed Sun.
With outlets in Edinburgh, Haddington and Peebles and online ordering, Villeneuve Wines boasts more than 2,000 wines and around 150 malt whiskies, plus high-quality sherries and madeira. The management pride themselves on keeping their selection varied and ever-changing, and also buying from small suppliers overlooked by larger chains. Staff will happily help you decide what you should drink with your dinner.

■ WoodWinters

Whisky, Wine, Beer
91 Newington Road, Edinburgh
0131 667 2760, www.woodwinters.com
Mon–Sat 10am–7pm; Sun 1–5pm
See main entry in Central Scotland & Fife listings.

GREATER GLASGOW & CLYDESIDE

■ Artisan Roast

Coffee
15 Gibson Street, Glasgow
07776 428409, www.artisanroast.co.uk
Mon–Fri 8am–7.30pm; Sat 9am–7.30pm;
Sun 9am–6.30pm.
Café.
See main entry in Edinburgh & Lothians listing.

■ The Cave

Whisky, Wine, Beer
421/423 Great Western Road, Glasgow
0141 357 5550
Mon 3–10pm; Tue–Sat 10am–10pm; Sun
12.30–10pm.
Located next to Glasgow's Kelvinbridge, the Cave is one of the city's few remaining independent off-licences. Feast your eyes upon the impressive array of bottled beers from Scotland and

beyond, the selection of intriguing world and organic wines and some excellent malt whiskies. The staff will go out of their way to source unusual varieties for you, no matter how obscure the request. Blackboards detail frequent deals.

◼ Demijohn

Organic Foods, Whisky, Liqueurs, Oil and Vinegar.
382 Byres Road, Glasgow
0141 337 3600, www.demijohn.co.uk
Mon–Sat 10am–6pm; Sun 11.30am–5pm.
Web/mail order.
See main entry in Edinburgh & Lothians listing.

◼ Inverarity One to One

Whisky, Wine, Cigars
185a Bath Street, Glasgow
0141 221 5121, www.inverarity121.com
Mon–Fri 10am–6pm; Sat 10am–4pm.
Web/mail order.
The public front of a company that's been trading to some of Scotland's biggest restaurants since the early 90s, Bath Street is the older, bigger sibling of Montrose Terrace in Edinburgh. One of Glasgow's only independent wine merchants, it stocks around 700 wines, with a preference for smaller, family-run vineyards. Cigars range from a decent stock in Montrose Terrace to a walk-in humidor in Bath Street, and they stock four whiskies continuously.

◼ Peckham & Rye

Deli, Whisky, Wine, Beer
21 Clarence Drive, Glasgow
0141 334 4312, www.peckhams.co.uk
Mon–Sun 10am–10pm.
With nearly 30 years of experience and expertise behind them, Peckham's is one of the more established groups of specialist wine and food shops in Scotland. This branch is a specialist drinks shop, with shelves stacked floor to ceiling with rare and exceptional wines to suit all price ranges, specialist spirits and over 300 beers of the world. Other branches have more limited stocks of wine, although any item stocked in one branch can be quickly ordered into any other.

◼ Tchai Ovna

Tea
42 Otago Lane, Glasgow
0141 357 4524, www.tchaiovna.com
Mon–Sun 11am–11pm.
Café, Web/mail order.
Opened in 2001 and initially inspired by Czech Republic tea rooms, Tchai-Ovna has taken on a laidback personality all of its own. Tea-lovers, locals and students alike flock to the cafe, which stocks over 100 varieties of tea, from as far as India and as near as Edinburgh.

JA Braithwaite Ltd

Filled with wooden benches and wicker chairs, the café is reminiscent of being in someone's living room and regularly hosts music and literature nights. Locally made cakes and wholesome vegetarian and vegan food are also on the menu. (At the time of writing Otago Lane was under threat from property developers.)

SOUTHERN SCOTLAND

◼ Corney & Barrow

Wine
8 Academy Street, Ayr
01292 267000
www.corneyandbarrow.com
Mon–Fri 10am–5.30pm; Sat 10am–5.30pm. Closed Sun.
With over 200 years' experience, wine merchant Corney & Barrow increased its hold on the fine wine market in Scotland when it purchased Whighams of Ayr, wine purveyor in the region since 1766. This branch has been a wine shop for much of that time, and customers can still find a dazzling range of wines and vintages. Knowledgeable staff will offer assistance as well as wine storage, tastings and event supply, while an informative website offers online shopping. Despite the top-end clarets, burgundies and New World gems, there are bottles to suit every pocket, with the French regional variety particularly good for bargains.

◼ Robbie's Drams

Whisky
3 Sandgate, Ayr, South Ayrshire
01292 262135, www.robbiesdrams.com
Mon–Sun 10am–10pm.
Web/mail order.
This independent whisky retailer specialises in single malts, and also offers an extensive range of blended and grain whiskies as well as Irish whiskey, bourbon whiskey and interesting ranges from other countries. Owner Robin Russell prides himself on the store's diversity: from the hundreds available in store you'll find everything from special monthly offers to collectors items and limited editions, closed and silent distillery bottles to its own range of single cask bottles. In-store tastings are available, and the knowledgeable staff will source more obscure bottles for you.

◼ Villeneuve Wines

Whisky, Wine
1 Venlaw Court, Peebles
01721 722500
www.villeneuvewines.com
Mon–Sat 9am–8pm; Sun 12.30–5.30pm.
Web/mail order.
See main entry in Edinburgh & Lothians listings.

CENTRAL SCOTLAND & FIFE

◼ The Bean Shop

Coffee, Tea
67 George Street, Perth
01738 449955, www.thebeanshop.com
Mon–Sat 9.30am–5.30pm. Closed Sun.
Web/mail order.
A haven for the coffee connoisseur, The Bean Shop has a staggering selection of the best gourmet coffee beans from around the globe. Choose from exotic, organic and fair-trade coffee to the famous Jamaica blue mountain coffee beans. A number of unique blends are designed to excite your palate – an Italian roasted gourmet blend is satisfyingly smooth, while the power of flavour behind the blend 67 will keep espresso drinkers happy.

■ Cairn o'Mohr

Coffee, Tea, Ice Cream, Wine, Cider
East Inchmicheal, Errol, Perthshire
01821 642781, www.cairnomohr.co.uk
Mon–Sun 10am–5pm.
Café, Web/mail order.

Cairn o'Mohr Winery is well worth a visit to sample the range of wines made from local fruits, flowers and leaves. New to the range is a cider. Tour the winery to see the wine-making process and try the café, which sells hearty bowls of soups, stovies of the day as well as daily specials. Or try unusual scones – gorgonzola and grape, anyone? And all served up in quirky surroundings.

■ House of Menzies

Wine
Castle Menzies Farm, Aberfeldy
01887 829666
www.houseofmenzies.com
Summer: Mon–Sat 10am–5pm; Sun 11am–5pm. Winter: Wed–Sat 10am–4pm; Sun 11am–4pm. Closed Mon/Tue.
Café, Web/mail order.

The House of Menzies is a unique example of what can happen when Scottish farmers decide to diversify. The doocot and barn at this working farm have been converted into a bright, contemporary space, housing no less than a bustling café, a gift shop and an award-winning New World Wine specialist. The wines here are clearly selected with knowledge and passion, and include some of the greats of Australia and New Zealand in particular.

■ The Scottish Real Ale Shop

Beer
The Lade Inn, Kilmahog, Callander
01877 330152, www.scottishrealales.com
Mon–Sat noon–6pm; Sun 12.30–6pm.
Café, Web/mail order.

Situated in Loch Lomond and the Trossachs National Park, the Scottish Real Ale Shop in Callander has been selling over 100 different Scottish beers since 2006. A one-stop shop for Scottish beers, real ale festival and brewing information, this is where to buy that elusive bottle from the Hebrides or delicious blonde from Islay. They hold a beer festival every year and summer tastings. Call into neighbouring Lade Inn – part of the family operation – for some lunch or try the beers produced on-site: Waylade, Ladeback or Ladeout.

■ The Spencerfield Spirit Company

Whisky
Spencerfield Farmhouse, Inverkeithing
01383 412144
www.spencerfieldspirit.com
Web/mail order.

Spencerfield was set up in 2005 when husband and wife team Alex Nicol and Jane Eastwood purchased the brands Sheep Dip and Pig's Nose from former employer Whyte & Mackay. After a little tinkering, they have taken the blends forward as individual but engaging and independent whiskies, and have recently added Edinburgh Gin to their range. As well as an online shop, the whiskies are stocked across the UK, and globally.

■ WoodWinters

Whisky, Wine, Beer
16 Henderson Street, Bridge of Allan
01786 834894, www.woodwinters.com
Mon–Sat 10am–7pm; Sun 1–5pm.
Web/mail order.

Husband and wife team Douglas and Cara Wood set up their wine merchants just over four years ago, and now have a branch in Edinburgh. Believing that everyone should be able to enjoy good quality wine at reasonable prices – without the need for supermarket-style discounting – their service is friendly and informative. Peruse (and sample) a selection of well-chosen old and new world wines, as well as champagne, whiskies, spirits, beers and ciders, plus cigars and luxury chocolates. Tasting events take place in-store every month.

NORTH EAST SCOTLAND

■ JA Braithwaite Ltd

Coffee, Tea, Kitchenware
6 Castle Street, Dundee
01382 322693
Mon–Fri 9am–5.30pm; Sat 9am–5pm.
Closed Sun (excl Dec.).

Braithwaite's has been trading since the 19th century, and walking in feels like stepping back in time. The tiny tea and coffee merchants is filled with wonderful smells from the secret age-old method of coffee roasting, and black-and-white photographs depicting the shop's history. The welcoming, cheery staff are on hand with lots of information should you feel overwhelmed. Old-fashioned tea tins, mugs and coffee grinders are also on offer in this wonderfully dimly lit vestige of how shopping used to be.

■ Gordon & MacPhail

Deli, Whisky, Wine, Beer
58–60 South Street, Elgin
01343 545110
www.gordonandmacphail.com
Mon–Sat 9am–5pm. Closed Sun.

Gordon & MacPhail proudly claims to be the world's leading malt whisky specialist. Allow the staff at their retail outlet to help you to choose from over 300 presentations of own-bottled single malts, aged from 5 to 70 years old, and a stock holding of more than 1,000 whiskies, including its own G&M Benromach from Scotland's smallest distillery. The store also showcases over 500 wines, a selection of champagnes, spirits, Scottish micro-beers and a deli with hand-made local chocolates.

■ MacBeans

Coffee, Tea, Kitchenware
2 Little Belmont Street, Aberdeen
01224 624757, www.macbeans.com
Mon–Sat 9.30am–5.30pm. Closed Sun.

Aberdeen's much-loved independent coffee and tea shop, tucked away on cobbled Little Belmont Street, selling speciality beans (many roasted on site) and loose leaf teas, as well as all manner of good quality tea- and coffee-making equipment and accouterments. If you're keen to try a cup, the Kilau Coffee Shop and art gallery across the road at 9a is supplied by MacBeans.

HIGHLANDS, ISLANDS & ARGYLL

■ Arran Brew Ltd

Beer
Cladach, Brodick, Isle of Arran
01770 302353, www.arranbrewery.co.uk
Easter–mid Oct: Mon–Sat 10am–5pm, Sun 12.30–5pm. Mid Oct–Easter Mon & Wed–Sat 10am–3.30pm.
Web/mail order.

Established in 1999, the award-winning Arran Brewery is set in the shadow of Brodick Castle. Naturally made and free from artificial additives and preservatives, the premium ales are produced in a micro-brewery using traditional production methods. An excellent visitors' centre allows you to watch the process, and a tasting is included in the price of the tour. You can buy gift packs of the beer from the shop or website, as well as hampers including other Arran products.

■ Loch Fyne Whiskies

Whisky
Inveraray, Argyll
01499 302219, www.lfw.co.uk
Mon–Sat 10am–5.30pm; Sun 12.30–5pm.
Web/mail order.

Regarded as one of the finest whisky retailers in the world by Whisky Magazine, this award-winning shop has been distributing the water of life since 1993. It offers several hundred single malts as well as the Loch Fyne, a mellow, well-regarded blend. Visitors can call into the shop, which also offers tasting, hip flasks, quaichs, Loch Fyne marmalade, books and miniatures, while worldwide mail order can be arranged by phone or through the website.

PHOTO: HUMA HYDER

DIRECTORY

CHEF'S CHOICE

JACQUELINE O'DONNELL ON WELL-BEHAVED SOFT FRUIT

It's exciting waiting on the first of the Scottish berries being picked. When we took our children to pick their own they nearly weighed my daughter on the way out as there were more over her cheeks then there were in the tubs.

I'm a great fan of Good Natured Fruit. Does this mean they say please and thank you? No, just that they are grown in the peace and harmony of the beautiful surroundings of the Angus countryside without the use of pesticides. These growers have all been cultivating soft fruit for generations, and I really appreciate the fact that they're grown here, not flown here, as our warm days and cool nights are ideal for growing and ripening the most scrumptious soft fruits. Their 'succulent' strawberries, 'ravishing' raspberries and 'brilliant' blueberries are treated with care and love to be as delicious as mother nature intended. They get ladybirds to do all the hard work eating potential pests like greenfly, which makes for such a sweet wee fruit.

I tend not to reserve soft fruits just for dessert – think about using them in the starter or a main course as they are honestly too good to wait until pudding. I have always enjoyed them as a side dish on our long hot summer nights (when we get them!) – chicken breast grilled on the barbecue with strawberry salsa or loin of Highland venison with balsamic raspberries and blueberries. Keeping it simple and Scottish makes it even tastier.
■ *Jacqueline O'Donnell is Chef/Patron Big Sis of the Sisters restaurants at Jordanhill and Kelvingrove in Glasgow, 0141 434 1179, www.thesisters.co.uk Good Natured Fruit is based at East Seaton in Angus, 01241 879989, www.goodnaturedfruit.co.uk*

■ L'escargot Blanc
17 Queensferry St, West End, Edinburgh
0131 226 1890
www.lescargotblanc.co.uk
Mon–Thu noon–3pm, 5.30–10.30pm; Fri/Sat noon–3pm, 5.30–11pm. Closed Sun. £10.90 (set lunch) / £21 (dinner)
This cheery West End bistro is linked to sister restaurant L'escargot Bleu in Broughton Street. Owners Frédéric Berkmiller and Betty Jourjon are still here, and the wine-dark coq au vin still comes to the table in those beguiling copper cooking pots. With a two-course prix fixe lunch/early evening menu along with a decent à la carte, there's something here for most occasions.

■ L'escargot Bleu
56 Broughton St, New Town, Edinburgh
0131 557 1600, www.lescargotbleu.co.uk
Sun–Thu noon–3pm, 5.30–10pm; Fri/Sat noon–3pm, 5.30–10.30pm. £22.50 (lunch/dinner)
The Auld Alliance between France and Scotland may have waned in politics, but it's very much alive on the plate. The staff at this engaging restaurant are as French as the posters and the red-chequered table cloths, but the free-range 'vicious but delicious' chickens are raised in the Borders by Linda Dick, while pork comes from rare-breed pigs that rootled through happy days in the shadow of East Lothian's Ballencrieff Castle.

■ First Coast
97–101 Dalry Road, West End, Edinburgh
0131 313 4404, www.first-coast.co.uk
Mon–Sat noon–2pm, 5–10.30pm. Closed Sun. £10.95 (set lunch) / £17 (dinner)
Being just off the beaten track has never been a major problem for First Coast, which has been welcoming satisfied customers since 2003. There's a good range of fish and meat, and the menu includes that rarest of beasts: a separate section for vegetarians. Quality ingredients and wonderful flavours are to the fore here, from a starter of tender slow-cooked salmon brought to life with pickled shallots and Guinness soda bread, to the strongly flavoured Filipino pork sisig.

■ The Garvald Inn
Main Street, Garvald, East Lothian
01620 830311, www.thegarvaldinn.co.uk
Tue–Fri noon–2.30pm, 6.30–8.30pm; Sat 12.30–2.45pm, 6.30–8.45pm; Sun 12.30–3pm. Closed Mon. £10 (lunch) / £15 (dinner)
A real community hub, Peter McQuade's bar-restaurant plays host to a steady stream of regulars with a mix of familiar modern pub staples and hearty but not heavy finer dining.

■ The Grain Store
30 Victoria Street, Old Town, Edinburgh
0131 225 7635
www.grainstore-restaurant.co.uk
Mon–Thu noon–2pm, 6–10pm; Fri noon–2pm, 6–11pm; Sat noon–3pm, 6–11pm; Sun noon–3pm, 6–10pm. £12.50 (set lunch) / £30 (dinner)
Something of an institution, the Grain Store has earned a reputation for using the best produce Scotland has to offer. While Scottish meat, game and seafood are plentiful, vegetarians are catered for, but with little imagination: a warm salad starter uses vegetables featured in other dishes. The lunch menu fares slightly better, offering goat's cheese salad and mushroom risotto. Desserts get things back on an even keel, and a fantastic selection of cheeses comes served with crumbly home-made oatcakes.

■ Henderson's Vegetarian Restaurant
94 Hanover Street, New Town, Edinburgh
0131 225 2131
www.hendersonsofedinburgh.co.uk
Mon–Wed 8am–10pm; Thu–-Sat 8am–10.45pm; Closed Sun. £9 (lunch) / £12 (dinner)
The deli upstairs and the recent addition of the contemporary art gallery add to the unique texture of this hallmark Henderson destination, now joined by a bistro round the corner and a café beneath St John's church in the West End. The kitchen/bakery is infamous for producing good quality veggie, vegan and gluten-free meals for all the right reasons. Children are welcome, and there's regular live music.

■ Iglu
2b Jamaica St, Stockbridge, Edinburgh
0131 476 5333, www.theiglu.com
Tue–Sat noon–3pm, 6–10pm; Sun noon–3pm, 6–9pm. Closed Mon. £18 (lunch) / £20 (dinner)
Provenance might be the buzzword of the moment, but Iglu has always been at the forefront of an ethical approach to eating and the proprietors pride themselves on their commitment to animal welfare and local sourcing. Twenty-eight-day-hung Aberdeen Angus rump steak served with hand-cut chips and roast garlic butter showcases Iglu's excellent meat, as does the wild boar burger with game jus. Friendly, informative service and comfortable surroundings are the icing on the cake.

■ The Kitchin
78 Commercial Quay, Leith
0131 555 1755, www.thekitchin.com
Tue–Thu 12.30–2pm, 6.30–10pm; Fri/Sat 12.30–2pm, 6.30–10pm. Closed Sun/Mon. £24.50 (set lunch) / £50 (dinner)

The Scottish Café and Restaurant

In a few short years, Tom Kitchin has shifted from new kid on the block to a place among Scotland's élite chefs. His motto, 'From nature to plate', acts as summary and guiding light to the impressive sourcing, presentation and quality of dishes in his Leith-based restaurant. The wine of the day changes with the menu, and a Monte Velho Branco from Portugal enriches and enhances the meal, which concludes with coffee and chocolate as you've never had before.

■ Lazy Lohan's
158 Canongate, Old Town, Edinburgh
0131 556 8999, www.lazylohans.com
Mon noon–3pm; Tue–Sat noon–3pm,
6–10pm; Closed Sun. £9.95 (set lunch) /
£17 (dinner)
Lazy Lohan's displays a strong identity and determined sense of purpose that belie its name and modest size. The Royal Mile bistro nails its colours to the mast in its mission statement, promising a commitment to healthy, sustainable food prepared using locally sourced ingredients wherever possible. The 'Lazy' of the title is an ironic reference to the ethos of the Slow Food movement, but there's undoubtedly a laid-back feel to the restaurant, reinforced by the unobtrusive service.

■ Loch Fyne Restaurant
25 Pier Place, Newhaven Harbour, Leith
0131 559 3900, www.lochfyne.com
Mon–Fri 10am–10pm; Sat 10am–10.30pm; Sun 10am–10pm. £10 (set lunch) / £19 (dinner)
Linked to, but separate from, the original Loch Fyne Oyster Bar in Argyll, the only Scottish outpost of the 47-branch chain is a temple to Scottish fish and shellfish. Juicy Loch Fyne oysters are served on

ice with a range of accompaniments, but the star of the starters is the home-made potted shrimp. Main courses range from the traditional (haddock, chips and peas) to the more adventurous (kiln-roasted salmon with mushroom, whisky and horseradish sauce).

■ Mussel Inn
61–65 Rose Street, New Town, Edinburgh
0131 225 5979, www.mussel-inn.com
Mon–Thu noon–3pm, 5.30–10pm;
Fri–Sun noon–10pm. £20 (lunch/dinner)
Serving up the freshest seafood from Scotland's shellfish farms, the Mussel Inn is a welcome port of good food amid Rose Street's pubs. Mussels are the star of the show, and come with a bewildering array of sauces: marinière, blue cheese and bacon – even a North African twist featuring ginger, coriander and cumin – while scallops play a strong supporting role. Add some tempting starters, side dishes and oyster options, and the stage is set for a great-quality feast.

■ The Old Bakehouse Bistro and Grill
Main Street, West Linton
01968 660830, www.west-linton.org.uk
Wed/Thu 5–9pm, Fri/Sat noon–9pm;
Sun 11.30am–9pm. Closed Mon/Tue. £9 (lunch) / £17 (dinner)
There's an old-time feel to the fixtures and fittings in this former village bakery, but the approach is contemporary and imaginative, with children's, high tea and Sunday brunch menus alongside a weekly market menu and main à la carte.

■ Ondine
2 George IV Bridge, Old Town, Edinburgh
0131 226 1888
www.ondinerestaurant.co.uk
Mon–Sat noon–10pm; Sun noon–4pm.

£14.95 (set lunch) / £27 (dinner)
One of the newest additions to Edinburgh's restaurant scene is tucked up a staircase on George IV Bridge. A sweeping bar dominates the dining room, perfect for sampling the varied crustacean menu and sipping white wine. Sustainability and conservation are critical to chef Roy Brett, who works closely with the Marine Stewardship Council. The trouble will be choosing. Like the eponymous mythical sea spirit, Ondine might just take your breath away.

■ pickledgreen
158 Rose Street, City Centre, Edinburgh
0131 220 0477, www.pickledgreen.co.uk
Mon–Thu 10am–2pm, 5–10pm; Fri
10am–3pm, 5–10pm; Sat 10am–10pm;
Sun 10am–4pm. £10 (set lunch) / £15 (set dinner)
Pickledgreen is a new addition to Edinburgh's dining scene and the Scots-Belgian bistro and café has spent its early months finding its feet. The location and layout are a challenge: the street-level entrance has the look of a deli and takeaway, and the restaurant upstairs is easily overlooked. Efforts have been made to make the menus affordable and well-versed in local, seasonal sourcing. Hopefully any teething problems can be fixed quickly, as the restaurant is friendly and well intentioned.

■ Plumed Horse
50–54 Henderson Street, Leith
0131 554 5556, www.plumedhorse.co.uk
Tue–Sat noon–1.30pm, 7–9pm. Closed Sun/Mon.
£24.50 (set lunch) / £45 (set dinner)
Since opening in 2006 and its subsequent acquisition of the Michelin star, the Plumed Horse has demanded – and garnered – a lot of attention from food critics and lovers of eating out. Chef/proprietor Tony Borthwick's personal touches are evident throughout the restaurant, from the décor and striking artwork through to the carefully honed menus. These take the form of set-priced menus at both lunch and dinner, with a seven-course tasting option available in the evening.

■ La Potinière
Main Street, Gullane, East Lothian
01620 843214, www.la-potiniere.co.uk
Wed–Sun 12.30–1.30pm, 7–8.30pm.
Closed Mon/Tue. (Closed Sun eve Oct–May). £18.50 (set lunch) / £40 (set dinner)
Award-winning food is often accompanied by a great deal of pomp, but this modest East Lothian restaurant is decorated simply and relies on the appreciative chatter of

diners for atmosphere, letting the food do the talking much of the time. Being two of the founder members of the Scotch Beef Club, owners/chefs Mary Runciman and Keith Marley believe in using only the freshest and the finest ingredients. The menu is brief – just two choices per course – and changes regularly according to the seasons.

Restaurant Martin Wishart
54 The Shore, Leith, 0131 553 3557, www.martin-wishart.co.uk
Tue–Fri noon–2pm, 6.45–9.30pm; Sat noon–1.30pm, 6.30–9.30pm. Closed Sun/Mon. £24.50 (set lunch) / £60 (dinner)
There is something inherently tasteful about Restaurant Martin Wishart. The place exudes calmness and warmth, and may encourage dangerously expensive lingering. This is not, however, a bad thing. The cooking at Wishart's is akin to culinary precision engineering. Flavours are arranged like cogs, each one playing an integral part in the whole. Of course, nothing weighs in at an everyday price, but then nor should it: Wishart's is not an everyday restaurant.

The Scottish Café and Restaurant
National Gallery of Scotland, The Mound, City Centre, Edinburgh, 0131 226 6524 www.thescottishcafeandrestaurant.com
Mon–Sat 8–5pm; Sun 10–5pm; late opening Thu till 6pm. £10 (café lunch) / £20 (restaurant lunch)
This café and restaurant in the National Gallery of Scotland is the latest offering from the branch of Contini dynasty renowned for Centotre and Zanzero. However, while an Italian influence is apparent, the main focus is on quality Scottish food. Starters include Dickson's of Cockenzie smoked salmon; heather honey-roasted beetroot or venison carpaccio with rocket and Loch Arthur cheddar, while mains include Buccleuch sirloin steak, roast Scottish seabass and venison stew. Fabulous views.

Seadogs
43 Rose Street, City Centre, Edinburgh 0131 225 8028
www.seadogsonline.co.uk
Mon–Sun noon–4pm; 5–10pm. £10 (lunch) / £14 (dinner)
David Ramsden continues to refine his innovative style with Seadogs, the latest addition to his restaurant empire, which began at The Dogs in Hanover Street. The menu has many of the original Dogs ideas – dishes for sharing and hearty seasonal grub at low prices. A smoked mackerel starter is served on toast with a peppery rhubarb jam – a combination that really works. Puddings are hearty affairs, just like Mum used to make.

Urban Angel

The Ship on the Shore
24–26 The Shore, Leith, 0131 555 0409 www.theshipontheshore.co.uk
Mon–Sun noon–10pm. £12 (set lunch) / £21 (dinner)
At first glance, the Ship might seem like it's been lifted straight out of a novel, so easy is it to imagine smugglers sitting in the cosy bar and plotting their next act of derring-do. In truth this is a friendly seafood restaurant that takes Scottish fish seriously, but never feels out of touch. The excellent-value lunch and early dining menu encapsulates all that the Ship does best – ideal for initiating yourself in the old tavern's charms.

Spoon Café Bistro
6a Nicolson Street, Old Town, Edinburgh 0131 557 4567, www.spooncafe.co.uk
Mon–Sat 10am–10pm; Sun 12pm–6pm. £10.50 (lunch) / £16 (dinner)
Spoon Café has done a great job in choosing new premises – this huge open space is prettily decked out and includes a kids' play area. Known for serving Edinburgh's best soup, Spoon's menu now includes more restaurant-style dishes. The vodka and beetroot home-cured salmon is a light and tangy starter, while for mains a trout fillet is beautifully cooked with a salted, crispy skin and cider vinegar dressing. Spoon Café is perfect for a pre-Festival Theatre visit.

The Sun Inn
Lothianbridge, Dalkeith, 0131 663 2456 www.thesuninneskbank.co.uk
Tue–Sat noon–2pm, 6pm–9pm; Sun noon–7pm. £15 (lunch) / £20 (dinner)
Given its location within easy reach of Edinburgh the Sun Inn could just settle for being yet another ye old inn that peddles out microwaved pub grub.

Thankfully they have a grander vision. Local produce features heavily on a menu with starters like Strathdon Blue soufflé, with he highlight of the mains a 'Pig on a Plate' – crispy belly pork on creamy mash with pork loin and apple sauce and Findlay's black pudding.

Sweet Melindas
11 Roseneath St, Southside, Edinburgh 0131 229 7953
www.sweetmelindas.co.uk
Mon 6–10pm; Tue–Sat noon–2pm, 6–10pm. Closed Sun. £12.50 (set lunch) / £22.50 (set dinner)
Cosy, welcoming and charming are just three of many adjectives to describe this delightful little restaurant. With seafood from Eddie's next door, arguably the city's best fishmonger, diners are assured of a freshness normally found only right by the sea. From the home-made soda bread that arrives as you place your order, to the Valrhona truffles accompanying your coffee, Sweet Melindas is all about those little extra touches, and is all the more special for that.

Tailend Restaurant
14–15 Albert Place, Leith Walk, Edinburgh, 0131 555 3577 www.tailendrestaurant.com
Mon–Sun 11.30am–10pm. £7.95 (set lunch) / £15 (dinner)
Sit-in fish'n'chip restaurants often conjure up sad images of greasy cafés with rubbery fish that tastes rather like licking the Formica tables on which it's served. Not so at Tailend, where crisp and fresh are the order of the day. Pedestrian traffic at the takeaway business next door is constant but never intrudes into the main restaurant, where modern decor in cool tones of green and blue speak of the sea.

Tony's Table

58a North Castle Street, New Town, Edinburgh
0131 226 6743, www.tonystable.com
Tue–Sat noon–2.30pm, 6.30–10pm, Sun 5–9pm, Closed Mon. £11 (lunch) / £18 (dinner)
At Tony's Table, executive chef Tony Singh's team serve up uncomplicated but out-of-the-ordinary food in genuinely relaxed surroundings. The list of mains makes it clear that the more expensive cuts of meat go to Tony's other higher-end Edinburgh restaurant, Oloroso, but with beautifully cooked diced pork belly and 'cow pie' on offer, this doesn't seem like a great loss. Don't be fooled by the flying pig motif – restaurants this good really do exist.

Urban Angel

• 1 Forth Street, New Town, Edinburgh
0131 556 6323, www.urban-angel.co.uk
Mon–Sat 9am–late; Sun 9am–5pm.
• 121 Hanover Street, New Town, Edinburgh
0131 225 6215, www.urban-angel.co.uk
Mon–Sat 9am–late; Sun 10am–5pm.
£19.50 (lunch/dinner)
From stylish premises in Hanover Street and Forth Street, the Urban Angel team serve up hearty portions of ethical grub to Edinburgh's trendy foodies for whom organic, fair trade and free-range are key considerations. Urban Angel 'favourites' can seem a bit dull in comparison to the exciting list of daily specials, along the lines of braised ox cheeks and smoked haddock and pea risotto, but Urban Angel offers reliably good eating with a squeaky clean conscience.

The Vintners Rooms

The Vaults, 87 Giles Street, Leith, Edinburgh, 0131 554 6767
www.thevintnersrooms.com
Tue–Sat noon–2pm, 7–10pm. Closed Sun/Mon. £19 (set dinner)
Maitre d' Silvano Praino extends a warm welcome in this delightful slice of France in Leith. Head chef David Spanner demonstrates considerable talent with a wafer-thin octopus carpaccio accompanied by locally sourced lobster. Main courses are likewise traditional yet inventive: a perfectly aged piece of beef sirloin with a marrow ham hock croquette is packed full of rich beefy flavour. Beautiful presentation is married with superb work in the kitchen, which makes for a memorable experience.

Wedgwood the Restaurant

267 Canongate, Old Town, Edinburgh
0131 558 8737
www.wedgwoodtherestaurant.co.uk
Mon–Sat noon–3pm, 6–10pm; Sun 12.30–3pm, 6–10pm. £10 (set lunch) / £25 (dinner)
From the elegant décor to each stellar dish, Wedgwood the Restaurant fulfils its promise of hosting the perfect night out. Much thought has been put into the tasteful dining room, where the gentle atmosphere allows the food and wine to be centre of attention and guests are encouraged to enjoy their 'deciding time' with a glass of champagne and the day's amuse-bouche selection. This chic establishment is a refreshing stop along the tartan-clad Royal Mile.

The Witchery by the Castle

Castlehill, Royal Mile, Old Town, Edinburgh
0131 225 5613, www.thewitchery.com
Mon–Sun noon–4pm, 5.30–11.30pm.
£13.95 (set lunch) / £40 (dinner)
The Witchery by the Castle has been wowing locals, tourists and celebrities for more than 30 years. Guests can choose to dine in either the darkly luxurious Witchery or the spookily-decorated Secret Garden. Staff are attentive, allowing guests to enjoy the excellent fare – such as a shared main course of beef Wellington, which is tender and flaky and arrives with a jug of red wine jus, buttery mash and green beans – and magnificent setting. A memorable experience.

GREATER GLASGOW & CLYDESIDE

An Lochan

340 Crow Road, West End, Glasgow
0141 338 6606, www.anlochan.co.uk
Tue–Sat noon–3pm, 6–9.30pm; Sun noon–3pm. Closed Mon.£9.95 (set lunch) / £23 (dinner)
An Lochan's roots lie in Tighnabruaich, where the original hotel and restaurant are still based. The Glasgow outpost offers an impressive dining room bathed in creams and whites, giving that special-occasion feel. The small menu shows dedication to locality and seasonality, though the execution needs work. If you fancy sampling a little of everything, go for the seafood platter of mussels, scallops, oysters, smoked salmon and langoustines, all cooked simply to let the produce shine.

Arisaig

1 Merchant Square, Merchant City, Glasgow, 0141 553 1010
www.arisaigrestaurant.co.uk
Mon–Wed noon–2.30pm, 5–10pm; Thu–Sun noon–10pm. £11.95 (set lunch) / £20 (dinner)
It feels as if Arisaig has always belonged in its new home, and even the menu exudes assurance. The kitchen has the wisdom to keep fried squid rings simple, lightly coated in flour and perfectly crunchy. A smoky kipper is combined with poached oyster – an intense mix, but a cheese sauce just about holds things together. It's also nice to see a restaurant approaching gluten-free cooking as a shift towards food that feels, and might even taste, better.

Bistro at One Devonshire Gardens

1 Devonshire Gardens, West End, Glasgow
0141 339 2001, www.hotelduvin.com
Mon–Thu noon–2.30pm, 6–10pm; Fri noon–2.30pm, 6–10.30pm; Sat 6–10.30pm; Sun 12.30–3pm, 6–10pm.
£14.50 (set lunch) / £35 (dinner)
One Devonshire Gardens has long been synonymous with elegant, up-market eating. Celebrities such as George Clooney and Justin Timberlake have dined there, and chefs including Andrew Fairlie and Gordon Ramsay have run the kitchen. These days in the capable hands of the Hotel Du Vin chain, it provides excellent service and exudes confident class, although aesthetically it appears a little dated. The menu, contrastingly, shines with style and exquisite taste – although be prepared to dip into your pocket accordingly.

The Butcher Shop Bar and Grill

1055 Sauchiehall Street, West End, Glasgow, 0141 339 2999
www.butchershopglasgow.com
Mon–Sun noon–2pm, 6–10pm. £12 (lunch) / £20 (dinner)
In keeping with the trend over the last few years of original and left-field openings along the Argyle Street strip from Kelvingrove to Finnieston comes this new bar and grill at the southern end of Kelvin Way. The venture blends a cocktail bar with a smart steakhouse offering bespoke steaks, burgers, charcuterie, calamari and other grilled fish, along with Sunday roasts, a weekend brunch offer and late-night supper options.

Café Gandolfi

64 Albion Street, Merchant City, Glasgow
0141 552 6813, www.cafegandolfi.com
Mon–Sun 9am–11.30pm. £14.50 (lunch) / £14.50 (dinner)
In the gastronomic dark ages of the late 70s/early 80s, Seumas MacInnes' Café Gandolfi stood as a beacon of hope, and it still retains its unique blend of homeliness and sophistication. Standards range from haggis and neeps to smoked venison with deliciously creamy gratin dauphinoise, and there are great daily specials. Glasgow was

just coming out of its tearoom era when the city's first cappuccino maker arrived with this establishment, and the quality of the coffee has never faltered.

■ Cafezique

66 Hyndland Street, West End, Glasgow
0141 339 7180
Mon–Sun 9am–10.30pm. £10 (lunch) / £15 (dinner)

Discerning locals, students and foodies flock to Mhairi Taylor's buzzing West End café-restaurant, next to her highly respected delicatessen, Delizique. Cafezique's simple interior and unobtrusive staff make for an informal but uncompromising dining experience. The emphasis is on the quality of the ingredients, and the menu confidently and imaginatively reflects this, with dishes divided into 'wee things' and 'big things'. The trick is to leave room for the generous desserts. Cafezique is everything you want in a local bistro.

■ Cail Bruich

• 725 Great Western Road, West End, Glasgow
0141 334 6265, www.cailbruich.co.uk
Tue–Fri noon–3pm, 5–9.30pm; Sat 10am–3pm, 5–9.30pm; Sun 10.30am–3.30pm, 5–9pm; Closed Mon. £10.50 (set lunch) / £26 (dinner)
• Sommerville Weir Hall, Faith Avenue, Quarriers Village, Bridge of Weir, Inverclyde
01505 610956, www.cailbruich.co.uk
Tue–Fri 11am–3pm, 5–10pm; Sat 10am–3pm, 5–10pm; Sun 11am–3.30pm. Closed Mon. £11.50 (set lunch) / £23 (dinner)

For a small place, Cail Bruich aims high and frequently hits its marks. The menu is reassuringly short, leaving chef Paul Charalambous time to develop the sophistication of his seasonal dishes. A velvety parsnip velouté is given sparkle by a dollop of bright lemon and herb gremolata and has a vibrant nutty undertow courtesy of some cooked chestnuts. From the mains a venison loin is pan-fried to perfection. Leave room for the pastry chef's theatrical and adventurous sweets.

■ Cookie

72 Nithsdale Road, Southside, Glasgow
0141 423 1411
www.cookiescotland.com
Mon 9am–6pm; Tue–Thu 9am–10pm; Fri/Sat 8.30am–11pm; Sun 10am–6pm].
£12 (lunch) / £15 (dinner)

Since opening in December 2009, Cookie's quickly built up a devoted following. Its informal dining room is peppered with funky design pieces and there's a tiny cook shop. The menu changes often to reflect the seasonal

produce key to Cookie's ethos. Many items double as mains and starters, and dishes are cooked to order before your eyes. The wine list is worth perusing; directly imported by management, you'll not find these anywhere else, and most are available by the glass.

■ Crabshakk

1114 Argyle Street, West End, Glasgow
0141 334 6127, www.crabshakk.com
Tue–Sat 11am–10pm; Sun noon–6pm. Closed Mon. £18 (lunch/dinner)

Despite the small but irritating matter of the spelling (not handy when Googling), Crabshakk's peachy-keen clientele means a full-to-bursting reservations book. The signature crab-cakes – flaky, sweet, fleshy and fresh – are unbeatable. It's hard not to demand extra bread with the scallops in anchovy butter to mop up the salty, buttery juices. Paired with an ice-cold bottle of Picpoul while anticipating fresh langoustines and skinny fries for your next course, you could probably die happy.

■ Dining Room

104 Bath Street, City Centre, Glasgow
0141 332 6678
www.diningroomglasgow.com
Mon–Sat noon–2.30pm, 5–10pm; Sun 5–10pm. £13.50 (set lunch) / £27 (dinner)

This exceptional new arrival joins Abode in bringing culinary sophistication to Bath Street. Chef Jim Kerr's reassuringly small menu offers starters such as a hot and sour prawn broth that's thick with spicy tomatoes and coriander – a balance of textures that signals his creative flair. From the mains a roast guineafowl is brightened with a vivid vermouth sauce rampant with leeks and grapes. Sweets are imaginative, and enthusiastic staff maintain an air of professionalism. An exemplary and exciting newcomer.

■ Fanny Trollopes

1066 Argyle Street, West End, Glasgow
0141 564 6464
www.fannytrollopes.co.uk
Fri–Sat noon–2pm, 5pm–midnight; Tue–Thu 5pm–midnight, Sun 3–9pm. Closed Mon (evening hours only, Jan–Feb).
£12.95 (set lunch) / £20 (dinner)

Don't be fooled by the shiny new neon sign – Fanny Trollopes is no follower of fashion, and in the kitchen they're continuing to serve up huge, expertly cooked portions of simple fare using excellent local produce. The menu tends to change daily, depending on what's in season, but you can always count on hearty meat dishes and at least one well-chosen catch of the day. This is informal dining that knows what it's doing.

■ Fusion

2 Hopeton Street, Gourock
01475 633998
www.fusionrestaurant.org.uk
Tue–Fri noon–2pm, 5–9.30pm; Sat 5–9.30pm. Closed Sun/Mon. £10 (set lunch) / £21 (dinner)

Simple, accomplished Scottish cuisine from Mary Robb and Evelyn Docherty in an unassuming but elegant and contemporary restaurant above a pub.

■ Gamba

225a West George Street, City Centre, Glasgow
0141 572 0899, www.gamba.co.uk
Mon–Sat noon–2.30pm, 5–10.30pm. Closed Sun. £16.95 (set lunch) / £29 (dinner)

In ten years Gamba has established itself as one the best places to eat fish in the city. Soft jazz plays and staff give discreet yet attentive service. An amuse-bouche may come in the form of a small, crumbly pastry case, filled with rich smoked salmon pâté – which sets the tone for the meal as classic flavours rub shoulders with Asian-inspired offerings to make an interesting and varied menu, cooked to perfection.

■ Gandolfi Fish

84 Albion Street, Merchant City, Glasgow
0141 552 9475, www.cafegandolfi.com
Sun, Tue–Thu noon–10pm; Fri/Sat noon–11pm. Closed Mon. £14.50 (set lunch) / £22 (dinner)

Modern, polished but above all buzzing, Gandolfi proves that you can be serious about fish without taking yourself too seriously. Less rustic and more cosmopolitan in décor than its sister-neighbour Café Gandolfi, the chic glass frontage, bright lights and solid dark wood merge comfort with class. Daily specials and staff will direct you to the best of that day's haul from the fish-market, but their trademark fish pie and fish'n'chips are always popular choices.

■ Guy's

24 Candleriggs, Merchant City, Glasgow
0141 552 1114
www.guysrestaurant.co.uk
Tue–Wed 5–10.30pm; Thu noon–10pm; Fri/Sat noon–11.30pm; Sun 12.30–9.30pm. Closed Mon. £8 (set lunch) / £23 (dinner)

Guy's restaurant is exactly that: proprietor Guy Cowan has devised the bulging and diverse menu, decorated the place in his unique, Italian style, and hand-picked all the staff. He also leads the kitchen. The menu traverses many cuisines and has a massive range of choice, from classic French dishes, Italian pastas and several well-sourced Scottish meat and fish dishes. Desserts

Crabshakk

are a wonderful way to finish a fantastic meal in a sophisticated atmosphere.

■ Heart Buchanan
380 Byres Road, West End, Glasgow
0141 334 7626
www.heartbuchanan.co.uk
Mon–Sat 9am–6.30pm; Sun 10am–6.30pm. £7.50 (lunch)
Heart Buchanan takes pride in selling fresh, home-made produce prepared with love and attention. The breakfasts are wonderful, from the pain au chocolate to porridge with fruit compote and cream. For lunch there is a selection of specials including soup and sandwiches as well as salads, also on sale in the neighbouring Heart Buchanan deli. The café also runs cookery and wine-tasting classes, plus the bakery is available for private dining parties.

■ Lebowskis
1008 Argyle Street, West End, Glasgow
0141 564 7988, www.lebowskis.co.uk
Mon–Sun noon–9pm. £8 (lunch) / £12.50 (dinner)
Lebowskis doesn't wallow in its theme – a half-hidden portrait of the eponymous Dude looks down and there is Lebowski-inspired white Russians. A dedication to local suppliers means the best regional produce never has far to travel to the kitchen, where the focus is on pub food of the highest quality. Mains include Aberfoyle steak and ale pie, west coast mussels, haggis lasagne and the self-proclaimed undisputed best burger in Scotland – a real pleasure.

■ The Left Bank
33–35 Gibson Street, West End, Glasgow
0141 339 5969, www.theleftbank.co.uk
Mon–Fri 9am–10pm; Sat/Sun 10am–10pm. £9 (lunch) / £13 (dinner)
With its design-led décor, exposed stonework and left-field soundtrack, it's no wonder this place is regularly name-checked in guidebooks. But this is not just a case of style over substance; the food here really delivers. From breakfast options including eggs mornay and porridge with manuka honey, lunches of roasted sweet potato falafel or coconut and lime Keralan chicken, and beyond, every dish is well thought out, carefully sourced and, most importantly, wonderfully well executed.

■ MacSorley's Music Bar
42 Jamaica Street, City Centre, Glasgow
0141 248 8581, www.macsorleys.com
Sun/Mon noon–6pm; Tues/Wed 12–8pm; Thu–Sat noon–9pm. £14 (lunch/dinner)
Nestled under the arches of Central Station, MacSorley's retains old-time charm while hosting live music and DJs. On the pub grub front, the rebranding of the kitchen as Biadh at MacSorley's Music Bar shows a desire to raise the game. The menu now offers quality Scottish produce in confident and inventive dishes. There are also large slates offering meat, fish or cheese with bread and pickles, or simple fish and chips wrapped in newspaper.

■ Martin Wishart at Loch Lomond
De Vere Cameron House Hotel, by Balloch, Dunbartonshire, 01389 722504
www.martinwishartlochlomond.co.uk
Wed–Fri 6.30–10pm; Sat noon–2pm, 6.30–10pm; Sun noon–2.30pm, 7–10pm. Closed Mon/Tue. £35 (set lunch) / £60 (set dinner)
When the chance came for Edinburgh uber chef Martin Wishart to return to the kitchens where he cut his culinary teeth at Cameron House it proved too tempting to resist. Under head chef Stewart Boyles the result is as spectacular as the glitzy resort around it. You could dine à la carte, but the six course tasting menu excels. Loch Fyne crab sparkles with white radish and Basque pepper while smoked organic Shetland salmon is lifted further by Hebridean samphire and crowdie.

■ Michael Caines @ ABode
129 Bath Street, City Centre, Glasgow
0141 221 6789, www.michaelcaines.com
Tue–Sat noon–2.30pm, 6–10pm. Closed Sun/Mon. £12.95 (set lunch) / £32 (dinner)
Though the decor is less than thrilling, the creativity behind the kitchen door more than makes up for it. From thoughtful touches of artisan breads, a smooth amuse-bouche, quirky pre-dessert jelly and petits fours with coffee to the careful attention of the waiting staff, there's a sense that Michael Caines is trying hard – and succeeding – to impress. Drawing from the finer side of Parisian cuisine, almost every dish has ambitious flavour and texture combinations. A stand-out dining experience.

■ Mount Stuart
Mount Stuart Visitor's Centre, Isle of Bute
01700 503877, www.mountstuart.com
Mon–Sun noon–8.30pm. Closed Oct–April. £9 (lunch) / £14 (dinner)
Mount Stuart, home of the Marquesses of Bute, is at the heart of the revival of interest in island-produced food. With Alison Sykora at the helm in the café-restaurant which takes up the glass-walled first floor of the attractive modern visitor centre, the food of Bute and Argyll has a real champion, with Drumachloy Rose Veal, Plan Farm lamb and Fyne Ales joining salad, fruit and veg plucked from the estate's kitchen garden.

■ Mussel Inn
157 Hope Street, City Centre, Glasgow
0141 572 1405, www.mussel-inn.com
Mon–Thu noon–2.30pm, 5–10pm; Fri/Sat noon–10pm; Sun 5–10pm. £21 (lunch/dinner)
See main entry in Edinburgh & Lothians.

■ No. Sixteen
16 Byres Road, West End, Glasgow
0141 339 2544, www.number16.co.uk
Mon–Sat noon–2.30pm, 5.30–10pm; Sun 1–3pm, 5.30–10pm. £9.95 (set lunch) / £21 (dinner)
With only 40 covers and serving reliably excellent food since 1991, No.16 has had little trouble filling its minuscule interior with a loyal crowd over the years. French-influenced dishes predominate on a changing menu that makes the

CHEF'S CHOICE

ALAN REID ON HARDIESMILL FARM'S BEEF

My kitchen window looks up over the fields to Caberston Forest, where roe deer wander down to the garden. Woodpigeon, pheasant and partridge are in abundance, with grouse on the moors beyond, and in the field there are usually either sheep or cows grazing away.

Not far away is Hardiesmill Farm, from where we source the finest pure-bred Aberdeen Angus beef. Robin and Alison Tuke are passionate about their product and, during a recent visit and farm tour, we followed the process from field to fork. After smelling the grain and feed, we then tasted various cuts cooked in the farm kitchen. You can then taste the feed in the beef. Only the best is used and the results are fantastic.

Being part of the Scotch Beef Club, recording the source to prove that the beef is Scotch could not be easier. Our guests always comment on the quality and flavour of our beef and, with mushrooms from the forest, we have everything to create dishes using only local and foraged produce.

We usually serve a medallion of fillet with either slow-cooked oxtail or ox cheek in Traquair ale, which is brewed just across the River Tweed at Traquair House, served with locally grown vegetables. I guess this must be chef's heaven as far as local produce is concerned.

■ *Alan Reid is chef proprietor at Windlestraw Lodge, Walkerburn, Peeblesshire www.windlestraw.co.uk. Hardiesmill Farm is in Gordon, Berwickshire www.hardiesmill.co.uk*

best of seasonal local ingredients, and if there's the odd disappointment among the starters – a broth of Puy lentils is underwhelming, for example – it's more than compensated for by satisfying mains such as slow-braised blade of beef or pan-fried bream with salsify.

■ R34 at India of Inchinnan

Greenock Road, Inchinnan, Renfrewshire
0141 533 4069, www.r34restaurant.com
Mon–Wed 8am–5pm; Thu 8am–9.30pm; Fri 8am–10.30pm; Sat 10am–10.30pm; Sun 11.30am–5.30pm. £10 (lunch) / £22 (dinner)
Part canteen, part fine-dining restaurant, chef/owner John Shields' operation is housed in the impressive extension to an A-listed Art Deco former rubber factory, with weekend evening dining and brunches most catching the imagination.

■ Red Onion

257 West Campbell Street, City Centre, Glasgow
0141 221 6000, www.red-onion.co.uk
Mon–Thu/Sun noon–10.30pm; Fri/Sat noon–11pm. £15 (lunch/dinner)
The stylish frontage to this popular restaurant – run by John Quigley and his wife – disguises a large and airy dining space with a welcoming ambience. Scottish classics and European and Asian dishes dominate a varied menu – a rich French onion soup and a pan-fried haggis sit alongside chicken liver parfait and fish-cakes. A dozen mains handle local produce and global flavours – from beef braised in beer with horseradish dumplings to a Malaysian curry.

■ Restaurant at Blythswood Square

11 Blythswood Square, City Centre, Glasgow, 0141 248 8888
www.blythswoodsquare.com
Mon–Fri 7–10am, noon–2.30pm, 6–10pm; Sat/Sun 7–10am, noon–3pm, 6–10pm.
£15 (set lunch) / £25.50 (dinner)
This redevelopment of the RAC Club is a worthy successor. One enters through the bar – with a playful nod to the environs' disreputable past as red lights shine from the windows. The menu is divided into 'classic' and 'contemporary' Scottish with swathes of Europe. Cremeux of foie gras has a rich, buttery meatiness that comes through at the end, after sherry vinegar and candied kumquat in a dish tasting of vanilla, then intense fruit, then toffee from a spiced croquant. Brilliant.

■ The Sisters

• 36 Kelvingrove Street, West End, Glasgow
0141 564 1157, www.thesisters.co.uk
Tue–Thu noon–2.30pm, 5–9pm; Fri/Sat

noon–2.30pm, 5–9.30pm; Sun noon–8pm. Closed Mon.
• 1a Ashgrove Gardens, 512 Crow Road, West End, Glasgow
0141 434 1179, www.thesisters.co.uk
Tue–Thu noon–2.30pm, 5.30–8.30pm; Fri/Sat noon–2.30pm, 5pm–9.15pm; Sun noon–7pm. Closed Mon.
£14.95 (set lunch) / £24 (dinner)
Few Glasgow foodies would presume such status without having dined at one of The Sisters' two establishments, where one can expect locally sourced and deftly prepared food with big flavours. Few dishes are unfamiliar, but the execution sets them apart and main courses have a refined heartiness. With puddings, one waiter is only half-joking when he speaks of potential rioting were puff-candy meringue with honeycomb ice-cream taken off. Though its replacement would no doubt be fantastic.

■ Stravaigin Café Bar

28 Gibson Street, West End, Glasgow
0141 334 2665, www.stravaigin.com
Mon–Fri 10am–10.30pm; Sat/Sun 11am–10.30pm. £12.95 (set lunch) / £16 (dinner)
Rustic interiors create an air of laid-back charm in this informal part of the Stravaigin stable. Situated above the renowned restaurant, the café bar specialises in superior pub grub and attracts a sussed crowd who've twigged that their brunch, lunch or dinner is being served from the same exceptional kitchen. Culinary flair and presentation are maintained with a smattering of cheffy touches. And how many bistros are so particular about quality that they keep their own flock of sheep?

■ Stravaigin 2

8 Ruthven Lane, West End, Glasgow
0141 334 7165, www.stravaigin.com
Mon–Fri noon–11pm; Sat/Sun 11am–11pm. £9.50 (set lunch) / £21 (dinner)
A walk down Ruthven Lane brings you to what feels like a small cottage – the second offering from the Stravaigin group. The seasonal and changing à la carte menu is succinct and fuses excellent British produce with Asian and Mediterranean flavours, a perfect example of their 'think global, eat local' ethos being a ramekin full of creamy potted paprika langoustines – crunchy, fresh red pepper and hazelnut salsa accompanies, mopped up with fragrant rosemary focaccia fingers.

■ Tattie Mac's

61 Otago Street, West End, Glasgow
0141 337 2282, www.tattiemacs.co.uk
Mon–Sun 11am–10pm. £10.95 (set lunch) / £18 (dinner)
Tattie Mac's is that rare thing: a

Toravaig House, Isle of Skye

Where to eat and drink in **Scotland**

Each business receives an annual visit by an assessor to ensure that they are maintaining high standards.

Businesses are assessed on • Hospitality and service • Quality and presentation of food and drink • Quality and freshness of ingredients • Housekeeping and hygiene.

So you can be assured of a great eating experience wherever you see the EatScotland logo. EatScotland Silver and Gold awards indicate excellent and outstanding places to dine.

Scottish TOURIST BOARD
SILVER

Scottish TOURIST BOARD
EatScotland

Scottish TOURIST BOARD
EatScotland GOLD

Discover EatScotland eating establishments throughout the country, as well as information on Scotland's fantastic produce and events, at **EatScotland.com**

Arbroath Smokies,
Portsoy Boat Festival
Aberdeenshire

SCOTLAND OF FOOD & DRINK
Nurtured at Source
Enjoyed the World Over

Live it. Visit *Scotland.*
eatscotland.com

genuinely stylish eating place serving inventive, carefully made food at accessible prices. Despite a name suggesting a baked potato shop, the menu presents a modern European approach to fine local ingredients, with French and Italian influences, plus restrained Asian flavours. The bistro menu with two courses for a little over a tenner (not Sunday nights) is the real bargain. An enterprising wine list, great décor and attentive service complete a thoroughly enjoyable experience.

■ Two Fat Ladies
• 118a Blythswood Street, City Centre, Glasgow, 0141 847 0088
www.twofatladiesrestaurant.com
Mon–Thu noon–3pm, 5.30–10pm; Fri/Sat noon–3pm, 5.30–11pm; Sun noon–3pm, 5–9pm. £16 (set lunch) / £25 (dinner)
• 88 Dumbarton Road, West End, Glasgow, 0141 339 1944
Mon–Thu noon–3pm, 5.30–10pm; Fri/Sat noon–3pm, 5.30–10.30pm; Sun 1–9pm.
£13.50 (set lunch) / £25 (dinner)
• Two Fat Ladies at the Buttery, 652 Argyle Street, West End, Glasgow 0141 221 8188
Mon–Sat noon–3pm, 5–10.30pm; Sun 12.30–9pm. £15.50 (set lunch) / £33 (dinner)
Under the expert eye of owner Ryan James and his Two Fat Ladies banner, the Buttery continues to flourish as a well-loved Glasgow institution, demonstrating exemplary standards of service and a confident, imaginative hand in the kitchen. At £25.95 the fillet of Scotch beef is the most expensive main course on the menu, but it more than lives up to its price tag. Desserts are equally ambitious and tempting, with a perfect crème brûlée the stand-out sweet of the evening.

■ Ubiquitous Chip
12 Ashton Lane, West End, Glasgow 0141 334 5007
www.ubiquitouschip.co.uk
Mon–Sat noon–2.30pm, 5.30–11pm; Sun 12.30–3pm, 6.30–11pm. £24.95 (set lunch) / £20 (dinner)
An institution in Glasgow since the 1970s, the Chip is as popular with couples and families as it is arty types, businessmen, media darlings and politicians. Unpretentious of décor and atmosphere, it serves Scottish-sourced produce of the highest quality and freshness with imagination and flair – albeit with precipitous prices to match. The wine list is epic, the menu dripping with appeal. Steep costs and sometimes small portions aside, it's hard to recommend this perennial favourite highly enough.

Martin Wishart at Loch Lomond

SOUTHERN SCOTLAND

■ The Black Bull
Market Place, Lauder, Berwickshire 01578 722208, www.blackbull-lauder.com
Mon–Sun noon–2.30pm, 5pm–9pm. £15 (lunch/dinner)
This very popular 18th-century coaching inn is situated in perfect walking and cycling country. It serves a great range of well cooked, no-nonsense food from soup and ham and cheese omelette to Border beef fillet, lamb and spinach curry? Eat in the cosy bar area or the slightly grander Georgian dining room. All the beef is sourced from the market at nearby St Boswells; local cheese and ice-cream are also a regular feature.

■ Braidwoods
Drumastle Mill Cottage, Saltcoats Road, by Dalry, Ayrshire
01294 833544, www.braidwoods.co.uk
Tue 7–9pm; Wed–Sat noon–1.45pm, 7–9pm; Sun noon–1.45pm. Closed Mon. (May–Sep closed Sun). £22 (set lunch) / £42 (set dinner)
Having won a Michelin star in 2000 – still held to this day – Braidwoods exudes a quiet confidence. The small dining room boasts a handful of linen-clad tables, and ostentation is limited to a few colourful original paintings on the walls.

■ Burts Hotel
Market Square, Melrose
01896 822285, www.burtshotel.co.uk
Sun–Thu noon–2pm, 6–9.30pm; Fri/Sat noon–2pm, 6–10pm. £18 (lunch) / £29.50 (set dinner)
Tucked into the heart of Melrose, Burts has location on its side. The Hendersons are the hands-on family

behind this 18th-century old dame. The bar offers old favourites like haddock and chips, but also nods to local produce with scampi from Eyemouth, as well as 28-day hung steaks from Melrose's Martin Baird Butchers. Head chef Trevor Williams is at the helm through in the restaurant, where safe mains such as halibut and beef fillets are backed up with decadent sole, tiger prawn and lobster ravioli.

■ The Caddy Mann Restaurant
Mounthooly Farm, Crailing, Borders 01835 850787, www.caddymann.com
Sun–Thu noon–2pm; Fri/Sat 7pm–9pm. £14 (lunch) / £23
Slow baked Borders lamb leads the way for the traditional Scottish food available here at lunchtimes and weekend evenings.

■ Chuchus
1 Cubrieshaw Street, West Kilbride, Ayrshire
01294 829956, www.chuchus.co.uk
Tue noon–3pm; Wed–Sun noon–3pm, 5–9pm. Closed Mon. £11 (lunch) / £21 (dinner)
An interesting little place with warmth, charm and personality, it's imaginatively fashioned from the decayed waiting room of West Kilbride's station. With the maxim 'Coffee, cocktails and cuisine', it has established itself as a favourite haunt of the local population.

■ Fins Restaurant
Fencefoot, Fairlie, Ayrshire
01475 568989, www.fencebay.co.uk
Tue–Sat noon–2.30pm, 7–9pm; Sun noon–2.30pm. Closed Mon. £13 (set lunch) / £20
It's a seafood restaurant, it's a farm

shop, it's a self-catering cottage – in short, it's a little food haven on the west coast, between Largs and Ardrossan. The restaurant serves hot and cold seafood platters, with seasonal catches from local waters including langoustines, scallops and squat lobster tails.

■ Fouters Restaurant
2a Academy Street, Ayr
01292 261391, www.fouters.co.uk
Tue–Thu noon–2pm, 5–9pm; Fri/Sat.
Closed Sun/Mon. £15 (lunch) / £23
Ayr's landmark restaurant was once 18th-century bank vaults, but with space for only about twenty covers the dining room is cosy and intimate all the same. The menu places a heavy emphasis on Scottish ingredients – whether wood pigeon, Stornoway black pudding or Moray Firth seafood.

■ Horseshoe Inn
Eddleston, near Peebles
01721 730225, www.horseshoeinn.co.uk
Tue–Thu noon–2.30pm, 7–9pm; Fri/Sat noon–2.30pm, 6.30–9.30pm; Sun noon–2.30pm. Closed Mon. £18 (lunch) / £35
Just the right side of Peebles to be handy from Edinburgh the Horseshoe Inn still feels very much the historic coaching inn. And while good comfort food is the order of the day in the cosy bar/bistro, wonders are afoot in the fine dining restaurant run by Frenchman Patrick Bardoulet. West Coast crab is lifted with a citrus crust and sits alongside a classic cheese soufflé to start, with Borders beef served up with braised oxtail in a fine signature dish.

■ The Lodge at Carfraemill
Carfraemill, Lauder, Berwickshire
01578 750750, www.carfraemill.co.uk
Mon–Sun 7.30am–9pm. £10 (lunch) / £20
A well-known landmark on the A68, Jim and Jo Sutherland's inn displays a deep commitment to Borders' food, with hearty day-to-day food always available alongside more crafted specialities.

■ MacCallum's of Troon Oyster Bar
Harbourside, Troon, Ayrshire
01292 319339
Tue–Sat noon–2.30pm, 6.30–9.30pm. Sun noon–2.30pm. Closed Mon. £15 (lunch) / £20 (dinner)
A harbourside seafood restaurant run by fishmongers, with a much-loved fish and chip stop (the Wee Hurrie) next door. Expect an array of fruits of the sea and not too much fussing at all.

■ 1906
Turnberry Resort, Turnberry, Ayrshire
01655 331000www.turnberryresort.co.uk/1906-restaurant
Mon–Sun 7.06–10pm. £35 (dinner)

This grand old dame of the Ayrshire coast has had an elegant, expensive makeover and now serves sophisticated high-end, Escoffier-inspired French classics using Scottish-sourced produce.

■ Osso Restaurant
1 Innerleithen Road, Peebles
01721 724477, www.ossorestaurant.com
Mon 11am–4.30pm; Tues–Sat 11am–4.30pm, 6pm–9pm; Sun 11am–4.30pm.
£14 (lunch) / £19 (dinner)
Ally McGrath's Osso Restaurant not only acts as a showcase for the chef's polished food preparation skills with some creative evening dining, but it's also Peebles' premier coffee-hang out and reliable lunch stop.

■ Smith's at Gretna Green
Gretna Green, Dumfriesshire
01461 337007
www.smithsgretnagreen.com
Mon–Sun noon–9.30pm. £18 (dinner)
A contemporary bespoke hotel in the heart of Gretna Green is revolutionary enough. But this one offers a good standard of smart comfort food at very reasonable prices, with interesting fish and game dishes, as well as fresh vegetarian options. Menus change every three months with the seasons.

■ The Sorn Inn
35 Main Street, Sorn, East Ayrshire
01290 551305, www.sorninn.com
Tue–Fri noon–2pm, 6–9pm; Sat noon–9pm; Sun noon–8pm. Closed Mon.
£14.95 (set lunch) / £18.95 (set dinner)
The Sorn Inn has earned plaudits for putting a quiet little Ayrshire village on the map, among them a much-prized Michelin Bib Gourmand for good food at moderate prices – now held for five years. The old whitewashed inn houses a relaxed restaurant combining fine dining and brasserie-style elements, and owner-chef Craig Grant's menu also manages to balance the elaborate and the homely.

■ The Sunflower Restaurant
4 Bridgegate, Peebles
01721 722420, www.thesunflower.net
Mon–Wed noon–3pm; Thurs–Sat noon–3pm, 6pm–9pm. Closed Sun.
£15 (lunch) / £16 (dinner)
As bright and breezy as its name suggests, this cosy little haunt just off the High Street is an oasis. Val and Andrew Brunton are the affable owners with Val's precise but unfussy cooking the star. Local produce has joint star billing with meat fresh from the local butcher, wine from a Peebles wine merchant and organic ice cream from Over Langshaw Farm in the Borders. Val is a dab hand at vegetarian cuisine too with numerous options served all day long.

■ Trigony House Hotel
Closeburn, Thornhill, Dumfriesshire
01848 331211, www.trigonyhotel.co.uk
Mon 6pm–9pm; Tue–Sun noon–2pm, 6pm–9pm. £22 (dinner)
Getting the balance between quality, comfort and good taste is hard to achieve, but this undemonstrative former shooting lodge in the rolling hills of Dumfriesshire manages admirably, with some simple but deceptively skilled cooking and good local sourcing.

■ Whitmuir – The Organic Place
Whitmuir Farm, Lamancha, Peeblesshire
01968 661908
www.whitmuirtheorganicplace.co.uk
Mon–Sun 10am–6pm. £15 (lunch/dinner)
A dynamic driving force in organic farming, Pete Ritchie and Heather Anderson's mixed farm now has one of Scotland's best-stocked organic farm shops and a large, smart farm café using homegrown and local produce. Chef Didier Nemesien's menu is rich in farm-produced ingredients, with an impressive range of daily specials supplementing soups, omelettes, platters and a mixed grill.

■ Windlestraw Lodge
Tweed Valley, Walkerburn, Scottish Borders
01896 870636, windlestraw.co.uk.
Mon–Sun 6.30pm–8.30pm. £44.50 (set dinner)
Alan and Julie Reid's secluded country house hotel by the banks of the Tweed near Innerleithen has six guest bedrooms and a dining room that makes more effort than most to show off the produce of the area. The fixed menu includes home-made ravioli, woodpigeon, guinea fowl and venison.

CENTRAL SCOTLAND & FIFE

■ Andrew Fairlie at Gleneagles
Gleneagles Hotel, Auchterarder, Perthshire
01764 694267, www.andrewfairlie.com
Mon–Sat 6.30–10pm. Closed Sun. £75 (set dinner)
Scotland's only Michelin two-star restaurant, this is one of the country's most sought-after upmarket dining experiences. It's not, however, an intimidatingly grand affair: set in a modestly sized room in the heart of Gleneagles hotel, it is stylish rather than stuffy, decorated with leaf motifs and framed contemporary artworks. Six-course dégustation and market menus are available, the dishes deceptively simple yet imbued with flavour and care.

■ The Apron Stage

5 King Street, Stanley, Perthshire
01738 828888
Wed–Thu 6.30–9.30pm; Fri noon–2pm,
6.30–9.30pm; Sat 6.30–9.30pm. Closed
Sun–Tue. £21 (dinner)
Running one of the most pleasant and
engaging small restaurants in Scotland
from a tiny open kitchen, Shona
Drysdale and Jane Nicoll (with some
help from Tony Heath) cook to a nightly
blackboard menu of local specialities
and comforting bistro classics.

■ Ardeonaig Hotel

South Road, Loch Tay, Perthshire
01567 820400
www.ardeonaighotel.co.uk
Mon–Sun noon–10pm. £15 (lunch) / £35
(set dinner)
On the shores of Loch Tay, this coaching
inn has been sensitively upgraded in
contemporary styled small hotel by
imaginative owner Pete Gottgens. A
South African native, his enthusiasm for
Scottish produce has seen him establish
his own herd of black-face sheep and
shooting estate, as well as ensure a
supply of veg, herbs and salad from
local gardens. Recently refurbishments
have included a state-of-the-art kitchen
and wine cellar with dining tables.

■ Barley Bree

6 Willowbrae Street, Methill, Perthshire
01764 681451, www.barleybree.com
Wed–Sun noon–2pm, 6–9pm. Closed
Mon/Tue. £14 (lunch) / £22
Fabrice Bouteloup, former head chef at
the Atrium in Edinburgh, runs and own
this cosy, stylish and seasonal-food
oriented restaurant with rooms in the
centre of the small village of Methill, a
few miles from Crieff.

■ Biscuit Café

Sandhaven, Culross, Fife
01383 882176, www.culrosspottery.com
Mon–Sun 10am–5pm. £11 (lunch)
Set in a small conservatory at the back
of the Culross Pottery, the modest
image of this daytime operation is
enhanced by its positive attitude to
local and seasonal produce, as well
as a commitment to home-cooked
food. From the brief menu of soup,
sandwiches, platters and proper home
baking, local ingredients are to the fore.

■ The Byre Inn

Brig O'Turk, by Callander, Perthshire
01877 376292, www.byreinn.co.uk
Mon–Sat 11am–11pm; Sun noon–11pm.
£13 (lunch) / £16
A historic wayside pub in the heart of
the Trossachs serving sophisticated and
imaginative food including salt cod fritters,
pheasant coq au vin and braised mutton.

■ The Cellar

24 East Green, Anstruther, Fife
01333 310378
www.cellaranstruther.co.uk
Tue–Thu 6.30–9pm; Fri/Sat noon–
2.30pm, 6.30–9.30pm. £19.50 (set lunch)
/ £34.95 (set dinner)
With Scotland's Fisheries Museum
next door, this former cooperage and
smokery is steeped in fishing history
as well as a life-long appreciation of
the bounty of the sea. With its stone
walls and beamed ceilings the Cellar
lacks sea views but is still a wonderfully
atmospheric dining space; Peter
Jukes' top-notch seafood menu has
unelaborate but supremely assured
dishes such as smoked fish stew or East
Coast halibut with greens, pine nuts,
smokey bacon and sauce hollandaise.

■ Cross Keys Hotel

Main Street, Kippen, Stirlingshire
01786 870293
www.kippencrosskeys.co.uk
Mon–Sat noon–9pm, Sun noon–8pm. £12
(set lunch) / £16
A classic village tavern injected with
a dose of contemporary style, good
taste and culinary flair, with all-day food,
outdoor dining, roaring log fires and
three overnight rooms.

■ Deans at Let's Eat

77–79 Kinnoull Street, Perth
01738 643377, www.letseatperth.co.uk
Tue–Sat noon–2pm, 6.30–9.45pm. Closed
Sun/Mon. £20 (lunch) / £25
Willie Deans has guided the discerning
reputation of this popular Perth dining
spot with his confident execution of
modern classic dishes.

■ Glenskirlie House

Kilsyth Road, Banknock, Stirlingshire
01324 840201
www.glenskirliehouse.com
Mon noon–2pm; Tue–Sat noon–2pm,
6–9.30pm; Sun 12.30–2pm, 6–9.30pm.
£15 (lunch) / £28 (restaurant) / £16 (grill)
This sophisticated and grand family-run
hotel has built a sturdy reputation for
quality over the years without losing
its modern touch. The bar, grill and
restaurant menu is capable of delivering
some thrilling and inventive cooking.

■ inDulge

22 High Street, Auchterarder, Perthshire
01764 660033, www.indulge-now.co.uk
Mon–Sat 9.30am–4.30pm. Closed Sun.
£10 (lunch)
The town of Auchterarder might be
on the culinary map thanks to the
Gleneagles Hotel and Andrew Fairlie's
two Michelin star restaurant, but
Amanda Young and Colin McNicoll's
lovely deli and café on the High Street,

InDulge. Sandwiches are never routine
and the day's lunch specials will
invariably sound wonderfully intriguing
and tempting.

■ The Inn at Lathones

Largoward, by St Andrews, Fife
01334 840494, www.theinn.co.uk
Mon–Sun noon–9.30pm. £27 (lunch/
dinner)
This unprepossessing looking, white-
walled inn is home to Scotland's
smallest music festival and the food's
pretty glamorous too. Chef Richard
Brackenbury changes his offering three
times a year to follow the seasons. A
tian of potted crab with lobster butter,
crayfish tails and herb salad is a light
contrast to the luxurious foie gras crème
brûlée. Baked turbot with hand-dived
scallops and leek and potato crumble
is a comforting combo, as is the no-
nonsense, mixed game steamed pudding
on a slice of Stornoway black pudding.

■ Lake of Menteith Hotel & Waterfront Restaurant

Port of Menteith, Stirlingshire
01877 385258, www.lake-hotel.com
Mon–Sun noon–2.30pm, 6.30–9.30pm.
£16 (lunch) / £39.95 (set dinner)
Less than an hour from the centre
of Glasgow, the elegant Waterfront
Restaurant offers views through
bullrushes across Scotland's only lake
through to the mysterious island of
Inchmahome. Less formal dining is also
available in the Port Bar.

■ The Library Tea Room

Balquhidder, Perthshire
www.mhor.net
Mon & Wed–Sun 10am–5.30pm. Closed
Tue. (Closed Nov–Mar). £8 (lunch)
The village library is now a tea room
at the heart of the Lewis family's Mhor
empire, which extend to the hotel at
the end of the road and the bakery
and fish café in Callender. Run by Lisa
May Lewis, wife of hotel chef Tom and
a talented chef in her own right, the
timber-lined interior, fire-engine red
Gaggia coffee machine and chalkboard
of well-crafted specials declare the
warmth and good attitude of the place.

■ Mhor Fish

75–77 Main Street, Callander, Perthshire
01877 330213, www.mhor.net
Tue–Sun, 10am–9pm. £12 (lunch/dinner)
With the Lewis family of the nearby
Monachyle Mhor hotel at the helm
the fish counter and café are in the
hands of true loyalists to good food.
Fish and crustacean delights are
heaped up in the window tempting in
shoppers and diners alike. The dining
space is no setting for romance, but

The Peat Inn

it also sports an à la carte menu and serves crisp white wines to go with the fishy delights. You could just visit their chippie next door; even there the batter is laced with sparkling water and cooked in dripping.

■ Monachyle Mhor

Balquhidder, Perthshire
01877 384622, www.mhor.net
Mon–Sun noon–1.45pm, 7–8.45pm. £20 (set lunch) / £46 (set dinner)
The mercurial Lewis family have been ticking all the boxes long before the boxes themselves became fashionable offering a boutique hotel hideaway in an 18th-century rural farmhouse and steadings, farming their own land and cultivating a proper kitchen garden. Head chef Tom Lewis brings out the best in his ingredients with the likes of Tamworth pork fillet and belly, kohlrabi choucroute and wild mushrooms. Sunday lunches are great value, but for the full experience a lingering dinner and a night hidden away in one of the suites around the back beckons.

■ The Old Rectory Inn

West Quality Street, Dysart, Kirkcaldy, Fife, 01592 651211
www.theoldrectoryinn.com
Tue-Sat noon-2pm, 7-9.30pm; Sun 12.30-2.30pm. £13 (lunch) / £16 (dinner)
Hidden behind a plain, whitewashed wall in the historic burgh of Dysart the Old Rectory Inn carries the atmosphere of its Georgian setting with elegance and ease. The loyal local following enjoyed by proprietors Maxine and Spencer Barrie reflects the care and thought they put into their menus, with home-smoked salmon, slow-braised beef and intriguing dishes such as mussel, barley and ham broth showing confidence in classic food and an awareness of modern trends.

■ Ostlers Close

25 Bonnygate, Cupar, Fife
01334 655574, www.ostlersclose.co.uk
Tue–Fri 7–9.30pm; Sat 12.15–1.30pm, 7–9.30pm. Closed Sun/Mon. £28 (lunch/dinner)
For nearly 30 years Ostlers Close has been the hidden secret of fine Fife dining. Tucked down a Cupar close, owners Amanda and Jimmy Graham keep their menu seasonal and clearly invest time and care sourcing or growing their ingredients. Jimmy's foraged chanterelle mushrooms enrich his meat dishes or add texture to a herby risotto and local damsons create a tangy sorbet and a plum-scented gin to counterbalance a silky dessert of vanilla pannacotta. It's not flash, or big, but it is a beacon of great Scottish cuisine.

■ The Peat Inn

Peat Inn, near St Andrews, Fife
01334 840206, www.thepeatinn.co.uk
Tue–Sat 12.30–1.30pm, 7pm-9pm. £16 (set lunch) / £32 (set dinner)
The Peat Inn has existed on this spot since the 1700s and with chef-proprietor Geoffrey Smeddle picking up a Michelin Star in 2010 has become (once again) one of Scotland's most cherished destination restaurants. There's little that's ostentatious, with a series of charming small dining rooms making up the restaurant. A variety of menus offer remarkably good value dining for this level of cooking and service.

■ Real Food Café

Tyndrum, Stirlingshire, 01838 400235
www.therealfoodcafe.com
Sun–Fri 10am–10pm; Sat 9am–10pm. £10 (lunch/dinner)
The Real Food Café transformed an old Little Chef into a fish and chip (and more) stop that buys its produce from local farmers, artisan suppliers and sustainable fish sources. With its open-plan kitchen and eating area, as well as outdoor tables, this has become an important wayside stop for those travelling to and from the Highlands on the A82.

■ Room With A View

Forth View Hotel, Aberdour, Fife
01383 860402
www.roomwithaviewrestaurant.co.uk
Wed–Sat noon–2.30pm, 6pm onwards; Sun noon–2.30pm. Closed Mon/Tue. £15 (lunch) / £21 (dinner)
A fish restaurant situated within the Forth View Hotel at Aberdour's craggy Hawkcraig point. A friendly, family-run ambience pervades, with amazing views across the Forth estuary from the elegantly clad windows. Chef Tim Robson's short menu changes weekly and offers choices such as salmon fillet poached in sweet elderberry and grape court bouillon or seabass on a bed of crab meat, shrimp and pak choi.

■ The Roost Restaurant

Forgandenny Road, Kintillo, Bridge of Earn, Perthshire, 01738 812111
www.theroostrestaurant.co.uk
Tue/Wed noon-2.30pm; Thu-Sat noon-2.30pm, 6.30-9pm; Sun noon-3pm. Oct–May closed Thu eve. £12 (lunch) / £25 (dinner)
The simple setting for the Roost, with its roof beams and stone floor, is one way this appealing Perthshire restaurant avoids pretension. The menu, with its lunchtime mix of crafted sandwiches and locally sourced food, is another. But with experience cooking for David Wilson, among others, Tim Dover is a chef with pedigree, and whether you're tucking into a venison burger or a evening main of baked Shetland plaice, it shows.

■ The Royal Hotel

Melville Square, Comrie, Perthshire
01764 679200, www.royalhotel.co.uk
Mon–Sun noon–2pm, 6.30–9pm. £14 (lunch) / £22 (dinner)
Long a favourite of the hunting, fishing and shooting brigade this grand old dame deep in rural Perthshire enjoys a much wider appeal these days. Choose from the lighter Hotel Menu in the informal bar area or even dine outside in the walled garden on a warm day. The restaurant menu tightly nods towards Scotland with a twist with home cured gravlax before moving on to pan fried venison glazed with stilton or Scottish hake wrapped in proscuitto.

Sangster's

51 High Street, Elie, Fife
01333 331001, www.sangsters.co.uk
Summer: Tue 7–8.30pm; Wed–Fri
12.30–1.30pm, 7–8.30pm; Sat 7–8.30pm;
Sun 12.30–1.30pm. Closed Mon. Winter:
Wed 7–8.30pm; Thu-Fri 12.30–1.30pm,
7-8.30pm; Sat 7–8.30pm; Sun 12.30–
1.30pm. Closed Mon & Tue
£20 (set lunch) / £30 (set dinner)
New(ish) Michelin star in tow, Bruce
Sangster runs a solo show in the kitchen
while wife Jackie takes care of front
of house. With just 26 covers in the
front room of a terraced property the
atmosphere is certainly not ostentatious;
the food, however, is far from home
cooking. Intense flavours, technical
dexterity and attention to detail are
here; quail arrives meltingly tender
having languished sous-vide in a water
bath, while pork fillet stuffed with black
pudding comes as neat discs alongside
pommes dauphinoise and red cabbage.

The Seafood Restaurants

• Bruce Embankment, St Andrews
01334 479475
www.theseafoodrestaurant.com
Mon–Sun noon–2.30pm, 6.30–10pm. £22
(set lunch) / £45 (set dinner)
• 16 West End, St Monans, 01333 730327
Mon–Sun noon–2.30pm, 6.30–10pm. £22
(set lunch) / £38 (set dinner)
The eye-catching, glass-walled Seafood
Restaurant sits right beside the Old
Course in St Andrews. Elegant yet
unstuffy, with contemporary cooking
that's assured at every turn. The pub
atmosphere of the pre-dinner drinks
area in St Monans is a contrast to the
light-filled restaurant beyond, with its
Forth-filled views. Head chef Craig Millar's
menu is mainly fish (sustainability and
provenance noted), but there are other
options, such as a ham hock terrine
accompanied by a bright piccalilli.

63 Tay Street Restaurant

63 Tay Street, Perth
01738 441451, www.63taystreet.co.uk
Tue–Sat noon–2pm, 6.30–9.30pm. Closed
Sun/Mon. £19 (lunch) / £26 (dinner)
Perth's dining scene has really been
in the ascendancy in recent years
with Graeme Pallister, chef patron at
63 Tay Street, at the forefront of the
renaissance. His sourcing is impressively
local and honest with Perthshire berries
and mushrooms from Aviemore, not
to mention lamb from Andrew Fairlie's
brother, but his food is more than
simple: the standout is sautéed local
beef rib with oxtail and horseradish

The Wee Restaurant

17 Main Street, North Queensferry, Fife
01383 616263

The Wee Restaurant

www.theweerestaurant.co.uk
Mon–Sun noon–2pm, 6.30–9pm. £16.75
(set lunch) / £25 (set dinner)
Wee it may be but the power house in
the kitchen really lifts this place, tucked
under a leg of the Forth Bridge, to a high
level. Simple set menus are packed with
delight: melting rabbit boudin balanced
by a rich black pudding and super-
fresh salad leaves, or a classic veal
blanquette modernised with a delicate
light sauce and home made pasta that's
a triumph of balance and well-married
flavours. Chef Craig Wood sources
well, combines ingredients with flair and
cooks them briefly. One of Fife's best.

NORTH EAST SCOTLAND

The Blue Marlin

9 Reform Street, Monifieth, Angus
01382 534001, www.thebluemarlin.co.uk
Tue–Thu noon–2pm, 5.30–late; Fri/Sat
noon–2pm, 6pm–late. Closed Sun/Mon.
£9.95 (set lunch) / £27
Steve Hyatt's seafood restaurant, with
a basic and unpretentious beach-house
style interior, brings local and exotic
fish and shellfish together in a menu
that also blends simple grills with global
flavours from South African to Mexican.
An early-bird menu offers good value.

Buchanans Bistro

Woodend Barn, Burn o' Bennie, Banchory, Aberdeenshire
01330 826530 , www.buchananfood.com
Mon-Sun 9am-10pm. £11 (lunch) / £15
(set dinner)
Set in a bright, large and pleasantly
laid out extension to Royal Deeside's
primary arts space, this new café-bistro
is run by highly respected local cooks
and caterers Val and Calum Buchanan.

Dishes are at once informal and expertly
constructed, displaying an enthusiastic
embrace of local, seasonal, organic and
artisan food – expect to find menus put
together on the basis of what's fresh
from the adjoining allotment or local
woods that day.

But 'n' Ben

Auchmithie, by Arbroath, Angus
01241 877223
Mon 7–10pm; Wed–Sat noon–2.30pm,
7–10pm; Sun noon–2.30pm. £10 (lunch)
/ £16
In its attractive cottage setting in cliff-top
Auchmithie, the But 'n' Ben has been
consistently good for years. Expect
to find wonderful, fresh oysters and
fish including a tasty Arbroath smokie
pancake. Home cooking and properly
honest fare predominate, with generous
portions and a pudding trolley is always
groaning with gateaux, cheesecakes
and apple pie.

Eat on the Green

Udny Green, Ellon, Aberdeenshire
01651 842337, www.eatonthegreen.co.uk
Sun & Wed/Thu noon–2pm, 6.30–8.30pm;
Fri noon–2pm, 6–9pm; Sat 6–9pm.
Closed Mon/Tue. £19.95 (set lunch) / £49
(set dinner)
Craig Wilson's popular and well-
respected restaurant is something of a
flag-bearer for rural Aberdeenshire. A
French style of cooking prevails in the
upmarket style dishes, but this is a place
with its roots in the local area.

Jute

152 Nethergate, Dundee
01382 909246, www.dca.org.uk
Mon–Sat 10am–4pm, 5–9.30pm; Sun
10am–8.30pm. £14 (lunch) / £21 (dinner)
Jute offers a bit of everything for those

interested in checking out Dundee Contemporary Arts, or indeed anyone just passing. A reasonably priced snack menu is available alongside a full dinner menu. Fish and vegetarian options are a big feature on the dinner menu, including a gorgeous mushroom and blue cheese risotto, though my companion labelled the rib-eye steak delicious. Mid-range to expensive prices, quality this high is tough to find elsewhere in the city centre.

■ The Milton
Milton of Crathes, North Deeside Road, Crathes, Banchory, Aberdeenshire
01330 844566, www.themilton.co.uk
Mon/Tue 9.30am–5pm; Wed–Fri
9.30am–9pm; Sat 9.30am–9.30pm; Sun
10am–5pm. £16 (lunch) / £23
A flexible, well-run restaurant with options for all times of day and an engaged attitude to Deeside's impressive range of produce.

■ Paula McEwen Restaurant
239 Great Western Road, Aberdeen
01224 587002, www.paulamcewen.com
Restaurant: Tue–Sat 5.30pm–9.30pm;
Bar & Lounge: Mon–Sun 12.30–8.30pm.
£14 (lunch) / £23.50 (dinner)
A recent addition to the West End, Paula McEwen's kitchen claims an impressive collective CV, including her own experience at the Witchery in Edinburgh. Whether your mood craves burger-comfort or truffle-roasted chicken sophistication, the range between the bar and the restaurant menus will oblige.

■ The Playwright
11 Tay Square, Dundee
01382 223113, www.theplaywright.co.uk
Mon–Sun noon–2.30pm, 5pm–9.30pm.
£16.95 (set lunch) / £32 (dinner)
The Playwright has labelled itself 'uniquely intimate', which cannot be argued with. Offering some of the most inventive fine-dining food in Dundee, with a price list to match, it aims high. It succeeds, although the grazing menu is the one if you are on a budget. Lunch and pre-theatre also offer reasonable value at £16.95 for two courses, whereas evening à la carte can see starters fetching around £12.

■ The Quay
1–4 Wharf Street, Montrose, Angus
01674 672821
www.thequaymontrose.co.uk
Wed/Thu & Sun 11.30am–midnight;
Fri/Sat 11.30am–1am. Closed Mon/Tue.
£21.50 (set dinner)
A smart new restaurant and bar on the riverside in Montrose with a sophisticated and stylish interior of neutral off-white colours. It has quickly established a local reputation for its

contemporary bistro food including fresh seafood in imaginative combinations.

■ Silver Darling
Pocra Quay, North Pier, Aberdeen
01224 576229
www.silverdarlingrestaurant.co.uk
Mon–Fri noon–1.45pm, 7–9.30pm; Sat
7–9.30pm. Closed Sun. £15.50 (set lunch)
/ £31 (dinner)
In a unique setting on the upper floor of Aberdeen's old Custom House at the mouth of the harbour, owner-chef Didier Dejean bring high-level French culinary skills to bear on fine local seafood.

■ La Stella
28 Adelphi, Aberdeen
01224 211414, www.lastella.co.uk
Mon–Thu 11.30am–2.30pm, 5pm–10pm;
Fri/Sat 11.30am–10pm. £11.95 (set lunch)
/ £28.95 (set dinner)
Well known as Le Bonne Baguette for many years, La Stella, now under the direction of Chris Tonner and Lynsey Yule, is a smart contemporary bistro focusing on hearty local ingredients served with enthusiastic originality and a touch of internationalism.

■ The Tolbooth
Old Pier, Stonehaven, Aberdeenshire
01569 762287
www.tolbooth-restaurant.co.uk
Tue–Sat noon–2pm, 6–9.30pm; Sun
noon–3pm, 5–8pm. (Oct–Apr closed
Sun). £12.95 (set lunch) / £23 (dinner)
A location right beside an old stone harbour is about as ideal as you could ask for in a North East seafood restaurant. The catch from the creel boats based here often makes its way up to the restaurant, set in a sixteenth-century building.

HIGHLANDS, ISLANDS & ARGYLL

■ The Albannach
Baddidarroch, Lochinver, Sutherland
01571 844407, www.thealbannach.co.uk
Tue–Sun 8–10pm. Closed Mon. £55 (set
dinner)
A dark wood dining room in the hotel is the backdrop for a set five course menu described as a 'showcase for all things local, free range and wild'. Twenty years under the same ownership, the Albannach was recognised with a Michelin star in 2010.

■ The Royal an Lochan
Shore Road, Tighnabruaich, Argyll
01700 811239, www.anlochan.co.uk
Mon–Sun noon–3pm, 5.30–9pm. £23
(lunch) / £35 (set dinner)
The sublime setting, tucked on the water

CHEF'S CHOICE
TONY HEATH ON HERBS

There is nothing quite like wondering through a herb garden in the summer, brushing and touching the herbs as you pass. It is an instant hit, very sensual, uplifting and magical.

Too many people think that, because we don't live on the shores of the Mediterranean, herbs are something exotic and unavailable. In fact, almost all the herbs you'd want can grow perfectly well in Scotland.

A kitchen without herbs is like a car without an engine. Fresh herbs can lift a dish or sauce from being mediocre to exquisite. I would never make a salad without adding quantities of freshly chopped/torn parsley, basil, mint, lemon balm, chives or coriander. They are the seasoning for my salads.

Although I grow many of my own herbs, as a professional chef I feel blessed to have a supplier like Scotherbs just 15 minutes along the road in Longforgan. To see and smell the vast quantities of freshly cut herbs being trimmed and packed is, for me, just as exciting as seeing a catch of freshly landed langoustines or a bunch of new season asparagus. I get the instant desire to 'do' something in the simplest of ways to capture the freshness and wonderful natural flavours.

■ The former chef-proprietor of Let's Eat in Perth, Tony Heath can sometimes be found helping his partner Shona Drysdale at the Apron Stage in Stanley. He also runs a small cook school at Kinfauns, Perth, 01738 861119, www.tony-heath-cook-school.co.uk. Scotherbs supply of fresh culinary herbs and salad leaves to retailers, wholesalers and food manufacturers, 01382 360642, www.scotherbs.co.uk

by the Kyles of Bute, could not be more apposite for a seafood feast. On the dedicated seafood menu (there is also another menu with meatier choices) the starter plump king scallops are plucked fresh from Loch Fyne, while the massive langoustines are landed at Tarbert.

■ The Anderson
Union Street, Fortrose, by Inverness
01381 620236, www.theanderson.co.uk
Mon–Sat 4–11pm; Sun 12.30–11pm. £12 (lunch) / £19

Scottish ingredients are given an international makeover in this restaurant and bar in Fortrose, near Inverness. A Manhattan seafood chowder is loaded with Moray Firth spoots and crab meat, or there is a decidedly un-Highlands-style venison Puebla, with roe deer fillet cooked in chocolate and chilli sauce. For those who feel like making a long weekend of it, there are nine ensuite bedrooms above the dining room.

■ Applecross Inn
Shore Street, Applecross, Wester Ross
01520 744262
www.applecross.uk.com/inn
Mon–Sun noon–9pm. £15 (lunch) / £15

The heart of the tiny coastal community, the Applecross Inn is always alive with locals and visitors. Local lobster is cooked simply and left for you to spend the rest of the night tackling. Or maybe just enjoy a pint of squat lobster tails – the moreish pistachios of the shellfish world. Red meat lovers are not left out with venison from the Applecross Estate and everyone gets to share the views over the unmistakable Cuillin ridge.

■ Ardanaiseig Hotel
Kilchrenan, Taynuilt, Argyll
01866 833333, www.ardanaiseig.com
Mon–Sun 12.30–2pm, 7–8.45pm. £25 (set lunch) £50 (set dinner)

There can be few finer escapes for a romantic getaway than Ardanaiseig, a stately old country house hotel hidden on the banks of Loch Awe. Gary Goldie has been head chef for over a decade and his assured touch is evident. Herbs, vegetables and fruit from the hotel's garden find their way into the likes of pan-roasted halibut with wild mushrooms in a Muscat sauce. Foodies will enjoy their mushroom foraging excursions and the cookery courses.

■ Argyll Hotel
Isle of Iona, Argyll, 01681 700334
www.argyllhoteliona.co.uk
Mon–Sun 12.30–1.30pm, 7–8pm. £18 (dinner)

The Argyll Hotel makes fine dining feel all rather homely and unpretentious with meat sourced from Mull, seafood

from the waters around the island and organic vegetables from the restaurant's own garden. A weekend brunch menu is also available.

■ The Boath House Hotel
Auldearn, Nairn, Inverness-shire
01667 454896, www.boath-house.com
Mon–Sun orders taken 12.30–1.15pm, 7–7.30pm. £21 (set lunch) / £65 (set dinner)

Michelin-starred head chef Charles Lockley is in charge of the cooking at this Georgian mansion, which has been operating as a luxurious country house hotel since a large-scale refurbishment in the 90s. Those popping in for a champagne afternoon tea or upmarket dinner are reminded of Boath House's smart-casual dress code, and for those looking to make a night of it, there are eight opulently decorated rooms upstairs. Booking is essential.

■ Busta House Hotel
Busta, Shetland
01806 522506 , www.bustahouse.com
Mon–Sun noon–2.30pm, 7–9pm. £17 (lunch) / £35 (set dinner)

At Busta House Hotel, unsurprisingly, Shetland produce plays a starring role in the dining experience. Shetland hill lamb, free-range pork and organic salmon from Unst, Muckle Roe mussels, halibut from Bressay and Yell Sound scallops. A nod to neighbouring Orkney is also made with beef and cheese on a menu heavily influenced by island life.

■ Café Fish
The Pier, Tobermory, Isle of Mull
01688 301253, www.thecafefish.com
Mon–Sun noon–3pm, 6–9pm. £12 (lunch) / £20

Perched above the old ferry waiting room on the pier overlooking Tobermory Bay, Lindsay McDonald and Liz McGougan cook up shellfish from the restaurant's own boat along with other fish and produce from the Isle of Mull.

■ cafébarge
The Harbour, Tarbert, Loch Fyne
01880 820000, www.cafebarge.co.uk
Mon/Tue & Thu–Sat 11.30am–9pm; Sun 12.30–9pm. Closed Wed. £8 (lunch) / £14

An intriguing new arrival moored to the harbour wall in Tarbert, this is a large Dutch barge with herbs and lettuce growing in containers on deck and converted below into a surprisingly spacious, modern looking tapas café. Dishes are small, simple and pleasantly unfussy, with seafood in the vanguard and some tasty vegetarian options to complement. No meat is served. Typical are three scallops fried in olive oil and

garlic, local crab meat with oatcakes, surf clams marinière or a whole globe artichoke with dressing. Coffee and snacks are served through the day, and a short wine and beer list is available.

■ The Captain's Galley
The Harbour, Scrabster, Caithness
01847 894999,
www.captainsgalley.co.uk
Tue–Sat 7–9pm. Closed Sun/Mon. £42.50 (set dinner)

A renovated old Scrabster ice house and salmon bothy, Jim Cowie's much-lauded restaurant is one of the few dining destinations on the north coast, serving up fish straight from the pier along with local shellfish and MSC-certified options.

■ The Ceilidh Place
14 West Argyle Street, Ullapool
01854 612103, www.theceilidhplace.com
Mon–Sun 8.30am–9pm. £10 (lunch) / £21

At the beating cultural heart of Ullapool, the Ceilidh Place is a rendezvous for travellers, musicians, philosophers and anyone else drawn to good conversation, good food and good living.

■ Chez Roux
Rocpool Reserve, Culduthel Road, Inverness
01463 240089, www.rocpool.com
Mon–Sun noon–2pm, 7pm–10pm. Bar menu available Mon–Sun noon–10pm. £12.95 (set lunch) / £21

Albert Roux's first venture north of the border (subsequently joined by two more) at boutique Rocpool Reserve hotel offers suprisingly well-priced dining showing off both French classicism and local ingredients.

■ Chez Roux
Inver Lodge Hotel, Lochinver, Sutherland
01571 844496
www.inverlodgehotel.co.uk
Mon–Sun noon–2pm, 7–9.30pm. Bar menu: Mon–Sun noon–6pm. £21 (dinner)

Perched above the fishing village of Lochinver, among the unique landscape of Assynt, Inver Lodge Hotel is the setting for one of Albert Roux's three Scottish restaurants, offering fine modern European cuisine.

■ The Coll Hotel
Arinagour, Isle of Coll
01879 230334, www.collhotel.com
Mon–Sun noon–2pm, 6–8.30pm. £18 (dinner)

You will have travelled a long way to get here by boat, plane or ferry, but the chances are that much of what you eat here will not. Fresh island vegetables, herbs, meat and fish overflow, from Coll

cafébarge

crab salad with Coll egg, anchovy and black olives to Coll mutton loin chops with a herb crust served with sautéed potatoes & Coll greens. Dine in the bar area or the dining room in this old whitewashed hotel and then enjoy a digestif and a chat to the locals as the sun melts over the Hebrides.

■ Crannag Bistro
Dornoch Road, Bonar Bridge, Sutherland
01863 766111, www.crannag.com
Tue–Sat 5–9pm. £18 (dinner)
Bonar Bridge lies at the confluence of four salmon rivers and the Crannag Bistro acts as a meeting point for various dining styles and inspirations. Run by Ian and Kathy Smith, this bistro serves easy-going food such as Dornoch Firth mussels or a Bonar Burger, all made with local ingredients. Takeaway pizzas and fish and chips are also available across the road at the Smith's other enterprise, the Curry Company, as are ready meals.

■ The Creel
Front Road, St Margarets Hope, South Ronaldsay, Orkney
01856 831311, www.thecreel.co.uk
Tue–Sun 7pm–8.30pm. Closed Mon (Closed mid Oct–March). £32 (set dinner)
Alan Craigie's superbly creative skills focus on the best that Orkney's seas, shores and land produce. Choices range from home-made fishcakes in shellfish bisque to seared diver-caught scallops presented with a wholesome chunk of steamed cod, braised fennel and spinach. Carnivores can't complain though with a choice of North Ronaldsay mutton baked in pastry to start or tender, slow-braised brisket and roast rib-eye for main.

■ Creelers
Home Farm, Brodick, Isle of Arran
01770 302810, www.creelers.co.uk
Tue–Sat 12.30–2.30pm, 6–9.30pm; Sun 1–3pm, 6–9.30pm. Closed Mon. £20 (dinner)
Sister restaurant to Tim and Fran James' Creelers in Edinburgh, serving fish from the adjoining smokehouse and shellfish from the surrounding waters.

■ The Cross
Tweed Mill Brae, Ardbroilach Road, Kingussie
01540 661166, www.thecross.co.uk
Tue–Sat 7–8.45pm. Closed Sun/Mon. £47 (set dinner)
Imaginative and assured cooking with well-sourced ingredients. Organic chicken and eggs come from the Moray coast, game from local estates, Highland beef, Shetland lamb and prime fish from Scrabster and Fraserburgh, with shellfish from Kyle of Lochalsh. Wild mushrooms are picked locally, with soft fruits coming courtesy of Alvie Estate.

■ Ee-usk
The North Pier, Oban, Argyll
01631 565666, www.eeusk.com
Mon–Sun noon–3pm, 6–9.30pm. £15 (lunch) / £24
Gaelic speakers may pick up on the clue in the name – which translates as fish. A place for groaning seafood platter, lightly cooked fish, crisp white wines and window tables with the best of those spectacular bay views.

■ Gallan Head Restaurant and Hotel
Aird Uig, Isle of Lewis, 01851 672474, www.gallanheadhotel.co.uk
Mon 7–9.30pm; Tue–Sun noon–2pm, 7–9.30pm. (Nov–Mar open Thu–Sat only).

£21 (lunch/dinner)
Sitting on a rocky outcrop in a former RAF building, the restaurant offers, in their own words, fine dining at the edge of the Atlantic.

■ Hay's Dock
Hay's Dock, Lerwick, Shetland
01595 741569, www.haysdock.co.uk
Mon–Sat 10.30am–4pm; Sun noon–5pm; Thus–Sat 7–11pm. £10 (lunch) / £22
With panoramic views of Lerwick Harbour the restaurant offers a wide range of eating options from daytime snacks to more adventurous dishes based on Shetland and Orkney produce.

■ Inver Cottage
Strathlachlan, Strachur, Argyll
01369 860537, www.invercottage.co.uk
Wed–Sat 10.30am–late; Sun 10.30am–5pm. Closed Mon/Tue. £18 (dinner)
Whether it's a cappuccino and some wickedly tempting home baking, a light and tasty lunch dish or something special from the dinner menu, Inver Cottage puts quality local ingredients to use in a fresh and imaginative way. With stunning views across the bay to ruined Old Castle Lachlan (home of the MacLachlan clan for over 1000 years), the dining room offers a relaxed and comfortable atmosphere. Inver Cottage craft gallery and shop also sells an unusual selection of artwork and gifts.

■ Isle of Eriska Hotel, Spa and Island
Ledaig, by Oban, Argyll
01631 720371, www.eriska-hotel.co.uk
Mon–Sun 7.45–9pm. £40 (set dinner)
Fort William-born Robert MacPherson has been the steady but innovative chef at the helm here since 1987. As the hotel sits on its own island seafood fittingly features strongly in dishes such as Loch Linnhe brown crab ravioli with ginger, mango emulsion and avocado puree. Choose between the likes of Kinlochlaich Farm pork loin, belly and cheek or roasted Oban turbot on the decadent main menu. The quartet of dining spaces each have their own charms with the light conservatory and the Morning Room most appealing.

■ The Kilberry Inn
Kilberry Road, Kilberry, Argyll
01880 770223, www.kilberryinn.com
Tue–Sun 12.15–2.15pm, 6.30–9pm. Closed Mon. (Nov/Dec dinner on Fri/Sat only.) £18 (lunch) / £25 (dinner)
Zip past on the scenic road down to Kintyre and you could be forgiven for thinking that this is just another cute whitewashed cottage. However, this culinary oasis has won a string of awards for cooking that nods to France

CHEF'S CHOICE
CRAIG WOOD ON HIS FISH SUPPLIER

I've worked in Australia and the States, and regularly go to France on holiday, and I really believe that Scotland undersells itself with its fish. The cold waters lend themselves to great quality. Even in Australia where everyone was raving on about their fish, I'd be thinking, this isn't a patch on what we have in Scotland. David Lowrie is a family-run fish merchant and wholesaler from Anstruther and he supplies all the best restaurants in Fife. He seems to have all the right contacts with the fishermen to get the best langoustine and lobster coming into places like Pittenweem and Anstruther. It's right off the boats and always so fresh. When you touch it, feel it, work with it, it gives you the satisfaction and confidence as a chef that your dishes are going to be great.
■ *Craig Wood is the chef/proprietor at the Wee Restaurant, North Queensferry.*

but always stays defiantly local with the likes of Isle of Bute rose veal rump pan-roasted with shallots, pancetta and pavé potatoes. Seafood features heavily too with a local bounty of lobster, scallops and langoustines frequent stars on the menu.

■ Kinloch Lodge
Sleat, Isle of Skye
01471 833333, www.kinloch-lodge.co.uk
Mon–Sun noon–2.30pm, 6.30–9pm.
£24.75 (set lunch) / £52 (set dinner)
'Authentic, charming and discreetly luxurious' is how author and cook Claire Macdonald describes her Highland hotel. The restaurant bears witness to her vision and attention to detail with Roux-brothers' trained chef Marcello Tully winning a Michelin star for his kitchen in 2010.

■ Kishorn Seafood Bar
Kishorn, Strathcarron, Ross-shire
01520 733240
www.kishornseafoodbar.co.uk
Mar–Nov Mon–Sat 10am–5pm, Sun noon–5pm; Jul–Sep Mon–Sat 10am–

9pm, Sun noon–5pm. £11 (lunch/dinner)
Since 1996 this place has been stemming the tide of Scotland's exported seafood at least long enough to let diners willing to travel this far north to enjoy affordable world class Scottish food. The seafood platter here is surely the finest in the country, overflowing with king scallops, queen scallops, langoustines, crabs, oysters, mussels and squat lobster tails. More log cabin than restaurant choose to dine inside amidst the aromas of garlic butter or recline at a bench outside and admire the loch and mountain views.

■ The Lime Tree
The Old Manse, Achintore Road, Fort William
01397 701806
www.limetreefortwilliam.co.uk
Mon–Sun 6.30–9.30pm. £26 (dinner)
Good dining has struggled to find a home in Fort William, but young local chef Ross Sutherland's cooking at the Lime Tree hotel and art gallery has been turning many head with his intricate, sophisticated style and high standards.

■ Loch Fyne Oyster Bar and Seafood Restaurant
Clachan, Cairndow, Argyll
01499 600236
www.lochfyne.com
Sun–Thu 9am–5.30pm; Fri/Sat 9am–7pm. £22 (lunch/dinner)
Knowledge, flair and expertise are the hallmarks of this truly remarkable operation whose passion for fresh sustainable seafood is written into every line of the business plan. The operation seeds, feeds, catches, processes and cooks much of the diverse menu on offer while white fish are landed by specially chosen small boats down in Cornwall. Pick up produce from the adjoining shop or make use of the new oyster shed in the car park for a takeaway.

■ Lochleven Seafood Café
Onich, by Kinlochleven, Lochaber
01855 821048
www.lochlevenseafoodcafe.co.uk
Mon–Sun noon–3pm, 6–9pm. £21 (lunch/dinner)
Sitting on the shores of Loch Leven, the Seafood Café grew from its roots as a shellfish distribution centre. Public demand for the seafood arriving at its doors each day led to the creation of a relaxed and informal bistro led by head chef Barry Moran, formerly of Andrew Fairlie's kitchen at Gleneagles. Mussels, oysters, lobster, crab and razor clams make up most of the menu, though meat and vegetarian options are available.

■ Mountain Café
111 Grampian Road, Aviemore
01479 812473
www.mountaincafe-aviemore.co.uk
Mon–Sun 8.30am–5pm. £8 (lunch)
Kiwi Kirsten Gilmour has imported her homeland's easy-going café culture and made-from-fresh approach to Aviemore. Serving breakfasts, lunches and home-baked treats in-between, everything is made on the premises, using as much local produce as possible – the bread, scones and daily specials are inventive.

■ Ninth Wave Restaurant
Bruach Mhor, Fionnphort, Isle of Mull
01681 700757
www.ninthwaverestaurant.co.uk
Mon–Sat 7–9pm. £36 (set dinner)
An intimate restaurant in a modern croft from a husband-and-wife team based by the Iona ferry, the Ninth Wave produces ambitious, smart cooking with ingredients sourced from local fishermen and crofters.

■ Ord Ban
Rothiemurchus Centre, Inverdruie, Aviemore
01479 810005, www.ordban.com
Mon–Sun 9.30am–9pm. £12 (lunch) / £19 (dinner)
In a former schoolhouse, this smart café-restaurant offers a short but well-versed home-cooked menu from breakfast/brunch through to supper, with special 'supper club' music events and film screenings at weekends.

■ The Pierhouse
Port Appin, Argyll, 01631 730302
www.pierhousehotel.co.uk
Mon–Sun noon–2.30pm, 6–9pm. £28 (dinner)
Located at the mainland terminus of the five-minute Lismore passenger ferry, the Pierhouse is part of the Seafood Trail and serves restaurant and bar meals overlooking Loch Linnhe.

■ Seafood Cabin
Skipness Estate, by Tarbert, Argyll
01880 760207, www.theseafoodtrail.com/members/seafood-cabin.php
May–Sep Mon–Sun 11am–6pm. Closed Sat. £8 (lunch)
A monument to simplicity and resourcefulness, the Seafood Cabin on Skipness Estate, next door to a ruined castle and with views to the peaks of Arran over the Kilbrannan Sound, is a wooden shack/café open in the summer months selling crab, prawns and locally smoked fish, served in rolls or platters with homegrown salad leaves.

■ Summer Isles Hotel
Achiltibuie, by Ullapool, Wester Ross

Seafood Cabin

01854 622282
www.summerisleshotel.co.uk
Mon–Sun 12.30–2pm, 8pm prompt.
Nearly everything you eat here is home
produced or locally caught. From
scallops, lobsters, langoustines, crabs,
halibut and turbot to salmon, venison,
big brown eggs and wholesome brown
bread fresh from the oven, chef Chris
Firth-Bernard shows his Michelin star
and Scottish Chef of the Year worth,
producing local, delicious and healthy
food.

■ Sutor Creek

21 Bank Street, Cromarty, Inverness-shire
01381 600855, www.sutorcreek.co.uk
Wed–Sun 11am–8.30pm. Closed Mon/
Tue. £11 (lunch) / £16 (dinner)
Pizzas are the main draw at this
Cromarty harbourside restaurant on
the Black Isle, and fresh, local seafood
makes for some very memorable
toppings. On Saturday nights the wood
fired pizza oven is also put to good use
roasting local meats in preparation for
Sunday lunch the following day. Wine
tastings, book clubs and themed nights
also appear on Sutor Creek's social
calendar. Check website for details.

■ Temple Seafood

The Pier, Gallanch Road, Oban, Argyll
01631 566000
www.templeseafood.co.uk
Thu–Sun, 6pm & 8pm sittings. Closed
Mon–Wed. £18 (set dinner)
Pine wooden beams and rough stone
pillars give this restaurant an instant
air of ramshackle beauty; indeed it is
affectionately referred to by the locals
as 'The Shack'. The menu changes
daily, depending on the catch of the
day, with fresh seafood served simply
without fuss.

■ The Three Chimneys

Colbost, Dunvegan, Isle of Skye
01470 511258
www.threechimneys.co.uk
Mon–Sun 12.30pm–1.45pm, 6.15–9.45pm
(evenings only in winter). £27.50 (set
lunch) / £55 (set dinner)
That a cosy restaurant set in a century
old crofter's cottage in the wildly remote
northwestern corner of Skye has made
it into many lists of onto global hit lists
is seriously impressive. Remarkable
chef Shirley Spear and her wine loving
husband Eddie may have taken some
of the pressure off by bringing in head
chef Michael Smith, but her passion for
local produce reinvented in continuously
imaginative ways never wanes in dishes
such as grilled Mallaig skate and Sconser
scallops with Orbost parsley mash, fennel
confit, surf clam & hazelnut velouté.

■ Tigh an Eilean Hotel

Strathcarron, Sheildaig, Wester Ross
01520 755251, www.tighaneilean.co.uk
Mid–Mar to end–Oct Mon–Sun 7–
8.30pm. £45 (set dinner)
An idyllic spot among the hills and
islands of the west coast, there's smart
dining with sea views, quality ingredients
and carefully prepared dishes in the
hotel and a much more informal set up
alongside in the Coastal Kitchen.

■ The Torridon

Torridon, Achnasheen, Wester Ross
01445 791242, www.thetorridon.com
Mon–Sun 7–8.45pm. £45 (set dinner)
This old world luxury country house
hotel looks more like a castle than
a hotel as it stands guard over the
brooding eponymous loch and
spectacular mountains. Head chef
Jason 'Bruno' Birkbeck, who grew up in
the (by comparison) urban Lake District,
recreates some of this drama on the
plate by fusing the fine larder of local
ingredients with some French twists on
his epic five course dinner menus. A less
grand option is on hand just a stone's
throw away at The Torridon Inn where
judicious use of local produce and solid
cooking elevate things above pub grub.

■ The Waterfront

1 Railway Pier, Oban, Argyll
01631 563110
www.waterfrontoban.co.uk
Mon–Sun noon–2.15pm, 5.30–9.pm;
Fri/Sat 5.30–9.30pm. £11.50 (set lunch) /
£16 (dinner)
As befits an outfit that owns two fishing
boats and sets up home on the end
of a pier the Waterfront's commitment
to fresh seafood and local sourcing is
impeccable. Flanked by a huddle of pier
head shops and the Oban ferry terminal,
the restaurant is based in a former
seaman's mission and offers panoramic
views of Oban bay. Chef Roy Stalker has
a nimble touch conjuring daily specials
from halibut, scallops, salmon, haddock
and many other Scottish ingredients.

■ The Whitehouse Restaurant

Lochaline, Morven, Argyll, 01967 421777
www.thewhitehouserestaurant.co.uk
Tue–Sat 12.30–2.30pm & from 6.30pm;
Sun 12.30–2.30pm. £23 (dinner)
Before it sets off on a food-mile heavy
journey to Europe, local seafood is
bought up by this restaurant in the
village of Lochaline, which is a twenty
minute ferry ride from the Isle of Mull. If
the ingredients aren't from the sea, then
the hillsides of Morvern and Mull are the
next obvious source. A relaxed place but
one well worth the detour to get here.
Takeaway picnics can be arranged.

FURTHER HELPINGS

Regularly updated websites with
information on Scottish restaurants
include:

• www.list.co.uk/eat-and-drink
An expanded on-line version of the
List's annually updated Eating &
Drinking Guide, with independent
reviews, maps, links and co mments.
• www.eatscotland.com
The official eating and drinking site
of VisitScotland, the national tourist
board, with lists of quality assured
restaurants, features and profiles.
• www.scottishfoodguide.com
Wendy Barrie's personal selection
of restaurants, places to stay and
producers around Scotland.

Sharpening your culinary skills

Scotland's budding cooks have plenty of options when it comes to learning their way around a kitchen. Whether you want to boil an egg, make luxurious chocolates or create a refined three-course meal, there are cook schools of many sizes, styles and approach. For those wanting to take it further and make a career out of cooking, there are various colleges around the country to help you on your way.

Bellini Cookery School
St George's West, 58 Shandwick Place, Edinburgh, EH2 4RT, 07889 460 267
www.bellinicookeryschool.co.uk
Run by chef Angelo Cimini and Gina Giubarelli, who ran Bellini restaurant in Edinburgh's New Town until 2009, the Italian-orientated cook school aims to teach people how to prepare delicious, healthy meals. Classes are informal and hands-on, and can be arranged for groups or individuals of any level of proficiency. Course topics change all the time, but incorporate the best of Italian cookery, whether cooking a romantic meal for two or dinner for a big group of friends.

Blar na Leisg
Drumbeg House, Drumbeg, Sutherland, IV27 4NW, 01571 833 325
www.blarnaleisg.com
A trip to the Highlands wouldn't be complete without sampling the local

fish. If tasting alone isn't enough, this small hotel can offer cookery classes to guide guests and visitors through the basics of making the most of the catch. Classes are available on a flexible basis, and can cover various dishes, all led by in-house cook Anne Strachan.

Bluebell Croft
15 Anaheilt, Strontian, Ardnamurchan, PH36 4JA, 01967 402226
www.bluebellcroft.co.uk
As well as being home to one of the best sited hot tubs in the UK, Bluebell Lodge also offers the chance to learn the art of smoking meat and fish at home, including a guide on building the smoker from scratch. The croft also provide workshops on Aga cooking to help to make the most of your range, all in the idyllic setting of five-star accommodation in a national nature reserve.

Braehead Cook School
7 Moorfields North Industrial Park, Crosshouse, Kilmarnock, KA2 0FE, 01563 550 008
www.braeheadfoods.co.uk
Aspiring cooks can choose from a huge range of classes, from making bread to stocks and sauces, 'Glorious Game' to 'Fusion Cooking'. Formats vary; day classes offer the chance to get involved, while evening demonstrations and dining are a quicker way to pick up some tips. New 'Fork Out Less' classes run for two and a half hours. Kids' classes are run over the summer months, and parties year-round cater for ages 5-16.

The Breadwinner Bakery School
20 Bruntsfield Place, Edinburgh, EH10 4HN, 0131 229 7247
www.thebreadwinner.co.uk
Throughout the winter months, this Bruntsfield bakery offers a heartwarming selection of intimate classes with Master Craftsman Baker Sean McVey. The breadmaking option takes you through the basics of making a sour starter with minimal use of chemicals and additives, with the chance to try your hand at other healthy breads. Alternatively, the pastry class features croissants, danishes and a savoury option to cheer up the darkest days of the year.

Cocoa Black Chocolate and Pastry School
Unit 7, Southpark Industrial Estate, Peebles, EH45 9ED, 01721 723764
www.cocoablack.co.uk
Co-owner and chef Ruth Hinks offers a range of classes at her chocolate and patisserie school to suit all ages and skill levels, from learning the basics of developing an appreciation of quality chocolate to creating tantalising

Cooking Mania

truffles, tarts and pastries. There are fun workshops for children to create seasonal chocolate treats, or more serious affairs such as the intensive two-day masterclass, designed for professional chefs and serious home cooks.

Coco of Bruntsfield Chocolate School

Unit A1, The Midlothian Innovation Centre, Pentlandfield, Roslin, EH25 9RE, 0131 228 4526 www.cocochocolate.co.uk/chocolate_school.htm

These one-day masterclasses began in 2008, giving people an insight into the extensive processes that go into making luxury chocolates. With no more than four to a class, maximum attention is assured for all topics covered, from tempering to making Coco's should-be-world-famous hot chocolate. At the end of the day, each attendee receives a Coco hamper with a selection of the chocolate they made in the class to take home and show off to their friends.

thecookschool.com

Broughtonknowe House, Broughton, Biggar, ML12 6HL, 01899 860 203 www.thecookschool.com

Headed up by Michael Muir and Rachael McQuaid, thecookschool. com offers monthly classes based on varying menus. The atmosphere is communal: participants all cook together rather than the 'show and do' styles of other schools, while the cookery days cover everything from fish to patisseries. Their rural base, outside Biggar, means that the day's efforts can be enjoyed, celebratory drink in hand, with a view of the Pentland hills. Although the website lists the upcoming class themes, private groups (including hen parties) can also be catered for.

Cook School by Martin Wishart

14 Bonnington Road, Edinburgh, EH6 5JD, 0131 555 6655 www.cookschool.co.uk

A wide variety of classes are offered between Wednesday and Saturday each week, from Oriental cookery to desserts and pastry. The coveted Martin Wishart masterclasses run on only ten dates a year, and book up well in advance. Children's classes are available over the summer, and wine-tasting evenings are being introduced on Thursdays. Class sizes are kept small, and there is an emphasis on the selection and provenance of ingredients as well as the cooking.

Edinburgh School of Food & Wine

PHOTO SCOTTISH-VIEWPOINT.COM

The Cookery School

Peckhams Building, 65 Glassford Street, Glasgow, G1 1UB, 0141 552 5239 www.thecookeryschool.org

Based in the Peckham's building in Glasgow's Merchant City, this school offers over 40 courses on everything from fish and seafood to stocks, sauces and desserts, with themes as diverse as modern Scottish, Indian, pasta, home-baking and classic Italian. One-day and evening classes are available, and there are also evening classes on wine and cocktail mixology. Most of the courses are aimed at adult cooks, but longer five-day courses – for both adults and kids – are held in the summertime. It also runs corporate and team-building courses, and hen parties are welcome too.

Cooking Mania

1/2 North West Circus Place, Edinburgh, EH3 6ST, 0131 220 2010 www.cookingmania.co.uk

Edinburgh's only 'fully child-friendly' cook school moved in 2010 to premises closer to central Edinburgh, and is offering an extended list of classes as a result. Unsurprisingly, there remains a strong emphasis on classes for little ones -- children's birthday parties are taken care of, as well as holiday workshops and Dad/Mum and Child sessions. Grown-ups aren't left out, with choices from men-only evenings to express entertaining. There are even holistic classes and demos, focusing on 'cooking for calm', fitness and slimming.

Coco of Bruntsfield

Cocoa Black Chocolate and Pastry School

Edinburgh New Town Cookery School

7 Queen Street, Edinburgh, EH2 1JE, 0131 226 4314

www.entcs.co.uk

Since opening its doors in December 2009, this dedicated cookery school has established itself as a feature of both the New Town and the Scottish culinary scene. Led by principal Fiona Burrell with a strong team of teachers, the ENTCS offers everything from one-day courses to six-month practical cookery diplomas. There are also specialist workshops for children and teenagers preparing to fly the nest to help them to survive on more than lukewarm beans and cider.

Edinburgh School of Food & Wine

The Coach House, Newliston, Edinburgh, EH29 9EB, 0131 333 5001

www.esfw.com

In contrast to its local rivals, Edinburgh's longest-established, fully-accredited school stands out for its sheer breadth of learning opportunities. Whether you're serious enough about a cooking career to spend six months training for a diploma or simply want a day out to put the sparkle back into home entertaining, you will find it at this 18th-century Newliston coach-house. Ian Pittrie and his team also cater for companies seeking unique team-building events, and wine- or whisky-tasting dinners.

Kinloch Cookery Demonstrations by Claire Macdonald

Kinloch Lodge, Sleat, Isle of Skye, IV43 8QY, 01471 833 333

www.claire-macdonald.com

With demonstrations described by The Washington Post as '. . . less cooking than high entertainment', these three-day cookery courses are a unique experience. Based in Lady Macdonald's home on the Isle of Skye,

the emphasis is not only on learning to cook, but also on learning to enjoy it. Practical, seasonal ingredients abound, ensuring new-found knowledge isn't left in the classroom; they are spun, however, into meals that smack of the the subtle luxury that pervades this Highland hideaway.

Nick Nairn Cook School

Port of Menteith, Stirling, FK8 3JZ, 01877 389 900

www.nicknairncookschool.com

In the heart of the Trossachs, this converted piggery now houses a celebrity cook school. Teaching a style of cooking in which the produce is king, students use fresh, organic herbs and vegetables from Nick's wife Holly's garden, along with eggs from their hens and smoked salmon from their smokehouse. Nick takes several Scottish cookery classes a month, and there is a full tuition calendar around this, offering day classes from Tapas to Thai, as well as three-day masterclasses.

Peckham's Cook School

29 South Clerk Street, Edinburgh, EH8 9NZ, 0131 668 3939

www.peckhamscookschool.co.uk

Not to be confused with the Glaswegian cook school in the Peckham's building, Edinburgh's shiny new Peckham's Cook School is nestled in the much-loved Newington branch of the Peckham's deli. Courses range from a couple of hours to a more intensive five days, while the wine-tasting sessions can help to match the right bottle with the right dish. Although initial interest has flooded them with corporate work, regular workshops are set to be a standard feature of the business.

Tony Heath "Cook School"

Ben Vorlich, Church Road, Kinfauns, Perth, PH2 7LD, 07778 990 341

www.tony-heath-cook-school.co.uk

With a focus on the intimate, Tony Heath primarily caters for pairs of people wanting to learn more about cooking in bespoke sessions. The use of inverted commas is entirely Heath's own: he presents a school in the loosest sense of the word. Although groups of up to five are catered for, he promotes a relaxed, hands-on atmosphere in his kitchen, where menus are designed around the participants. 'Classes' cover bread-making, vegetables, main courses and dessert.

West Highland Dairy

Achmore, Stromeferry, Ross-shire, EB53 8UW, 01599 577 203

www.westhighlanddairy.co.uk

The West Highland Dairy produces a range of cheese, yoghurt and ice cream, as well as offering workshops for those keen to learn their craft. With short courses running monthly and specialising in cheese, or butter, yoghurt and ice-cream, students will walk away with the fruits of their labour.

If you're interested in taking things a bit more seriously, there are plenty of places in Scotland to gain professional qualifications and great experience:

Aberdeen College

www.abcol.ac.uk/

Professional Cookery courses are available as a HNC, introductory level and City & Guilds Level 2 Diploma, which includes food classification and purchase.

Adam Smith College

www.adamsmithcollege.ac.uk

Representing Fife, Adam Smith College's prospectus features an NQ Intermediate 2 in creative cake production, an HNC in professional cookery and an evening course in creative and Indian cookery for beginners.

Elmwood College

www.elmwood.ac.uk

A wide selection of short courses cover a range of food production areas, including tending a successful allotment and pesticide regulation. The kitchen is also covered, with up to Level 2 City & Guilds diplomas or an HNC in professional cookery alongside leisure-based Italian and Thai cookery.

Federation of Scottish Chefs

www.scottishchefs.com

The aspiring professional can take one step further with the Federation, whose raison d'être is to 'promote excellence in the art of professional cookery' and whose culinary teams represent Scotland at some of the world's most prestigious culinary competitions each year.

Glasgow Metropolitan College

www.glasgowmet.ac.uk

The School of Food, Hospitality, Sport and Tourism offers a range of courses, from a more casual ten-week introduction to fine dining, to a one-year NQ in basic Food Technology. Baking is also, ahem, catered for with cake decoration classes and an SVQ in Bakery supported learning course. The shorter wine appreciation courses offer no official accreditation, but do have weekly sampling sessions with guidance on tasting.

thecookschool.com

Heriot-Watt University

www.undergraduate.hw.ac.uk

Those interested in a career in the drinks industry should look at the four-year BSc in Brewing and Distilling, which includes experience in the school's pilot plant. Alternatively, a BSc in Food Science and Technology lays solid groundwork for a career in food and drink production.

Jewel & Esk College

www.jec.ac.uk

Most levels of culinary experience will find a course that suits them, with Professional Cookery SVQs from foundation levels 1-3 and food hygiene qualifications available.

Motherwell College

www.motherwell.ac.uk

A few levels of professional cookery on offer, including SVQ and City & Guilds diplomas levels 1 and 2. Patisserie and baking are covered by SVQs levels 2 and 3, while a bespoke professional cookery one-day masterclass is designed to intensively improve skills for those already working withing the industry.

Queen Margaret University

www.qmu.ac.uk

Not a specialist in cookery as such, but was established in an attempt to improve, among other things, the diets of local people. Continuing on similar lines, the university now offers BSc courses in dietics and nutrition.

University of the Highlands and Islands

www.uhi.ac.uk

Professional Cookery is available for study at HNC and HND level at five of the UHI colleges: Lews Castle, Moray, North Highland, Orkney and Perth. The HNC in Hospitality also covers elements of food production and service.

West Lothian College

www.west-lothian.ac.uk

As well as certificates in food hygiene, West Lothian College has professional cookery courses at SVQs levels 2 and 3, with a Level 1 Food Preparation and Cooking course if you're just getting started. Evening classes in subjects such as modern fusion cooking are also available in 12-week blocks.

Or if the produce and manufacturing is of more interest:

The Scottish Agricultural College

www.sac.ac.uk

Courses include BASIS Certificate in Crop Protection, BSc in agriculture or poultry and various levels of rural business management.

Nick Nairn Cook School

Taste Travels

If you're travelling around Scotland looking out for good local food and drink, don't just focus on shops, markets, restaurants and pubs. The visitor attractions and activities listed here offer some pleasant culinary diversions along the way.

PHOTO: GLENGOYNE DISTILLERY

> DISTILLERIES

Combine sightseeing and a selection of fine malts with the **Malt Whisky Trail**, which takes in nine distilleries including Glenlivet, Glenfiddich and the lively action of the Speyside Cooperage. To learn more about the trail, go to www.maltwhiskytrail.com

You can earn your dram by finding more leisurely ways to get from one distillery to the next: the **Speyside Way** (www.speysideway.org), a walking and bike route, passes right by a number of famous distilleries on the banks of the Spey and its tributaries, while the West Highland Way long-distance footpath goes right past **Glengoyne Distillery**, near Killearn. You can take a bike and enjoy the scenery of Islay while hopping between its 9 distilleries (www.islayinfo. com), and there's an annual yachting event visiting various coastal distilleries on the West Coast of Scotland (www. worldcruising.com/classicmaltscruise)

A full guide to Scottish distilleries which offer tours can be found at: www.visitscottishheartlands.com/ whisky/tours.html

> WINERIES & BREWERIES

All the wine made at the quirky small **Cairn o'Mohr Winery** is made from berries, flowers and leaves that grow within a 20-mile radius of the farm on the rolling hills and woodland between Dundee and Perth. www.cairnomohr.co.uk

Highland Wineries is based at Moniack Castle, seven miles from Inverness. Although the products are no longer made at the castle, this Inverness property is still worth a visit for the chance to taste their Highland wines, liqueurs and preserves in a beautiful venue. www.moniackcastle.co.uk

Emile van Schayk's **Orkney Wine Company**, which makes traditional fruit wines and liqueurs including many from locally harvested fruit and flowers, has a small shop on Lamb Holm near the Italian Chapel on Orkney. www.orkneywine.co.uk

A number of Scottish breweries offer tours or a chance to view their beer-making in action. For a list of these, see p.108.

> DAIRIES

Cream O' Galloway
Rainton, Gatehouse of Fleet, Castle Douglas
www.creamogalloway.co.uk
The ice-cream production area, shop, café and visitor centre, along with the imaginatively constructed woodland adventure playground, will keep younger visitors occupied, while a farm tour is a regular part of the wildlife event programme, helping kids link nature and delicious food.

Connage Highland Dairy
Milton of Connage, Ardesier, by Inverness
www.connage.co.uk
Now with its own 'Pantry' selling farm produce and offering the chance to view the cheesemaking operation.

St Andrew's Cheese Company
Falside Farm, Anstruther
www.standrewscheese.co.uk
On certain days (commonly Mon & Tue) you can watch their traditional cheese being manufactured from the specially designed viewing gallery accessed from the café.

PHOTO: ALLANHILL FRUIT FARM, FIFE

> GOOD FOR KIDS

City farms are a great place to introduce children to the basics of where eggs, milk, crops and meat come from.

Gorgie City Farm
Edinburgh, www.gorgiecityfarm.org.uk

Knowetop Community Farm
Dumbarton
www.knowetopcommunityfarm.co.uk

To experience farming life, the website www.farmstay.co.uk has ideas about holidaying on a Scottish farm.

Other kid-friendly destinations include:

Muddy Boots
Balmalcolm Farm, Fife
01337 831 222
A farm shop with a range of activities, including grass sledging, large play areas and a quad train.

Cairnie Fruit Farm
Cupar, Fife, www.cairniefruitfarm.co.uk
Known for its top quality fruit and tearooms for the adults, there's a mega maize maze for the younger of heart.

> HERITAGE

National Museum of Rural Life
East Kilbride
www.nms.ac.uk
Learn about Scottish farming heritage at this museum with a full working farm.

Highland Folk Museum
Kingussie and Newtonmore
www.highlandfolk.com
Includes a history of agriculture in the Highlands and an activities programme.

Barony Mills
Birsay, Mainland, Orkney
www.birsay.org.uk/baronymill.htm
Tours are available of this ancient mill between 1 May and 30 September.

Blair Atholl Water Mill
Blair Atholl, Perthshire
www.blairathollwatermill.co.uk
The oldest working water mill in Scotland, with its own tea room.

The Scottish Fisheries Museum
Anstruther, Fife
www.scotfishmuseum.org
Scotland's principal fisheries heritage centre.

> ACTIVE

Trout farms offering the opportunity to spend some time honing your casting, learning the rudiments or stocking the freezer include **Drummond Trout Farm**, Loch Earn, Perthshire (www.drummondtroutfarm.co.uk), **Wellsfield Farm**, Stirling Road, Denny (www.wellsfield.co.uk) and **Rothiemurchus Estate**, Inverdruie by Aviemore (www.rothiemurchus.net).

For a full list of trout farms, try www.fishing-scotland.net

Fruit farms are a feature of the Scottish landscape in many areas: there's no better way to check your produce is fresh than picking it yourself. There are farms stretching from **Wester Hardmuir**, at Auldearn, by Nairn (www.hardmuir.com) to **Border Berries** near Kelso (www.borderberries.co.uk), with particular concentrations in Angus, Perthshire and Fife.

A good website for information on fruit farms is www.berryscotland.com. Many of them don't have their own site, so ring ahead for opening hours or to check what fruit is in season.

SCOTTISH FOOD AND DRINK CALENDAR

SEPTEMBER 2010

3–5 September
■ Dundee Flower and Food Festival
Camperdown Country Park, Dundee,
01382 433815
www.dundeeflowerandfoodfestival.com
A festival celebrating the best of the regions food and flora, featuring chef showcases, tastings, cookery demonstrations, crafts and activities to keep the children happy. Plus there will be plenty of gardening interest with demonstrations, exhibits and the National Vegetable Society's 50th championships.

4 September
■ Eat Scottish Venison Day
Various venues around Scotland.
www.scottish-venison.info
A day dedicated to raising awareness of the benefits of eating venison. Aside from the taste of a well-cooked steak, this often overlooked meat is also lower in fat than other red meats, thanks to the deer's diet of grass and vegetation. Also, keep a lookout for special venison dishes being served in restaurants in your area.

4–19 September
■ Scottish Food and Drink Fortnight
Various venues around Scotland
www.scottishfoodanddrinkfortnight.co.uk
An all encompassing event, headed up by Patron Lady Claire Macdonald, dedicated to promoting Scottish food and drink. There's a chance to join in the various public events around the country, or take advantage of the local recipes available on the website if your kitchen is too cosy to leave.

4–19 September
■ Flavour Fortnight
Various venues around Dumfries & Galloway
www.savourtheflavours.co.uk
Timed to coincide with the Scottish Food Fortnight, this inaugural festival is packed with a diverse range of events at various venues celebrating and showcasing the best of the region's food and drink, from tastings and demonstrations to talks, workshops and activities that are suitable for all the family.

Martin Wishart cookery demonstration

10–12 September
■ eatBute
Mount Stuart, Isle of Bute, PA20 9LR
www.eatbute.com
Produce from the Isle of Bute and Argyll are displayed in this three-day festival, including stalls and 'Meet the Buyer' events to encourage the development of relationships with local traders.

11 September
■ Whisky Live Glasgow
Glasgow Thistle Hotel Ballroom,
Cambridge St, Glasgow, 01603 633808
www.whiskylive.com/scotland/glasgow-2010/
The place to find the finest whiskies, with masterclasses on how to enjoy them properly and a whisky collectors' corner for those investment bottles.

11–18 September
■ East Renfrewshire Food Festival
Various venues throughout East Renfrewshire
www.dayvisitor.com
The East Renfrewshire Food Festival will be a celebration of Scottish food and drink as well as exploring ethnic cuisine. Events will include cooking demonstrations and farmers' markets, an event combining cooking and comedy with Hardeep Singh Kohli and family fun at Apple Day in Rouken Glen Park.

17–19 September
■ Edinburgh's Real Ale Festival
The Queen's Hall, Edinburgh
www.realalebus.co.uk
This three-day celebration and promotion of Scottish real ales aims to help breweries of all sizes take their ales and beers around the country for tastings and events.

18 September
■ Buchan's Larder
Various venues around Peterhead and surrounding areas
www.buchanslarder.com
A week of activities based in Peterhead, which has now taken over from the Peterhead Food Festival, celebrates the best produce this fertile corner of the country has to offer.

18 September
■ ScotFest
Cochrane Park, Alva, 01259 215111
A one-day event featuring the best in local food and drink, including a pop-up Beer and Cider Garden. Central FM have their own stage with live entertainment and music, while craft

ScotFest

stalls, face painting and birds of prey demonstrations promise to keep the whole family occupied.

23–28 September
Autumn Speyside Whisky Festival

Dufftown and surrounding area
www.spiritofspeyside.com/dufftown.php
Six days of whisky fun in Scotland's whisky centre of Speyside. Events on offer include tours of distilleries not normally open to the public, bus tours, and as many whisky tastings as you could ever want. Enjoy music, dancing, exhibitions, pipe bands and food and craft fairs as well as celebrating Scotland's national drink.

25 September
Living Food at Cawdor Castle

Nairn, IV12 5RD, 01667 404401
www.cawdorcastle.com
Billed as a celebration of organic food, this event includes lectures, demonstrations and live music to break up a delicious day.

OCTOBER 2010

7–9 October
Ayrshire Real Ale Festival

Concert Hall, Troon
www.camra.org.uk
Tasting sessions for local ales over this three-day celebration. Food will be available at all sessions, with entertainment provided on Friday evening and Saturday afternoon. CAMRA members get a reduced entry price.

21–24 October
Trossachs Mushroom Festival

Various venues around the Trossachs
www.mushroomfestival.co.uk
A Hong Kong-themed Mushroom Festival this year, with performances from the Hong Lok Dragon, Lion Dance Troupe and Chinese cookery demonstrations alongside the usual fungal fun.

22–24 October
Peebles Food Festival

Eastgate Theatre and Arts Centre, Eastgate, Peebles, EH45 8AD, 01721 725777
www.peeblesfoodfestival.com
Based in and around the Eastgate Theatre this year, the Food Festival will feature the chance to hear tips from chefs, demonstrations, young cook events and an indoor and outdoor food market.

22–24 October
BBC Good Food Show Scotland

Glasgow SECC,
www.bbcgoodfoodshow.com
Top chefs such as Gordon Ramsay and James Martin are plugged as the major attractions at this huge exhibition in Glasgow's SECC, but it's the hidden treasures of the Producers' Village where you might just find your next favourite wine or local artisan cheese. New for this year is the 'Masterchef' experience, including a clinic and cook-off competitions.

22–23 October
Alloa Octoberfest

Town Hall, Alloa
www.camra-forth-valley.co.uk
This popular beer festival, now in its nineteenth year, is organised by the Forth Valley branch of CAMRA. Discounts are available for CAMRA members.

NOVEMBER 2010

6–7 November
Taste of Dumfries & Galloway

Kirroughtree Visitor Centre, Newton Stewart
www.savourtheflavours.co.uk
Enjoy the flavours of Dumfries & Galloway at this tasty event celebrating the region's food and drink. There will be plenty of delicious goodies for visitors to sample, enjoy and buy as food and drink producers from across Scotland's south-west showcase their treats, share their passions and tell the story of their food and drink at this friendly event.

6–14 November
Shetland Food Festival

Various venues around Shetland
www.shetlandfoodfestival.co.uk
Founded in 2008, this festival seeps on to many of the Shetland islands, with food-related events including demonstrations and a Producers' Market crammed with local goods.

13 November
Glasgow's Whisky Festival

The Arches, 253 Argyle Street, 0141 565 1000
www.glasgowswhiskyfestival.com
The first-ever whisky festival based in Glasgow, showcasing the art of whisky-making around the world but with a nose for the distilleries and independent bottlers closest to the city.

21 November
Wild Harvest Autumn Food Festival

The Scottish Crannog Centre Kenmore, Loch Tay, 01887 830583, www.crannog.co.uk
The centre holds this annual autumn Food festival. Warm by the fires and taste Iron Age stews, breads, fish and meats in the beautiful setting of Loch Tay.

DECEMBER 2010

3–5 December
Foodies Christmas Festival

Assembly Rooms, 54 George Street, Edinburgh, 0871 230 5573
www.foodiesfestival.com/christmas
With over 80 stalls from speciality food and drink producers and the chance to meet some of Scotland's finest chefs, Foodies is becoming a fixture in Edinburgh's Christmas shopping.

Foodies Christmas Festival

The Scottish Real Ale Festival

JANUARY 2011

23–25 January
■ Scotland's Speciality Food Show
SECC, Glasgow
www.scotlandstradefairs.co.uk
This trade show is for small- and medium-sized food producers and distributors to exhibit to delicatessen owners, buyers and wholesalers. Often seen as a launch-pad for new businesses looking for exposure and new product launches from more established businesses.

25–29 January
■ Food Allergy and Intolerance Week
Various venues
www.allergyuk.org
It's becoming increasingly the case that a food intolerance doesn't have to mean avoiding delicious food, or baulking at the thought of a meal out. This week is dedicated to raising awareness of all kinds of food issues, from mild wheat intolerance to extreme nut allergies. Check the Allergy UK website for more details and information on dealing with problems.

FEBRUARY 2011

23 February – 7 March
■ Fairtrade Fornight
Various venues
www.sftf.org.uk
Scotland's Fair Trade record is looking increasingly impressive, especially since the foundation of the dedicated Scottish Fair Trade Forum. Established by a collection of campaigners, NGOs and the Scottish Government, with a smattering of volunteers, its main aim is to encourage ethical credentials in produce. Visitors can combine Scottish produce with Fair Trade-marked goods for a clean conscience and a healthy palate.

28 February – 2 March
■ ScotHot
SECC, Finnieston Quay, Glasgow, 0844 395 4000
www.scothot.co.uk/
An exhibition which brings together Scotland's hospitality industry, including the 28th Scottish Culinary Championships and the Scottish Chef's Hall of Fame.

APRIL 2011

Dates TBC
■ Celtic Food and Drink Festival
Scottish Crannog Centre, Aberfeldy, 01887 830 583, www.crannog.co.uk
A celebration of the finest produce from Perth's ancient past, including roasted meats, fish, herbs and drinks, with some historical activities to entertain the whole family while the cooking takes place.

28 April – 2 May
■ Spirit of Speyside Whisky Festival
Various venues around Speyside
www.spiritofspeyside.com
A collection of whisky-inspired events, with the aim to make the world appreciate a good dram in the proper manner. If it's the wrong time of year for a trip, check the website for some autumnal events taking place along the same malty lines.

MAY 2011

21–28 May
■ Islay Festival of Malt and Music
Various venues around Islay
www.theislayfestival.co.uk
Local talent and artists from the mainland form the backbone of the entertainment at Feis Ile. There are also children's shows, distillery open days, guided walks and sporting events.

Dates TBC
■ Taste of Edinburgh
Inverleith Park, Arboretum Place, Edinburgh, www.tasteofedinburgh.co.uk
Cooking classes, exhibitors and restaurant demonstrations have made Taste a feature in the Edinburgh food and drink calendar. The website is the place to check for the latest news on their 2011 event.

Dates TBC
■ 3 Harbours Seafood Festival
The Greenbelt, Edinburgh Road, Prestonpans
www.3harbours.co.uk/10.html
A sister strand to the 3 Harbours Arts Festival, this event focuses right down on the local community and heritage within the fishing industry. Features stalls, demonstrations and music.

JUNE 2011

4 June
■ Taste of Grampian
Thainstone Centre, Inverurie, 01467 623760
www.tasteofgrampian.co.uk
A day packed full of entertainment, crafts and, of course, fine food and

Tom Kitchin cookery demonstration

drink from the Grampian region. Previous events have included cookery demonstrations and events by local distilleries with a chance to try a dram.

12 June

▪ Open Farm Sunday
Farms around Scotland
www.farmsunday.org
A unique chance to have a nose around a working farm and meet those who produce your food and taste the results of their labours. Various activities are planned on this family-friendly day, including walks, rides and mini farmers' markets. Check the website for participating farms and events.

23–26 June

▪ The Royal Highland Show
Royal Highland Centre, Ingliston,
0131 335 6200
www.royalhighlandshow.org
The annual carnival of agriculture and entertainment returns with lots of Scottish food and drink to sample and enjoy, all accompanied by competitions, live music and theatre, and, of course, plenty of live animals.

Dates TBC

▪ The Scottish Real Ale Festival
www.scottishbeerfestival.org.uk
The annual celebration of Scottish ale where thousands gather to taste a wide selection of beers from approximately 30 Scottish breweries.

JULY 2011

1–3 July

▪ The Scottish Game Fair
Scone Palace, Perth
www.scottishfair.com
Held in the grounds of the gorgeous Scone Palace, this annual event has now become a great day out for all the family, and includes a very successful Food Hall. And as well as showing off the best produce Scotland has to offer, the Food Hall will also host demonstrations of cooking, butchery of venison, sausage making and chocolate making.

2–3 July

▪ Scottish Traditional Boat Festival
Various venues, Portsay
www.scottishtraditionalboatfestival.co.uk
Traditional boat building is the main focus of this festival, with a side helping of traditional crafts. However, food lovers are well catered for in the Food Fayre which prides itself on displaying the best in Scottish produce.

3 Harbours Seafood Festival

23 July

▪ The Sutherland Show
Dornoch Links, Dornoch, Sutherland
www.sutherlandshow.com
The Sutherland show is a great opportunity to sample fresh goods and check out the best local growers with the fruit and vegetable judging competitions. Families are well catered for with agricultural judging, dog show and pipe bands over the whole day.

Dates TBC

▪ Tarbert Seafood Festival
Various venues
www.seafood-festival.co.uk
Amid all the entertainment, music and crowning of princesses and queens, the Tarbert Festival is a great place to experience cooking demonstrations with a seafood twist, followed up by specialised menus at local restaurants and bistros.

Dates TBC

▪ Big Tent Festival
Falkland Estate, Fife
www.bigtentfestival.co.uk
This family festival is dedicated to living in an environmentally friendly way, which is reflected in the food on offer in their organic-crammed One Planet Food Village. Other events include music, comedy and art exhibitors.

Dates TBC

▪ Glasgow Merchant City Festival
Various venues around the Merchant City
www.merchantcityfestival.com
Tucked into the vibrant programme of performance, fashion and art is a chance to sample some fine food and drink. Last year saw international markets taking to the streets of the Merchant City, with a number of restaurants in the area running special menus and deals in honour of the celebrations.

AUGUST 2011

13–14 August

▪ Arbroath Seafest
Various venues around Arbroath
www.arbroathseafest.co.uk
Arbroath Seafest is an annual festival of the sea held along Arbroath's seafront and centring around the town's traditional harbour and new marina. Foodies will no doubt be attracted by the world-famous Arbroath Smokie, as well as the traditional haddock. The festival often sees some more unusual items being smoked, including suckling pig, venison and ostrich meat.

Dates TBC

▪ Gourmet Glasgow
Various venues around Glasgow
www.graonline.co.uk
A range of events held at restaurants throughout the city – the perfect opportunity to treat yourself to a superb value meal in some of Glasgow's finest restaurants.

Dates TBC

▪ Foodies at the Festival
www.foodiesfestival.com
A popular event held during the Edinburgh Festival, Foodies usually takes place over three days in Holyrood Park, at the foot of Arthur's Seat. Cookery demonstrations, samplings, a producers market, as well as tasters of the best shows in town.

Farmers' markets around Scotland

Use the table below as a ready reckoner to find out where farmers' and producers' markets are held on any given weekend of the year. Note that during December/January, many markets don't run to the usual pattern of dates. Fuller details about each market, including location, are given in the A to Z list opposite. For general news and updates, go to **www.scottishfarmersmarkets.co.uk**, or search for Scottish Farmers' Markets on Facebook.

Every Weekend	First Weekend of Each Month	Second Weekend of Each Month
Edinburgh (Castle Ter) Sat 9am-2pm	**Ayr** Sat 9am-1pm	**Ardrishaig** Sat 10am-1pm
Ellon Sat 8am-1pm	**Balloch** Sun 10am-3pm	**Balerno** Sat 9am-1pm
Stornoway (Dec-Apr) Sat 9am-11.30am	**Bishopbriggs** Sat 10am-2pm	**Banff** (Apr-Oct) Sat 9.30am-12.30pm
(Apr-Dec) 8.30am-1pm	**Campbeltown** Sat 10am-1pm	**Dingwall** Sat 9am-2.30pm
Ullapool Sat 9am-5pm	**Edinburgh** Sat 10am-6pm	**Dunfermline** Sat 9am-1pm
Wigtown (Easter-Oct) Sat 10am-4pm	(Ocean Terminal) Sun 11am-5pm	**Forfar** Sat 9am-1pm
	Edinburgh (Portobello) Sat 10am-2pm	**Glasgow** (Fort) Sat & Sun 10am-4pm
	Gatehouse of Fleet Sat 9.30am-1pm	**Glasgow**(Mansfield Pk)Sat 10am-2pm
	Glasgow (Queen's Park) Sat 10am-2pm	**Glenkens** Sat 10am-1pm
	Huntly Sat 9am-1pm	**Inverurie** Sat 9am-1pm
	Langholm Sat 9am-1pm	**Livingston** Sun 11am-4pm
	Lochwinnoch first Sun of Mar, Jun, Sep & Dec, 11am-2.30pm	**Moffat** Sun 10/11am-3pm
	Montrose Sat 9am-1pm	**Paisley** Sat 9am-1pm
	Overton Sat 10am-2pm	**Peebles** Sat 9.30am-1.30pm
	Perth Sat 9am-2pm	**Stirling** Sat 10am-4pm
	Peterhead Sat 10am-3.30pm	
	St Andrews Sat 9am-1pm	
	Stonehaven Sat 9am-1pm	

Third Weekend of Each Month	Fourth Weekend of Each Month	Last Weekend of Each Month
Balloch Sun 10am-3pm	(also see list for Last Weekend of Each Month)	(also see list for Fourth Weekend of Each Month)
Banchory Sat 9am-1pm		
Cupar Sat 9am-1pm	**Alford** Sat 10am-2pm	**Aberdeen** Sat 9am-5pm
Dumfries Sun 11am-3pm	**Blairgowrie** Sat 10am-3pm	**Fencebay** Sun 9am-2pm
Dundee Sat 9am-4pm	**Cairndow and Loch Fyne** Sat 10am-1pm	**Glasgow** (Fort) Sat & Sun 10am-4pm
Edinburgh Sat 10am-6pm	**Clarkston** Sat 9am-1pm	**Haddington** Sat 9am-1pm
(Ocean Terminal) Sun 11am-5pm	**Drumlanrig** Sun 11am-3pm	**Inverness** Sat 9am-2pm
Elgin Sat 9am-4pm	**Glasgow** (Mansfield Pk) Sat 10am-2pm	**Kirkcaldy** Sat 9am-1pm
Glasgow (Queen's Park) Sat 10am-2pm	**Kelso** Sat 9.30am-1.30pm	**Macduff** Sat 9.30am-12.30pm
Greenock Sat 9am-2pm	**Linlithgow** Sat 10am-2pm	**Orkney** Sat 9am-1pm
Hamilton Sat 9am-1pm	**Paisley** Sat 9am-1pm	**Paisley** Sat 9am-1pm
Kilmarnock Sat 9am-1pm		**Stoneykirk** (not Jan) Sun 11am-2pm
Lockerbie Sat 10am-2pm		
Portpatrick(Jun-Sep, Dec) Sun 1-4pm		
Tarbert Sat 10am-1pm		
Turriff Sat 9.30am-12.30pm		

Weekdays and irregular markets		
Applecross First Fri of each month 10am-1pm	**Falkirk** First Fri of each month 12-4pm	**Milngavie** First Wed of each month 10am-2pm
Baltasound Various Sundays throughout the year	**Hawick** Third Fri of each month 9.30am-1.30pm	**Oban and Lorn** First and third Thu (Mar-Dec) 10am-3pm
Cairngorms Various venues and dates throughout the year	**Jedburgh** First Fri of each month 9.30am-1.30pm	**Tingwall** Various dates throughout the year 10am-2pm
Colvend Third Fri of the month 9am-1pm	**Lochcarron** Last Fri of each month 11am-3pm	**Vidlin** Various dates throughout the year

A-Z OF FARMERS' MARKETS IN SCOTLAND:

Aberdeen Belmont Street, last Sat of each month, 9am–5pm, www.aberdeencountryfair.co.uk

Alford Alford Heritage Centre, fourth Sat of each month 10am–2pm, www.spanglefish.com/alfordfarmersmarket

Applecross Community Hall, first Fri of each month, 10am–1pm

Ardrishaig Chalmers Street, second Sat of each month, 10am–1pm

Ayr Kyle Centre car park, first Sat of each month, 9am–1pm, www.ayrshirefarmersmarket.co.uk

Balerno Main Street, second Sat of each month, 9am–1pm, www.balernovt.org.uk

Balloch Loch Lomond Shores, first and third Sun of each month, 10am–3pm, www.lochlomond shores.com

Baltasound Hall, Shetland, Various Sundays throughout the year, www.shetland.gov.uk/communitywork/northisles/Whatson.asp

Banchory Scott Skinner Square, third Sat of each month, 9am–1pm, www.aberdeenshire.gov.uk

Banff St Mary's car park, second Sat of the month (Apr-Oct), 9.30am-12.30pm

Bishopbriggs Huntershill Village, first Sat of each month 10am–2pm, www.bishopbriggs-farmersmarket.co.uk

Blairgowrie Community Market, fourth Sat of each month (Apr-Sep) 10am–3pm, www.strathmoreglens.org

Cairndow and Loch Fyne Loch Fyne Oyster Bar, fourth Sat of each month, 10am–1pm

Cairngorms Various venues and dates throughout the year, www.cairngorms-farmers-market.com

Campbeltown Royal Hotel yard, first Sat of each month, 10am–1pm

Clarkston Station car park, fourth Sat of each month, 9am–1pm, www.lanarkshirefarmersmarket.co.uk

Colvend Public Hall Third Fri of the month 9am-1pm

Crossford Overton Farm, first Sat of each month, 10am–2pm, www.lanarkshirefarmersmarket.co.uk

Cupar Bonnygate Car Park, third Sat of each month, 9am–1pm, www.fifefarmersmarket.co.uk

Dingwall High Street, second Sat of each month, 9am–2.30pm, www.dingwall.org.uk

Drumlanrig Drumlanrig Castle, fourth Sun of each month, 11am–3pm, www.drumlanrig.com

Dumfries Tarff Town & Country Car Park, third Sun of each month, 11am–3pm

Dundee High Street, third Sat of each month, 9am–4pm, www.dundeecity.gov.uk

Dunfermline Glen Gates, Bridge Street, second Sat of each month, 9am–1pm, www.fifefarmersmarket.co.uk

Edinburgh Castle Terrace, every Sat, 9am–2pm, www.edinburghfarmersmarket.co.uk

Edinburgh Ocean Terminal, first and third weekend each month, Sat (10am-6pm) Sun (11am–5pm), www.oceanterminal.com

Edinburgh Portobello Organic Market, Brighton Park, first Sat 10am-2pm, www.pedal-porty.org.uk/food

Elgin The Plainstones, third Sat of each month, 9am–4pm, www.aberdeenshire.gov.uk

Ellon Neil Ross Square, every Sat, 8am–1pm, www.aberdeenshire.gov.uk

Falkirk High Street, first Friday of each month, 12–4pm, www.falkirkbid.com

Fencebay Fairlie, last Sun of each month, 9am–2pm, www.fencebay.co.uk

Forfar Myre Park, second Sat of each month, 9am–1pm

Gatehouse of Fleet Main car park, first Sat of each month 9.30am-1pm, www.gatehouse-of-fleet.co.uk

Glasgow Mansfield Park second and fourth Sat of each month, 10am–2pm, www.scottishfarmersmarkets.co.uk; Glasgow Fort Shopping Centre, second and last Sat & Sun of each month, 10am–2pm, www.glasgowfort.co.uk; Glasgow Queen's Park, first and third Sat of each month, 10am–2pm

Glenkens Dalry town hall, second Sat of each month, 10am–1pm, www.st-johns-town-of-dalry-town-hall.co.uk

Greenock Clyde Square, third Sat of each month, 9am–2pm

Haddington Court Street, last Sat of each month, 9am–1pm, www.haddingtonfarmersmarket.co.uk

Hamilton New Cross, Quarry Street, third Sat of each month, 9am–1pm, www.lanarkshirefarmersmarket.co.uk

Hawick Town Centre, third Fri of each month, 9am–2pm, www.bordersfoodnetwork.co.uk

Inverness Highland Food Market, Tesco Extra, last Sat of each month, 9am–2pm, www.highlandfoodmarket.com

Huntly Huntly Square, first Sat of each month, 9am–1pm, www.aberdeenshire.gov.uk

Inverurie Market place, second Sat of each month, 9am–1pm, www.aberdeenshire.gov.uk

Jedburgh Market Place, first Fri of each month, 9.30am–1.30pm, www.bordersfoodnetwork.co.uk

Kelso Market Square, fourth Sat of each month, 9.30am–1.30pm, www.bordersfoodnetwork.co.uk

Kilmarnock Foregate Square, third Sat of each month, 9am–1pm, www.ayrshirefarmersmarket.co.uk

Kirkcaldy Town square, last Sat of each month, 9am–1pm, www.fifefarmersmarket.co.uk

Langholm Eskdale Sports Centre, first Sat of each month, 9am–1pm

Linlithgow The Vennel, fourth Sat of each month, 10am–2pm

Livingston Civic Square, second Sun of each month, 11am–4pm,

Lochcarron Lochcarron Hall, last Fri of each month, 11am–3pm, www.lochcarron.org.uk

Lochwinnoch Castle Semple Visitor Centre, first Sun of Mar, Jun, Sep & Dec, 11am-2.30pm www.clydemuirshiel.co.uk

Lockerbie Lockerbie Town Hall, Third Sat of each month, 10am-2pm, www.allaboutlockerbie.com

Macduff Fishmarket, last Sat of each month, 9.30am–12.30pm, www.aberdeenshire.gov.uk

Milgavie Douglas Street, first Wed of each month, 10am–2pm

Moffat Town Hall Second Sun of each month (except Nov when it is second Saturday and Jan when there is no market) 10am-3pm (May-Oct) 11am-3pm (Nov-Apr)

Montrose Town House car park, first Sat of each month, 9am–1pm, www.gable-enders.co.uk

Oban and Lorn Kintaline Farm, Benderloch, First and third Thu (Mar-Dec) 10am–3pm, 10am–3pm, www.lorn.org.uk

Orkney Masonic Hall Kirkwall, last Sat of each month, 9am–1pm

Paisley County Square, second and last Sat of each month, 9am–1pm, www.ayrshirefarmersmarket.co.uk

Peebles Eastgate car park, second Sat of each month, 9.30am–1.30pm, www.bordersfoodnetwork.co.uk

Perth King Edward Street and St John's Place, first Sat of each month, 9am–2pm, www.perthfarmersmarket.co.uk

Peterhead Drummers Corner, first Sat of each month, 10am–3.30pm, www.aberdeenshire.gov.uk

Portpatrick Village Hall, third Sun of each month (Jun-Sep & Dec), 1-4pm

St Andrews Argyle Street Car Park, first Sat of each month, 9am–1pm, www.fifefarmersmarket.co.uk

Stirling Port Street, second Sat of each month, 10am–4pm, www.stirlingfarmersmarket.co.uk

Stonehaven Market Square, first Sat of each month, 9am–1pm, www.aberdeenshire.gov.uk

Stoneykirk Village Hall, last Sun of each month (not Jan) 11am-2pm

Stornoway Point Street, every Sat, 11.30am (Dec-Apr), 8.30am-1pm (Apr-Dec), www.stornowayfarmersmarket.co.uk

Tarbert Harbour Front, Harris, third Sat of each month, 10am–1pm

Tingwall Tingwall Hall, Shetland Various dates throughout the year, 10am-2pm

Turriff High Street car park, third Sat of each month, 9.30am-12.30pm, www.aberdeenshire.gov.uk

Ullapool Seaforth car park, every Sat, 9am–5pm

Vidlin Vidlin Hall Shetland, various dates throughout the year, www.vidlinhall.co.uk

Wigtown Market Cross, every Sat (Easter-Oct), 10am–4pm, www.wigtownmarket.com

Seasonal Eatings

Enjoying local fruit, vegetables, fish and meat is often a matter of knowing the period in the year when they're ready and at their best. Produced in conjunction with NFU Scotland's What's on Your Plate campaign, this handy at-a-glance guide outlines what Scottish food is available when.

	JANUARY	FEBRUARY	MARCH	APRIL	MAY
VEGETABLES (indicating the optimum months for produce that still has a discernible seasonal growing pattern based on traditional, open air production in Scotland. The focus here is on fresh, local, new season produce rather than stored items such as carrots, leeks, onions and potatoes. Grains can now be stored so well that there is no seasonal pattern and they have not been listed.)	Brussels sprouts, Cabbage, Calabrese broccoli, Chicory, Kale, Leeks, Parsnips, Radicchio and other winter salad, Turnips	Brussels sprouts, Cabbage, Calabrese broccoli, Chicory, Kale, Leeks, Radicchio and other winter salad	Brussels sprouts, Cabbage, Chicory, Leeks	Cabbage, Chicory, Leeks, Purple sprouting broccoli, Radishes, Spinach, Spring greens	Asparagus, Cabbage, Carrots, Chicory, Cauliflower, Garlic, Lettuce, Purple sprouting broccoli, Radishes, Spinach, Spring greens
FRUIT (again, indicating optimum months for freshly picked outdoor produce. Some fruit, particularly berries, now have very extended seasons in poly-tunnel production. In addition, fruit such as apples and pears can be stored well for many months.)			Forced Rhubarb	Rhubarb	Rhubarb, Strawberries
FISH (*indicates best months for quality)	Langoustine*, Cod, Haddock, Monkfish*, Whiting*, Lobster*, Native Oyster	Langoustine, Cod, Crab, Haddock*, Monkfish*, Whiting*, Lobster*, Hake, Native Oyster	Langoustine, Cod, Crab*, Haddock*, Monkfish*, Whiting*, Scallops, Lobster*, Hake, Native Oyster	Langoustine, Cod, Crab*, Haddock*, Monkfish*, Whiting*, Scallops, Lobster*, Hake, Native Oyster	Langoustine, Cod, Crab*, Haddock*, Monkfish, Scallops, Lobster, Herring, Hake
GAME (with the exception of new-season lamb, available from August, the domestication of animals and consumer demand have largely removed the traditional seasonal pattern for farmed meat such as beef, pork and chicken; the same applies to eggs, milk and most dairy products. For more on small game, see panel at top of page.)	Red deer, Pheasant, Partridge, Duck, Goose, Woodcock, Common Snipe, Coot, Golden Plover, Hare	Red deer (hinds to 15 Feb), Hare			
WILD FOOD & HERBS			Mint, Sorrel, Wild garlic	Watercress, Wild garlic	Mint, Parsley, Watercress

It is legal to shoot a variety of birds, wildfowl and mammals in Scotland, but for many of these species, there is also a closed season during which time they must be left undisturbed to breed and disperse. As such, small game is generally unavailable during the spring and summer months.

Pigeon and rabbit are both technically regarded as pest species, so can be shot all year round. However, size and quality can be variable during the breeding season, and it is better to wait till autumn to take advantage of a well-fed crop of birds and bunnies. See: www.basc.org.uk/content/shootingseasons

compiled by

NFUScotland

JUNE	JULY	AUGUST	SEPTEMBER	OCTOBER	NOVEMBER	DECEMBER
Asparagus, Broad beans, Cauliflower, Carrots, Garlic, Lettuce, New potatoes	Beetroot, Broad beans, Cauliflower, Cabbage, Carrots, Celery, Courgettes, Garlic, Lettuce, Onions, Peas (shell), Peas (sugar snap), New potatoes, Shallots	Aubergines, Beetroot, Calabrese broccoli, Cauliflower, Cabbage, Carrots, Celery, Courgettes, French beans, Garlic, Lettuce, Onions, Peas (shell), Peas (sugar snap), Main crop potatoes, Runner beans, Shallots	Cabbage, Calabrese broccoli, Carrots, Cauliflower, Celery, Courgettes, French beans, Garlic, Leeks, Lettuce, Onions, Parsnips, Main crop potatoes, Runner beans, Shallots, Summer squash, Turnips	Brussels sprouts, Cabbage, Calabrese broccoli, Carrots, Cauliflower, Celeriac, Celery, Courgettes, Lettuce, Mushrooms, Onions, Parsnips, Pumpkin	Brussels sprouts, Red cabbage, Calabrese broccoli, Chicory, Leeks, Onions, Parsnips	Brussels sprouts, Red cabbage, Calabrese broccoli, Chicory, Kale, Leeks, Onions, Parsnips, Radicchio and other winter salad, Turnips
Gooseberries, Strawberries, Tayberries, Rhubarb, Redcurrants	Blackcurrants, Gooseberries, Loganberries, Raspberries, Redcurrants, Strawberries, Tomatoes, Blueberries	Blackberries, Blueberries, Gooseberries, Raspberries	Blackberries, Blueberries, Damsons, Plums, Pears, Raspberries	Apples, Elderberries Pears		
Langoustine, Cod, Crab*, Haddock, Mackerel*, Monkfish, Scallops, Lobster, Herring*, Hake, Squid, Octopus	Langoustine, Cod*, Crab, Haddock, Mackerel*, Monkfish, Scallops, Lobster, Herring*, Hake, Squid, Octopus	Langoustine, Cod*, Crab, Haddock*, Mackerel*, Monkfish, Whiting, Scallops, Lobster, Herring, Hake, Squid, Octopus	Langoustine, Cod*, Crab*, Haddock*, Mackerel*, Monkfish, Whiting, Scallops*, Lobster, Herring, Hake, Native Oyster	Langoustine*, Cod*, Crab*, Haddock*, Mackerel, Monkfish*, Whiting, Scallops*, Lobster, Hake, Native Oyster	Langoustine*, Cod*, Crab*, Haddock, Monkfish*, Whiting*, Scallops, Lobster*, Hake, Native Oyster	Langoustine*, Cod, Crab*, Haddock, Monkfish*, Whiting*, Lobster*, Native Oyster
	Red deer (stags from 1 July)	Red deer, Grouse (from 12 Aug), Ptarmigan (from 12 Aug), Blackgame (from 20 Aug), Common Snipe (from 12 Aug), Hare	Red deer, Partridge, Grouse, Duck, Ptarmigan, Blackgame, Common Snipe, Coot, Hare	Red deer (stags to 20 Oct; hinds from 21 Oct), Pheasant, Duck, Partridge, Grouse, Goose, Woodcock, Ptarmigan, Blackgame, Common Snipe, Coot, Hare	Red deer, Pheasant, Partridge, Grouse, Duck, Goose, Woodcock, Ptarmigan, Blackgame, Common Snipe, Coot, Hare	Red deer, Pheasant, Duck, Partridge, Grouse (to 10 Dec), Goose, Woodcock, Ptarmigan (to 10 Dec), Blackgame (to 10 Dec), Snipe, Coot, Hare
Parsley, Watercress	Fennel, Mushrooms, Parsley, Sage, Watercress	Basil, Mushrooms	Basil, Mushrooms, Watercress		Chestnuts	

Stamps of approval

There are many labels, marques and logos associated with food and drink in Scotland. Some seem self-explanatory but most carry important information. Peter Brown of the food certification company SFQC explains some of the details behind the claims made on Scotland's food and drink.

SCOTTISH ORIGIN	
Arbroath Smokies	Haddock, cured and hot-smoked (cooked) to a golden brown colour, attributed to the small fishing village of Auchmithie, near Arbroath - holds European PGI (Protected Geographic Indication) approval. www.scotland.gov.uk/Topics/Business-Industry/Food-Industry/PFNs
Mey Selections	Produced within a 100-mile radius of Prince Charles' Highland home at Castle of Mey in Caithness (and selected for inclusion within the brand). www.mey-selections.com
Orkney Beef, Orkney Lamb, Shetland Lamb	Beef and lamb from these islands, recognised as distinctive because of the use of traditional breeds and the island's unique topography, geology and climate - each hold European PDO (Protected Designation of Origin) approval. www.scotland.gov.uk/Topics/Business-Industry/Food-Industry/PFNs
'Scotch'	Whisky from Scotland - the term is legally defined and protected www.scotch-whisky.org.uk
'Scottish'	With some products this will mean it comes entirely from Scotland; for others it means the place of 'last substantial change'. So, unless stated otherwise, it's possible that it has originated elsewhere and been processed in Scotland. www.scotland.gov.uk/Topics/Business-Industry/Food-Industry/Origin
Scottish Crofting Produce Scottish Crofting Produce Highlands and Islands Croft Origin	Meat, fruit, vegetables, horticulture, trees, honey, yarn and woven goods from Scottish crofts. www.crofting.org/index.php/scpbrand
SCOTTISH ORIGIN + INDEPENDENTLY CHECKED STANDARDS	
Scotch Beef & Lamb	Has been born, reared and slaughtered in Scotland and is also farm-assured (see opposite), as well as carrying associated feed, transport, auction and abattoir assurance. Holds European PGI approval and it's all traceable back to farm. www.qmscotland.co.uk www.scotchbeefandlamb.com www.scotland.gov.uk/Topics/Business-Industry/Food-Industry/PFNs
Scottish Salmon Quality Approved Shetland Salmon	It's farm-assured (see opposite) and processor-inspected. Product is traceable & Scottish Farmed Salmon is PGI-approved. www.scottishsalmon.co.uk www.shetlandaquaculture.com www.scotland.gov.uk/Topics/Business-Industry/Food-Industry/PFNs

Scottish Quality Wild Venison	Wild venison from estates assessed annually against criteria for stalking, carcase-handling and hygiene in larders. www.sfqc.co.uk/processing/scottish_quality_wild_venison_sqwv
Specially Selected Pork	The same as for Scotch Beef and Lamb but not covered by a PGI. Sometimes used with the Scottish SPCA (Society for the Prevention of Cruelty to Animals) logo as Scotland's animal welfare charity endorses this scheme. www.qmscotland.co.uk

UK/WORLDWIDE INDEPENDENTLY CHECKED STANDARDS – APPLIED TO MANY SCOTTISH PRODUCTS

'Farm Assured'	Farms are assessed by an independent inspector to check animal welfare, staff competence, building safety/suitability, the avoidance of environmental damage and the safe use of medicines, pesticides and herbicides. www.qmscotland.co.uk www.sfqc.co.uk www.ndfas.org.uk www.assuredproduce.co.uk www.assuredchicken.org.uk www.sqcrops.co.uk
Freedom Food	Independently inspected farms to RSPCA standards – so you can be pretty sure animal welfare is a fairly high priority. The RSPCA calls it 'farm assurance with a difference' - i.e. with a welfare accent. Note also that Scottish SPCA decided not to establish its own scheme but rather to endorse some farm assurance schemes (see the example of pork, above). www.rspca.org.uk www.scottishspca.org
Organic	Europe sets minimum organic standards for everything produced as organic in the EU. Organic certification bodies, in turn, set their own standards, which have to be approved by the UK Government. The two most commonly seen in Scotland are those certified by SOPA (look out for UK3 on packaging) and the Soil Association (UK5). However, by no means has all food labelled by a UK organic certification body come from the UK. The certification body label is applied at the place of packing or processing and so could be different from the certification body that inspected the origin of the product. Around 700 Scottish farms and crofts are officially certified organic. www.defra.gov.uk/foodfarm/growing/organic/standards www.sopa.org.uk www.soilassociationscotland.org
Lion Quality	The little red lion printed on lots of eggs (alongside the 'best before' date) indicate that they have been produced safely and hygienically and that the eggs come from hens that have been vaccinated against salmonella. www.britegg.co.uk
Marine Stewardship Council	Fish and shellfish from independently inspected, sustainable fisheries from around the world. Has the support of important players such as WWF. www.msc.org
Red Tractor	Farm-assured (see above), plus checks at processing and packing. www.redtractor.org.uk